FEMINA
LIBIDO SEXUALIS

FEMINA
LIBIDO SEXUALIS

COMPENDIUM OF THE PSYCHOLOGY, ANTHROPOLOGY AND
ANATOMY OF THE SEXUAL CHARACTERISTICS OF THE WOMAN

BY HERMAN HEINRICH PLOSS,
MAX BARTELS and PAUL BARTELS

EDITED BY ERIC JOHN DINGWALL
ARRANGED BY J. R. BROSSLOWSKY

THE MEDICAL PRESS

1 9 6 5   NEW YORK

THE SEXUAL CHARACTERISTICS

MAN and woman differ from each other in several respects, and these differences are termed Sexual Characteristics. They include the special organs of sex, but are not confined to these organs. John Hunter (1728–1793) was the first to distinguish between primary and secondary sexual characteristics, and Darwin followed and emphasised this distinction, which has proved of great use in scientific investigation and was considered adequate for over a century. But the growth of knowledge proved the need for further categories—a need conclusively shown by the discovery of the *rôle* of the endocrine secretions. Poll has suggested the following classification of Sexual Characteristics :

I. *Essential* (or Germinal), in which he includes only the gonads or reproductive glands, *i.e.*, testes and ovaries respectively.
II. *Accessory*.
    (*a*) Subsidiary genital.
        (1) Internal (ducts, copulatory organs, vascular organs and accessory glands).
        (2) External.
    (*b*) Extragenital.
        (1) Internal (vocal and psychic peculiarities).
        (2) External (differences in general structure).

Hirschfeld [1] makes a further sub-division. He distinguishes :

I. Sexual Organs proper, which he further classifies as Secretory, Ducts, Conserving (or Reservoirs) and Copulatory Organs.
II. Further bodily differences in structure.
III. The Sexual Instinct.
    (*a*) The *Centripetal* trend, *i.e.*, the direction of desire.
    (*b*) The *Central* Impetus, *i.e.*, the force of desire.
    (*c*) The *Centrifugal* expression, *i.e.*, the release of desire.
    (*d*) The regulative mechanism, *i.e.*, the inhibition of desire.

A brief description of the female sexual characteristics is appended, based on the system suggested above.

The Primary Sexual Characteristics

These may also be described as *glandular* or *gonadal*. They manufacture the essential reproductive cells, whether male (sperms) or female (ova), and are the crucial factors in cases of indeterminate or intermediate type, however atypical the remaining bodily structure. Both testes and ovaries are glands of complicated structure containing tissue of different sorts. Only a part of these gonads is actually reproductive, *i.e.*, devoted to the formation of reproductive cells, or to spermatogenesis or oögenesis respectively, for they also contain tissues of endocrine accessory type. The pair of ovaries lie in the lower portion of the abdominal cavity and are attached to the broad ligaments of the uterus. They are about the size of small plums. They consist of :—

(*a*) Connective tissue (*stroma ovarii*), which forms both an exterior sheath (*tunica albuginea*), medulla and the *cortex*.

1.—Ovary. (After Kahn.) (*a*) Primordial ova ; (*b* and *c*) Ova ; (*d*) Ovarian vesicle ;
(*e*) Same in section ; (*f*) Outer wall ; (*g*) Ruptured vesicle.

(*b*) The cortex, which is rich in elastic tissue and blood vessels. The surface of the ovary is covered over with a layer of epithelium (Fig. 1).

The *cortex* interests us particularly.

The female reproductive cells first appear (Fig. 2) among the surface epithelial cells—which are small, smooth and cylindrical in form, whereas the oogonia are larger, rounder and lighter in colour. They have each a large nucleus with nucleolus. The cells of the germinal epithelium group themselves around the oogonia and form the primitive follicles, which descend and spread into the cortex. Each of these follicles consists of :—

(*a*) The essential egg cell or ovum :
(*b*) The epithelial cells ;
(*c*) The outer sheath of connective tissue.

Their normal development is as follows :

The follicular epithelium expands and swells, so that a *rim*, the *zona pellucida*, is formed around the ovum (Fig. 2). The formation of follicles begins in the embryo and continues into the early years of childhood. According to Sappey, a three-year-old child has about 400,000 follicles. Their number then begins to decline ; Henle estimates that a girl of 18 has about 36,000 follicles. The epithelial cells proliferate and between the layers appears a fluid, the *liquor folliculi*. This implies that the follicle is maturing ; its diameter is between 0·5 and 1·2 mm. It consists of :—

(1) The *theca folliculi*, with two layers :
(a) The fibrous *tunica externa ;*
(b) The *tunica interna*, which is vascular and full of cells, many of which are relatively large, spherical and of a yellowish tint and are therefore called theca lutein cells, with which we shall deal later in our study.
(2) The follicular epithelium or *membrana granulosa*, in which there is a mound,
(3) The *cumulus oophorus* ; in which lies
(4) The *ovule*. The cells of the *cumulus oophorus* immediately surrounding the ovule branch out from it, like rays, and form the *corona radiata*.

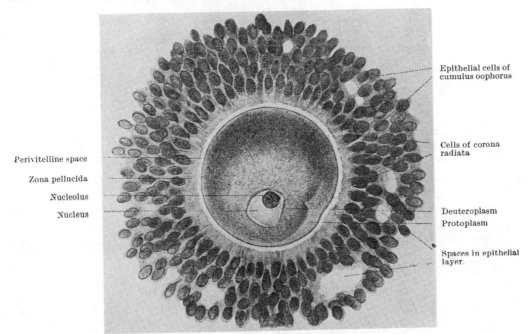

Epithelial cells of
cumulus oophorus

Cells of corona
radiata

Perivitelline space

Zona pellucida

Nucleolus

Nucleus

Deuteroplasm
Protoplasm

Spaces in epithelial
layer.

2.— Egg cell of an adult. (After Bumm.)

Only a small proportion of the actual number of follicles reaches maturity, but some of the follicles mature. They grow and swell to the size of a small cherry or hazel-nut on their exterior surface, which becomes thinner, and finally yields to the pressure of the follicular fluid. Suddenly the follicular protuberance splits or bursts, and ovule and liquid are discharged with great impetus. The ovule, at this stage of its evolution, is 0·2–0·25 mm. in dimensions, that is, it is just at the borderline of visibility. The follicular rupture and extrusion of the ovule are termed *ovulation*. We shall return to these processes, but must now consider the

Essential Sexual Characteristics

The first to consider, in woman, are the *ducts* (Fig. 3), known as oviducts, or Fallopian (uterine) tubes. They are tubular in form and extend from the cavity of the womb (*fundus uteri*) towards the pelvic wall on either side. At their junction with the womb they are extremely narrow ; they would hardly admit a pig's bristle. But they gradually widen out, and terminate in a funnel-shaped mouth (*ostium abdominale*) with fimbriated edges, somewhat resembling a red carnation in full bloom. The tubes are lined internally with ciliated epithelium, whose cilia tend

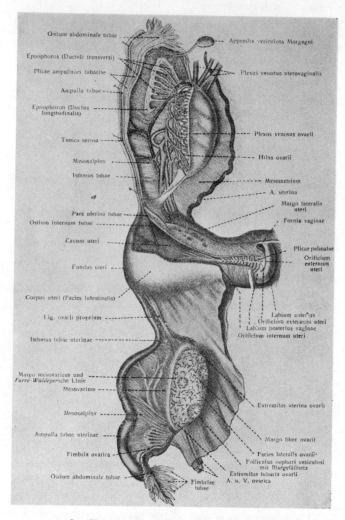

3.—Uterus with appendages. (After Oertal.)

to drive the contents towards the uterus. When the follicle bursts, some have thought that the funnel-shaped end of the oviduct clasps the ovary, and, with a sudden convulsive suction—like a sea anemone—the ovum is drawn into the tube.

The accessory sex ducts in woman further include the *Parovarium* (*Ep-oöphoron*). They are delicate whitish tubules at right angles to the tubes, but opening into another wider duct parallel with the oviduct. Their walls are relatively thick and lined with the same type of epithelial membrane as the Fallopian tubes, and they possess muscle fibres of their own. We do not yet know their function in the woman's organism, but structurally they would appear to correspond to the lobules of the *epididymis* in the man (see below). Moreover, they are always demonstrable, which is not the case with another accessory organ, the *Par-oöphoron*.

There are, further, the glands, termed, from their discoverer, glands of Bartholin (*glandulæ vestibulares majores*), corresponding to the bulbo-urethral glands in the male. These are duplex, have minute efferent ducts opening against the medial side of the margin of the labia minora, and are about the size of two peas or a bean. They lie (Figs. 4 and 6) right and left of the orifice of the vagina, and they pour

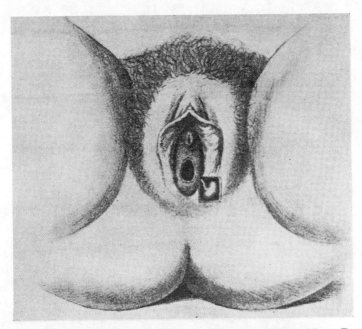

4.—External genitals showing gland of Bartholin. (After Meyer-Ruegg.)

out a secretion during sexual excitement, which lubricates the opening of the vagina.

The uterine group of sex organs includes the Uterus, or Womb, and the vagina. The latter is a muscular passage running upwards and backwards from the vulva into the body for a distance of between 7 and 8 cm. (posterior measurement). Normally its anterior and posterior walls are in apposition. The upper end widens into the vaginal vault or *fornix*, into which extends the lower portion of the uterus (*portio vaginalis*) with the opening (*orificium externum uteri*) or *external os uteri* (Figs. 3, 8 and 9). The adult uterus itself, in its non-pregnant state, is about the size and shape of a pear (Fig. 3). Its main body, or *corpus uteri*, is roughly triangular : wide at the upper extremity or *fundus*, from which the oviducts branch off at either side, and narrowing towards the lower extremity, or *cervix uteri*. The uterus is a mobile organ ; its exact position in the body depends, for example, on the respective pressure and fullness of bladder (in front) and rectum (behind). It is at an angle of about 80 degrees to the axis of the vagina.

Between the cervix and corpus is the so-called isthmus uteri, of which the length is typical and distinctive in the changing phases of growth and life. Before puberty, the isthmus is long relatively to the rest of the organ, and its walls are lax and thin. During puberty, it becomes comparatively shorter, and its walls thicken and grow firmer ; after the change of life it disappears.

Finally, we must enumerate the *conjugal* sex characteristics : they are the external genitalia, and include, in woman, the vestibule (Fig. 7) with the clitoris (Fig. 6) in front and the labia majora, or outer lips, on either side. The vestibule

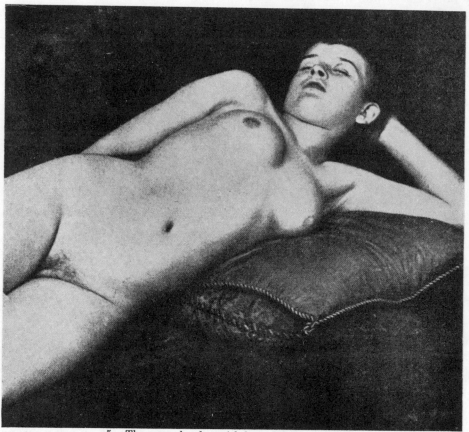

5.—The normal vulva with legs closed.   (After Stratz.)

contains the urinary orifice or meatus, the introitus or vaginal orifice and the openings of the minute ducts of Skene's glands (*ductus paraurethralis*).

In the virgin the outer lips or labia majora approach each other, so that the clitoris hardly protrudes. They have thick deposits of adipose tissue, are somewhat pigmented and covered externally with hair. Between them are the *labia minora* (*nymphæ*), or inner lips, which are always hairless. The upper folds arch over the clitoris in front and the lower merge into the *labia majora*, toward the perineum. The clitoris (Fig. 10), corresponding to the penis, has a glans (*glans clitoridis*) with prepuce, and consists of a cylindrical mass of erectile tissue so that it is capable of erection (see Kobelt). Two further erectile masses of tissue lie behind the labia minora ; they are the bulbs of the vestibule and serve to congest and expand the vulva, causing it to open slightly, or pout. Above the clitoris, on the exterior

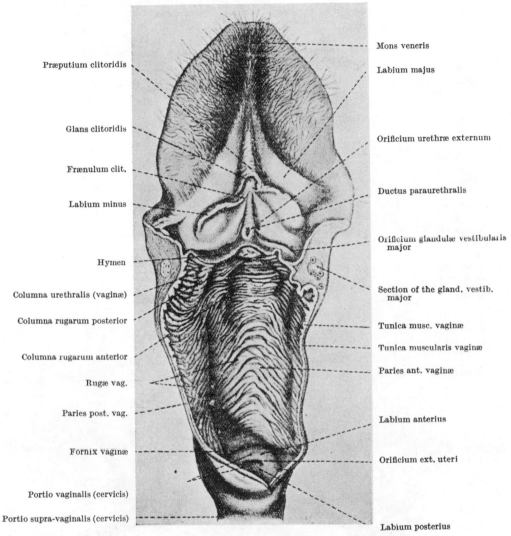

Præputium clitoridis

Glans clitoridis

Frænulum clit.

Labium minus

Hymen

Columna urethralis (vaginæ)

Columna rugarum posterior

Columna rugarum anterior

Rugæ vag.

Paries post. vag.

Fornix vaginæ

Portio vaginalis (cervicis)

Portio supra-vaginalis (cervicis)

Mons veneris

Labium majus

Orificium urethræ externum

Ductus paraurethralis

Orificium glandulæ vestibularis major

Section of the gland. vestib. major

Tunica musc. vaginæ

Tunica muscularis vaginæ

Paries ant. vaginæ

Labium anterius

Orificium ext. uteri

Labium posterius

6.—Dissection of vagina.   (After Halban-Seitz.)

surface of the body, is a thick cushion of fatty tissue (Fig. 5) called the *mons veneris* or *mons pubis*, which is covered with hair during sexual maturity. Gussenbauer has dealt with the vascular system of the genitals in detail, and to this the reader is referred.

The Determinative Sexual Characteristics

These are the glands of internal secretion, or ductless glands. The whole subject of these glands is of the highest significance and still far from fully explored,

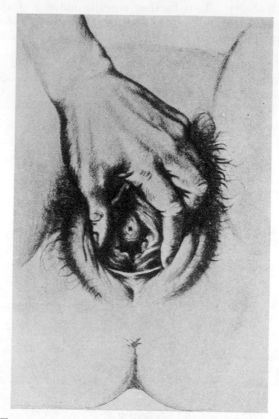

7.—External female genitals with separated labia. (After Polano.)

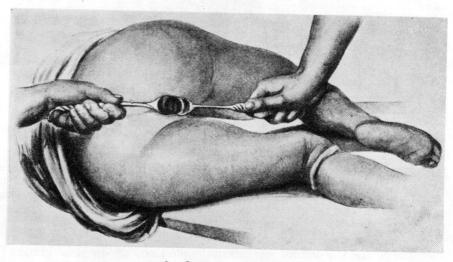

8.—Os uteri. (After Polano.)

but can only be dealt with very briefly here. We would refer readers to the works of Biedl, Leschke, Weil, Gley, Waldeyer. Classical medicine anticipated modern discovery by its doctrine of " humours." Aristotle, Hippocrates and Galen believed that blood, yellow and black bile and phlegm were the basic human substances. Their due proportion and interaction gave health and preserved life, their unbalance brought disease or death. The increase of exact knowledge in histology drew attention to neural structures and functions ; the nerves were considered the keys to human physiology and psychology and all was ascribed to " nervous correlation." The composition and circulation of the various liquid secretions in the body were neglected, and many important glandular structures were declared useless and " vestigial." But it could not be denied that operative removal of these caused the gravest injuries, and this drew attention to their study. In 1849 Berthold proved that the sexual urge was not obliterated even if all nerve supply to the gonads were cut off.

He then observed and recorded the changes in the whole organism which followed the removal of the male gonads by castration ; and the restoration of

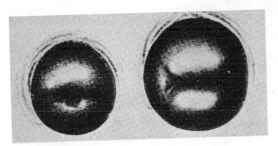

9.—Vaginal portion of the uterus showing the os uteri in (a) a nullipara and (b) a multipara. (After Oertel.)

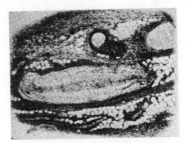

10.—Tactile corpuscle in the clitoris. (After F. Fränkel.)

normal functions and qualities following on the regrafting of the testes—not necessarily on their natural site.

But these epoch-making discoveries were soon forgotten, and when Brown-Séquard, at the end of the nineteenth century (1889), demonstrated that an injection of testicular extract was followed by general physical rejuvenation, he was simply ridiculed. Nevertheless, the conviction gradually grew that the secretions of certain glands were carried by the blood stream and caused the most pronounced results, independently of the nervous system. Claude Bernard championed this theory of the importance of the internal secretions. Bayliss and Starling termed these secretions hormones (ὁρμάω, set in motion). Aggregates of cells in the form of glands which secrete these hormones are termed endocrine glands (κρίνω, to separate). They differ from the glands previously studied and classified in that they have no ducts, but pour their secretions straight into the blood stream. And this has led to a change in our former concept of " glands," for we now know that, e.g., the red portion of the bone marrow secretes such substances. Not all these endocrine glands can be reckoned as determining sexual characters, but most of them have a share in determining sexual development. Some of the hormonic glands inhibit or hinder sexual development ; others again, promote it. Also some glands, the sexual glands, manufacture internal as well as external secretions. Moreover, all these glands have a definite effect on one another, and they form a system (Fig. 11) whose individual component organs are quite distinct, but closely interwoven by means of the circulation of the blood and the vegetative nervous

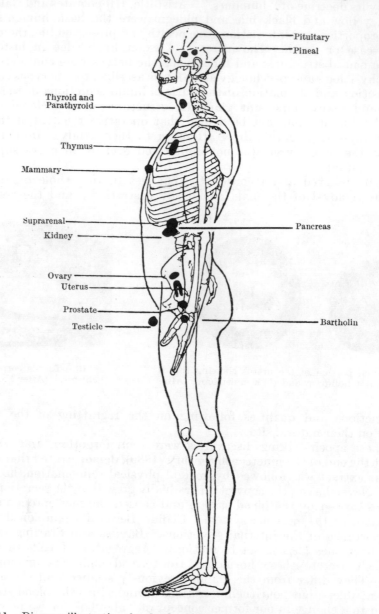

11.—Diagram illustrating the glands of internal secretion.   (After v. Reitzenstein.)

system. If any one of these endocrine glands is affected and its action either stimulated or decreased, the whole endocrine system is thrown out of gear and its harmony is disturbed. Let us briefly survey them. The first is the *hypophysis cerebri* or *pituitary gland* (*cf*. Fig. 12).   It is situated below the brain on the so-called sella turcica. It consists of two main portions, the anterior and posterior lobes. The posterior lobe is mainly composed of a mass of cells (*neuroglia*). From it two active hormones are obtained. Pitosin and pitressin are both present in Pituitrin. It increases the blood pressure and accelerates labour or brings it on prematurely by causing contractions of the uterus. The active principle of the posterior pituitary lobe has been put on the market in medical preparations such as Pituitrin, Pityglandol, Hypophysin, etc. It is said to produce normal parturition. Furthermore, the posterior lobe increases the consumption of oxygen, whereas the front lobe decreases it ; it causes increase of weight and promotes the peristaltic action of the intestine, thus causing rapid defæcation. If the posterior lobe is underdeveloped or affected by tumours, etc., an enormous development of fat, in peculiar distribution, ensues, accompanied by deficient metabolism and arrested development of the genitals, with cessation of the sexual impulse (*Dystrophia adiposogenitalis*). The distribution of adipose tissue becomes feminine ; it accumulates on the hips, buttocks, thighs and breasts. In men, the beard and pubic hair fall out and the voice does not "break." In women, the hairs on the pubes and in the armpits are also lost and the periods cease.

Two hormones are produced in the anterior lobe : (*a*) a growth-provoking one, and (*b*) a sex-maturing one. Oversecretion of the growth-provoking hormone produces gigantism or acromegaly, as described below. Under-secretion induces dwarfism. The sex-maturing hormone appears to be double.

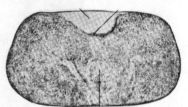

12.—Section through the pituitary of a pregnant woman (After Aschner.)

(1) Prolan A, which stimulates œstrus and maturation of the Grääfian follicle ;

(2) Prolan B, which stimulates Corpus Luteum formation, and so prevents abortion. The Zondek-Aschheim test for pregnancy, described on page 33, depends on the presence of Prolan B in the urine.

The functional disturbances of the anterior pituitary lobe are of interest to us. Excessive functional activity arising in adult life causes acromegaly ; the ribs increase in length and deform the thorax ; hands, feet and the bones of the jaw and skull become similarly misshapen. If this excessive hormonic activity occurs in early childhood, the ossification of the centres of the larger bones is delayed, growth is abnormally long, and gigantism results. Both in gigantism and acromegaly (Fig. 13)* there is frequently a later atrophy of both interior and exterior genitals, diminution of desire and even impotence. Deficient function of the anterior pituitary lobe causes a severe disturbance of metabolism, which is known as cachexia hypophyseopriva. Total destruction of this lobe leads to death, the body becomes abnormally thin and prematurely senile, hair and teeth fall out and sexual functions and emotions are extinguished. If atrophy of the pituitary occurs in children, a peculiar type of dwarf is said to be produced ; an infantile expression of countenance is generally combined with adiposity of the trunk and sometimes with deficient sexual development. This condition is known as *ateleiosis*, but this is a mutation and may not be due to changes in the pituitary only.

Another important endocrine organ is the *Epiphysis* (Figs. 14A and 14B) pineal gland, or conarium pinealis. It makes its appearance at the end of the fourth or beginning of the fifth week of embryonic life, increases in size and attains its greatest

* See F. R. B. Atkinson.

development in the early years of childhood.   From about the seventh year onwards there is a proliferation of connective tissue and an accompanying atrophy of the pineal cells, which suggests that the main activity of the gland ceases with the advent

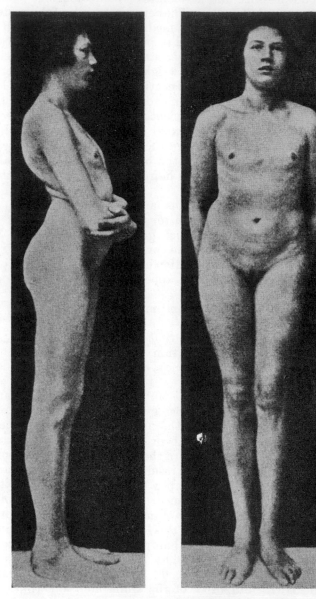

13.—Acromegaly.

of puberty. It appears, indeed, possible that the epiphysis inhibits the sexual evolution and must, therefore, cease to function before sexual maturity can supervene. The decrease of pineal secretion leads to abnormal precocity (*pubertas præcox*). In such cases menstruation is established before the seventh year and boys are capable of erection and ejaculation at the same age. Or this amazing precocity can be manifested intellectually, *e.g.*, in infant prodigies, Biedl applying

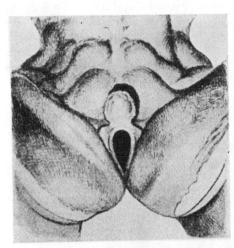

14A.—Pineal body in a 16-year-old virgin.

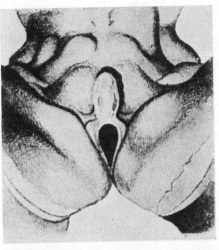

14B.—Pineal body in a 16-year-old primipara at the end of pregnancy.   (After Aschner.)

the term *apinealism* to such cases.   If the pineal gland is removed or destroyed, the result is a gross adipose deformity somewhat similar to that caused by obliteration

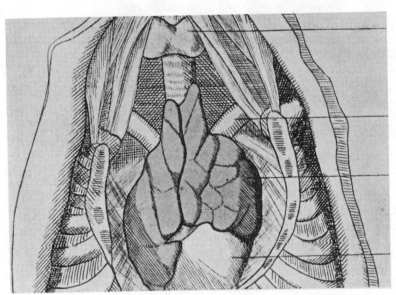

15.—Thymus and thyroid.   (After Merkel.)

of the *pituitary*. Leschke is probably right in assuming that both sets of diseased conditions are caused by the pressure of the affected glands on certain portions of the diencephalon. Pineal extracts are claimed to decrease sexual sensation, followed by increased uterine contractions in pregnant cases and a greater flow of milk during lactation. For a survey of recent literature see Jelliffe. The same effects are caused by the glandular activity of the *thymus* (Figs. 15 and 16). This gland is situated in the chest cavity above the heart, and it is large in children, decreases from between the 10th and the 14th year (at birth it weighs approximately 10–15 gm. ; at two years old, 25 ; at puberty, 40, and decreases to 15 or 10 gm. after the 45th year). The thymus also appears to be composed of different groups

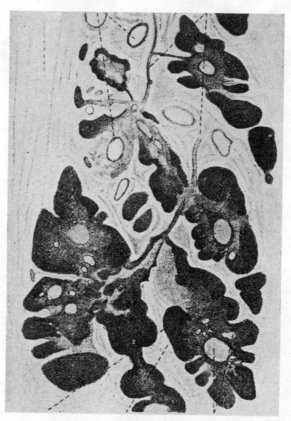

16.—Section of thymus in 13-year-old child, showing Hassall's bodies. (After Stohr.)

of cells, with different functions ; one group appears related to the spleen and the formation of blood. The other group has been supposed to promote the growth of the gonads, but inhibits their full functional activity. If the thymus is removed the testes grow much larger, but soon diminish again ; *i.e.,* their seminal portion is injured but the interstitial portion thrives. And, after castration, the thymus trebles in size.* Defective function of the thymus disturbs the osseous formation, but in a different way from the cerebral endocrine glands ; a condition resembling rickets is produced, owing to deficient lime. It has also been observed that extracts of the thymus gland are an antidote to muscular exhaustion. If the thymus does

* [These figures and assertions are disputed.]

not decrease after puberty a hypertrophy of the whole lymphatic system ensues. The sex organs atrophy and extreme obesity results ; the skeleton and growth of hair assume the characteristics of the opposite sex. (*Cf.* Marine and Oswald, and for recent work on the thymus see Hammar, C. Smith, Cooperstock and Park and McClure.)

A specially important endocrine organ is the thyroid gland (Figs. 15 and 17), so-called from its square shape (θυρεός). It affects almost all the metabolic manifestations and the whole physique, growth, sexual development and psychic qualities, in collaboration with the pituitary and suprarenal glands. This group is, therefore, collated under the term *synergetes*. Destruction of the thyroid is fatal to the health and causes premature death. It is supposed to secrete various distinct hormones, and also to possess the quality of neutralising certain toxic products of metabolism. In the course of research an American, Kendall by name, claimed to succeed in isolating one of the thyroid hormones. He called the resultant substance *thyroxine*, and its chemistry has been further elucidated by Harington. We must realise the preponderant influence of thyroid endocrines when we know that the whole of the blood in the dog flows, according to Tschuewsky, through this gland sixteen times in the twenty-four hours.* The thyroid is situated in the throat on either side of, and underneath, the larynx. Enlargement of the thyroid (goitre) is frequently accompanied by a special form of disease, Graves' disease. Sufferers from this complaint are always in a state of extreme agitation, the heart beats rapidly and the eyeballs protrude (hence the term exophthalmic goitre) : the metabolic and assimilative processes are much accelerated. These symptoms are generally accompanied by an enlargement of the thymus and an atrophy of the adrenal bodies, the ovaries and the pancreas.

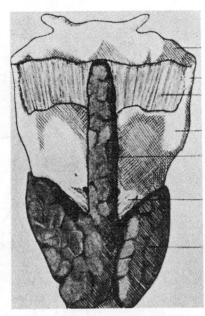

17.—Thyroid. (After Merkel.)

Deficiency of the thyroid is followed by other manifestations. The whole connective tissue of the body proliferates and becomes infiltrated with a mucoid substance of doubtful chemical nature. This process begins in the tissues of the face and the skin hardens and thickens so that the eyes have narrow slits and immobile lids. The degenerative process extends to the rest of the body, the hair falls out, finger and toe nails split, the movements become clumsy and difficult. This pathological condition is termed myxœdema, and we can distinguish a congenital form of it, in which there is thyroid deficiency from birth. Another complaint caused by thyroid deficiency is infantile myxœdema. Here the patients become apathetic and, finally, imbecile (Figs. 18A and 18B), as do also persons in whom the thyroid has been excised ; this condition is termed *cachexia strumipriva :* and is sometimes combined with a cretinism in which the goitre is not soft and vascular,

---

* [The supply of blood to the thyroid is considerable, more indeed in proportion to its size than that to the brain. It is clear that this implies that its functions are of great importance, which is becoming more and more fully recognised as experiments proceed.]

but hard and exsanguine. It is significant that the thyroid is enlarged during pregnancy, and similar observations are said to have been made in the case of girls who practised masturbation. During pregnancy the endocrine functions of the ovaries are stimulated, and seem to react on and enlarge the thyroid and thus

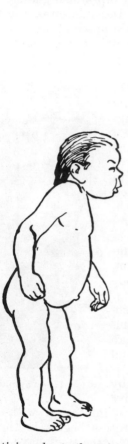

18A.—Cretinism, due to thyroid deficiency in a 15-year-old girl.

18B.—The same case after six years' treatment with thyroid extract. (After Slarek and Weygandt.)

increase metabolism, in order, so Weil suggests, to meet the needs of both mother and child (see Mayo and Plummer).

[Recent gynæcological work on the thyroid has been assisted by the mass of material which has been accumulated on the effects of feeding thyroid extracts and of thyroidectomy on the reproductive system in animals. The dependence of the ovary upon the action of the thyroid is becoming established, and cases of sterility and menstrual disorder are in consequence becoming more amenable to treatment (cf. L. Blanchard).]

The adrenal bodies are also enlarged in pregnant women. Leschke has demonstrated that thyroid changes always accompany functional changes in the ovarian apparatus (puberty, sexual intercourse, pregnancy, childbirth and the change of life). These sexual crises are also often the signal for the onset of Graves' disease, and in dissecting specimens of such cases we find the fairly constant symptom of ovarian atrophy, which manifests itself clinically in diminished or suppressed menstruation, in the exaggerated bone development and its osteomalacic accompaniments and in certain distinctive changes of the sex functions (Figs. 19 and 20). If the thyroid secretion is inadequate,

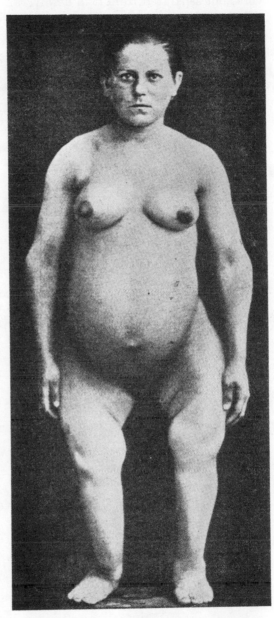

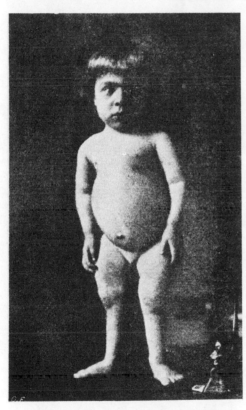

19.—Rachitic dwarf, five years old and 73·5 cm. tall. (After Guggisberg.)

20.—Case of extreme rachitis. (After Stratz.)

the resultant manifestations are confined to deficient growth of the body, particularly undevelopment of the sexual organs and lack of hair. Beside the thyroid gland are situated certain extremely small glandular bodies (generally four), which are known as the *parathyroids* (Fig. 21). It is specially significant that these parathyroids are adjacent to the thyroid, or even inside it, in the bodies of carnivora, but separated from it in herbivora.

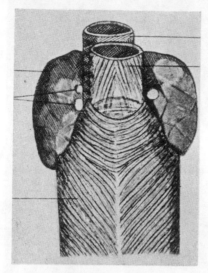

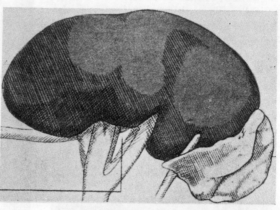

22.—Kidney with suprarenal gland. (After Merkel.)

21.—Accessory thyroid glands.
(After Merkel.)

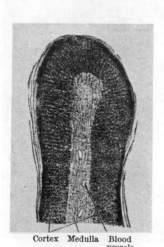

Cortex Medulla Blood
vessels
23A.—Section of the
suprarenal gland of a child.

23B.—Section through
suprarenal gland.

They develop out of the epithelia of the dorsal aspects of the third and fourth gill-clefts, and, in human beings, they are about 3–15 mm. long and 2–4 mm. wide. If they are not present in the organism, or if they do not perform their office, tetanic convulsions ensue, followed by death. Similar convulsive symptoms may not only sometimes be noted in the menstrual periods, but may appear spontaneously during pregnancy and lactation. During pregnancy they may be accentuated to the point of premature expulsion of the fœtus. Another fact of significance is that the parathyroid secretion also seems to affect the new-born child and to cause convulsions in some cases.

The parathyroids produce an internal secretion, "parathormone" (Collip), which controls the calcium metabolism of the body. Hyposecretion causes tetany and defects in the dental enamel. Hypersecretion causes diminution in the calcium of the skeleton, and osteitis fibrosa. In hyposecretion there is great diminution in the calcium content of the blood. In hypersecretion there is excessive calcium in the blood, with depletion of the lime and phosphorus in the skeleton and softening of bone in consequence.

One of the symptoms is an increase of ammonia and carbamic acid in the urine, which further contains free nucleic acid.

Leschke has shown that Koch found further substances in the urine of dogs affected by tetanus; such as methyl guanidine (and other guanidine compounds), histamine, choline and neurine : that is to say, toxic substances which had not been broken down.

The *Glandulæ suprarenales* (generally termed the adrenal bodies), Figs. 22, 23, and 24, are of the utmost importance in the endocrine system. They are in intimate relation to (without being functionally associated with) the kidneys, and consist of two separate glandular systems. Moreover, throughout the body there are minute portions of tissue resembling the suprarenal medullary substance : for instance, in the liver, the spleen or pancreas, in the male spermatic cord, along the course of the large veins of the abdomen, and of the sympathetic trunk, in the testes and the broad ligaments,

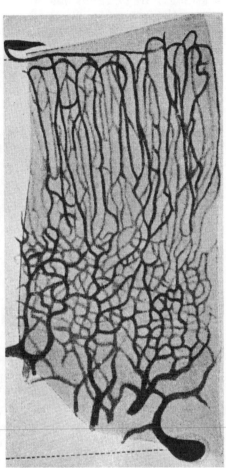

24.—Section through the suprarenal gland of a child. Cortex above and medulla beneath. (After Stöhr.)

the oviducts and ovaries. There are also certain glands whose structure resembles the suprarenals inasmuch as there are two different substances, cortical and medullary. These may be termed the true accessory adrenals (*Glandulæ suprarenales accessoriæ*). All these glandular structures form the adrenal or chromaffin system. The specific central adrenal hormone has been isolated and is known as adrenalin, or epinephrine. Adrenalin has a significant and manifold value for the living organism, but it is essentially a stimulant, an energiser. It causes a contraction of the vascular system and thus increases the blood pressure. The symptoms of Addison's disease are relevant here : the cause is known to be degeneration of the adrenal tissue, generally of tubercular origin.   The blood pressure falls, there are nervous disturbances, anæmia and marasmus, and the skin becomes dirty in appearance, brown and spotted.   The result is generally fatal.

It is possible to trace the presence of the *millionth fraction of a milligramme* of adrenalin.   It has a tonic and stimulant effect on the uterus.   Larger doses cause a strong flow of saliva and it is significant that increased salivary secretion is one of the accompaniments of sexual excitement in normal persons.   Indeed, the adrenal system has extremely powerful influence and interactions genitally, as has been demonstrated by J. F. Meckel as long ago as 1806.   A recent investigator, P. F. Richter, confirmed the paramount importance of the adrenal bodies in determining the essential female characteristics.   The structure of the adrenal cellular tissue closely resembles that of the ovarian corpus luteum.   The cortical portion of the adrenal body seems specially important in this respect.

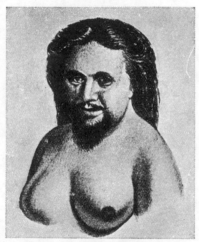   

25.—Bearded European woman.   26.—Mrs. Taylor, born in 1832
(After Ecker.)   in Lincoln, U.S.A.   (After Moll.)

[It had long been known that the cortex was indispensable to health, and that it probably produced a hormone which could be isolated.   Although complete chemical identification has not yet been achieved the hormone (*cortin*) is now being examined, and its effects are being tested both in men and animals.   It has proved of considerable value in cases of Addison's disease.]

In cases of tumours of the suprarenal cortex which involve hypertrophy of local tissue, there is degeneration of the uterus and the menses stop.   There is an increase of hair on the face and body, approaching the masculine type.   In young girls the sexual organs develop before their time, for the ovaries dominate ; but, in elderly women whose ovaries have atrophied, the adrenal bodies continue to function and there is a remarkable hirsute development ; the bearded women (Figs. 25 and 26) of museums and circuses owe their anomaly to disturbance of the suprarenal glands.

After castration there is a hypertrophy of the suprarenal cortex ; the same occurs in pseudo-hermaphroditism and in pubertas præcox.   Here, too, there is a strong growth of hair and often excessive fat.   In women there may be a tendency towards the masculine type in physique, hair growth (*hirsutismus*) and voice.   The converse effect is produced by the injection of ovarian secretion into normal persons ; there is an increase of the suprarenal cortex and this corresponds to certain pheno-mena of pregnancy and of rut in male animals ; *i.e.,* strong pigmentation and growth of hair.

The degeneration and atrophy of the cortex (*hypoplasia*) produces the same symptoms as that of the anterior pituitary lobe (see above) : premature senescence, baldness, loss of fat and flesh, etc. These symptoms constitute what is termed by Charcot, *geromorphism*, and by Variot, *senile nanism*. If the suprarenal cortex is destroyed, death ensues.

Leupold proved that there is a remarkable correspondence between the weight of testes and suprarenal bodies. In 52 out of 100 cases he showed the ratio to be 2·5–1. Further, he found that while the thymus gland is still demonstrable, the adrenal bodies weigh very little, but that, during puberty, the adrenals grow rapidly in weight, while the actual gonads develop more slowly, but for a longer period of time. It has been suggested that the adrenal bodies activate the involution or atrophy of the thymus and thus clear the way for the functions of the sexual organs.

[The interrelation of the ovaries and the suprarenal glands is now becoming more and more evident, and the study of cortical tumours and disturbances generally has tended towards the view that the adrenal cortex is intimately associated with male attributes since, in the case of women, the changes observable are nearly always in the direction of virilism. Collett reports a case in which a girl, only $1\frac{1}{2}$ years old, exhibited hair about the genitals, the labia and furrowed clitoris being well developed. Hair was also to be observed on the face, and the vocal cords were large. After removal of a tumour these appearances receded although hair again began to grow around the vulva two years later. Further advance in our knowledge is certain now that extracts are being prepared.]

The last-named glands (or gonads) are particularly important ; they have (at least) double purposes in either sex. They are glands of reproduction, in which capacity we have already briefly described them. They are also glands of internal secretion. It is still a matter of dispute as to which special portion of the gonadal tissues secretes hormones.

The initial experiments were made by Nussbaum several years ago. He removed the testes of male frogs, which then ceased to develop the pads or protuber-ances on the fore feet with which they normally grasp and hold their mate during copulation. These pads develop in the breeding season. Thus it was experimentally indicated that certain elements derived from the testes promoted the formation of male accessory organs and characteristics : in other words, that the testes had an endocrine secretion. Steinach continued this series of experiments by injections of testicular secretions from male frogs in heat into the bodies of castrated males of the same species. The castrates, before injection, had no urge to copulate and no special organs on their feet. A few hours after injection they became genitally active.

Up to that time the view was held by many men of science that sexual processes were a function of the nervous system. In how far was this view still tenable ? How far were nerves affected as well as glands ? It was already certain that the copulatory reflex of male frogs could be set in motion by mechanical stimuli. Could secretions of specific kind also affect the central nervous system ? Steinach injected his castrated frogs afresh but with a preparation from the spinal and cerebral substance of male frogs in heat. And the same copulatory reflexes duly appeared. But, when spinal and cerebral preparations from male frogs in a sexually quiescent state were injected there was no response.

It was clearly demonstrated that the secretion of the testes had a special chemico-erotic effect on the nervous system of normal male creatures.

Steinach carried his experiments a step nearer the human organism. He removed the testes of very young rats between three and six weeks old. All the typical qualities of the male animal remained in abeyance, *i.e.*, they remained immature. But, if testes were grafted into the bodies of these castrates (and not necessarily in their normal position) the distinctive male qualities developed, if and when the grafts healed and were functionally assimilated. Therefore he concluded that the testicular secretions determine not only the activity of the male sexual impulse, but also the male secondary characteristics. And it was specially illuminating to observe that in the testicular grafts the seminiferous tubules in which the sperms are generated became atrophied and disappeared, but the interstitial cell tissue throve and grew.*

The corresponding series of experiments on female rats included the removal and regrafting of ovarian tissues. The results were substantially in harmony with those obtained on the males. Ovarian excision inhibited the development of female characteristics and the activity of the female sexual functions, and successful ovarian regrafting restored both to normality. But the functions of the ovary are evidently more intricate in certain ways than those of the male gonads.

It is probable that there are other contributory portions of the testes as well as the interstitial cells, but their effects seem virtually the same (see Bouin and Benoit). The ovarian secretions have evidently greater variety, and it cannot be maintained that Steinach's term " gland of puberty " or " puberal gland " is happily chosen or often accurately understood. Of late, many have even disputed the endocrine activity of the interstitial cells. Following an earlier study by Kyrle—who maintained that they were purely trophic or nutritive—these opponents of Steinach either deny that the gonads are endocrines or consider them only secondarily and dependently active, in this sense. But, so long as they cannot produce more positive results, we have no reason to reject the other theory.

Continuing his investigations, Steinach proceeded to try to show that orchitic (or testicular) and ovarian secretions were essentially different ; that these essential essences of maleness and femaleness influenced the whole organism. Otherwise they might well be interchangeable and grafted ovaries need not affect the normal development of male creatures. But, if such grafts were followed by anomalies of feminine type, then the ovarian secretions must be held responsible. *Vice versâ*, female animals might be masculinised by orchitic grafts. Steinach in Vienna, Brandes in Dresden and Sand in Copenhagen, as well as other investigators, have tried to prove these facts. Young rats, guinea pigs and fawns were castrated and their testicles were sewn under the skin of females of their species. In about half the cases the grafts had healed successfully by the end of a fortnight and the results were as might have been expected. The males who had been grafted with ovarian tissues showed no further normal genital development : their scrotal organs remained of infantile size and shape—in fact, they were even less normal than castrated creatures. The typical breadth and thickness of the head and shoulders, characteristic of male mammals, did not appear : their heads and forequarters remained comparatively small and narrow ; the thorax, instead of expanding, was also narrower than in normal or adult castrated males. When they were X-rayed the bony formation was found to be quite feminine. The thick, coarse body hair,

---

* These interstitial cells are groups of cells between the seminiferous tubules of the testes. They are also known as Leydig's cells (*cf.* Kohn).

characteristic of males, was replaced by a softer and shorter coat. And the milk glands grew and became normally female, even under the microscope. They secreted a normal milk, full of fatty substance. As Steinach said : " If young guinea pigs are put close to these feminised adults the infant creatures at once recognise that they can give suck, and they nuzzle up to them. The feminised adults cherish the suckling young, give of their milk and show an evident satisfaction, attention and patience in the exercise of this complex function, equal to that of normal suckling mothers. The determinant deflecting power of the female puberal glands has made males into tender mothers and milk givers." Moreover, these feminised adults were no longer male in their sexual impulse ; they showed no interest in females of their species but received the attentions of the normal males who approached and copulated with them. The conclusion is that the ovaries secrete a substance which not only inhibits but reverses normal male development. The virilised doe rabbits and guinea pigs showed a masculine trend. Their mammary glands, uteri and exterior genitals did not develop normally ; in some cases they even regressed. Their softer and shorter fur was replaced by long, coarse hair and their skulls and shoulders broadened and thickened : sometimes they exceeded the normal males in these dimensions. Their sexual instinct became male in its direction ; they sought out the normal females and were at once able to detect whether or not the objects of their attention were ready to receive them. " As soon as they detected a normal female in oestrus they followed her incessantly, with demonstrations of courtship and attempts at pairing. Towards normal males they showed rivalry and indifference."

The Dresden zoologist, Professor Brandes, corroborates Steinach's results. He says :

" I have myself seen these feminised males in Steinach's laboratory. I was able to assure myself, by careful inspection of the external genitals—though these showed traces of atrophy—that the most characteristic feminine qualities were combined with a male body."

Brandes himself extended the experimental tests to deer.

" We have removed the testicles of a young male and grafted them into the lower abdomen of a doe, whose ovaries were grafted into his body. Both animals were, of course, very young. Both are reacting to the grafts already. The former doe has clearly recognisable rudiments of horns and the Adam's apple in the throat which is distinctively male ; and it is beginning the characteristic jumping and springing movements of male deer. The feminised male shows no sign of either horns or Adam's apple, but has mammary glands, which normally appear only after the young are conceived."

There can, therefore, be little doubt that both the secondary sexual characteristics and the direction of sexual urge and emotion are dependent on substances produced by the gonads, and that these gonads produce substances of opposite nature ; so that the male gonad or testicle activates the development of male characteristics and directs the urge towards the female, and that the female gonad or ovary operates in the contrary manner. It is not of much importance whether the interstitial cells, or other portions of the gonadic tissue manufacture these essential substances.

As Brandes remarks :

" The careful inspection of the glandular grafts, which had healed in their new site showed that both the spermatozoa with their tubules and the ova were quite atrophied, but that the connective tissue throve, and that there was a special proliferation of Leydig's cells (in the male organ) and lutein cells (in the female). We cannot, therefore, attribute the endocrine secretions to the reproductive cells, but must consider the proliferating interstitial tissue responsible.''

[For many years the nature and source of the testis hormone have received attention, but it is only with recent years that experimental work has made real progress. It is known that one hormone is very powerful, and it would appear from recent work that a second hormone is produced having some relation to the pituitary. The source of these hormones is still debated, but it would seem probable that both the interstitial cells and the germinal tissues share in the work of production. The work of Steinach, supported by Brandes (whose experiments were badly reported), gave rise to extravagant hypotheses which are not fully justified. Nevertheless, research has shown the extreme potency of the male hormones, and their interaction with the pituitary is being demonstrated.

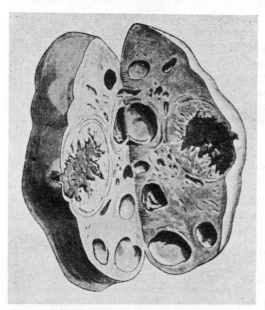

27.—Ovary of a healthy 19-year-old girl: section showing corpus luteum at menstruation. (After Kollmann.)

In discussing the effects of gland grafting and the injection of hormones and extracts the subjective factors must never be neglected. Undoubtedly much exaggeration has existed and possibly even a certain degree of charlatanry. In view of certain results in animals, however, it would be hazardous to reject the whole of the experiments as due to fraud, mal-observation or suggestion. Nevertheless, the influence of the latter (whatever may be the precise mechanism at work) is enormous. It may be perceived even in the cases of such radical operations as castration. A recent instance was a man, who, castrated at 25, was capable of leading an active life and satisfying his wife, if we can credit the report. Examination showed few serious physical disabilities beyond the loss of the testes. Moreover, a recent report that an examination of 23 palace eunuchs in China revealed the fact that 10 were suffering from gonorrhœa indicates that caution is suggested. (*Cf.* Rowe and Lawrence : McCartney. For plates illustrating the genitals of Peking eunuchs, see Matignon.)]

We must now consider the special female gonad or ovary. An ovary is depicted in Fig. 27. We have already given a brief description of the structure of these organs and the formation of ova. But what portions of the ovaries secrete the female hormones ? And are other tissues or organs also active in this sense ? Present-day biology attributes the ovarian hormones to the interstitial cells, follicles (Figs. 28, 29A, 29B, 30) and corpus luteum, which develop rhythmically as the follicles rupture. (Bucura, 1913, Sand, 1918.) There are also apparently endocrine qualities in the ovule after ovulation, the myometrial gland, the placenta, and even the actual embryo, and these probabilities do not exclude other possible sources of hormonic supply. We must distinguish between the *corpus luteum* (Fig. 31) of pregnancy (*corpus luteum gravi-ditatis*) and what has been called the spurious corpus luteum, which develops and disperses concurrently with an unfertilised ovum, which passes out of the body.* The corpus luteum can obviously bear no part in the actual physical evolution of the female organs; and Biedl correctly states that the anatomical structure of the uterus is not due to the corpus luteum but to the interstitial tissue. And, indeed, as we shall show, the corpus luteum is essentially preparatory and accessory to reproduction. In order to make this clear we must define the processes of ovulation and menstruation (Figs. 27 and 30).

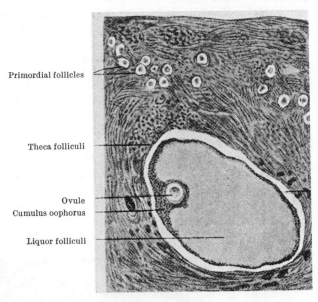

Primordial follicles

Theca folliculi

Ovule
Cumulus oophorus

Liquor folliculi

28.—Follicle from the ovary of a seven-year-old girl.

The life of woman has three main physiological stages: the pre-puberal, in which the general and genital organism is undeveloped; the adult, or sexually mature, which begins with puberty and continues till the climacteric, and

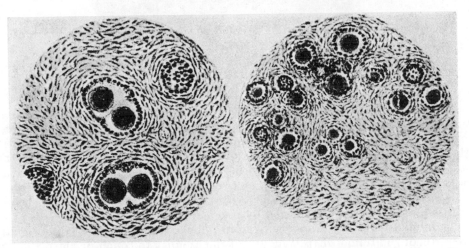

29A.—Primordial follicles containing two ova about to divide into follicles containing one. From the ovary of a 34-year-old woman. (After Lindemann.)

29B.—Primordial follicles from the ovary of a 25-year-old woman.

the final stage of physical and genital repose. Sexual maturity begins, as a rule, in temperate climates between 13 and 14 years of age; in southern lands, 11, 10 or even earlier, and in northern lands much later.* Its functional sign is menstruation, which

* [This is not now generally accepted.]

normally recurs till the climacteric, at average intervals of four weeks.   The average age for the climacteric is from 45–50 among women living in temperate climates. These changes must obviously be accompanied by alterations in the activity of the endocrine glands or the amount of endocrine secretions.   Thus, menstruation has normally certain recurrent symptoms : increased secretion of saliva, loss of appetite, or, on the other hand, sharp hunger, with tendency to diarrhœa, moods of depression or elation and excitability and swelling of the breasts.   In singers, also, there is generally a marked alteration in vocal range and even quality.   All these symptoms are more or less normal, and there are others of a pathological nature in some cases. During menstruation there is a loss of between 100–200 c.c. of dark red blood, mixed with cervical mucus, which is expelled from the os uteri through the vagina. In the course of each four-weekly cyclic interval between menstrual periods a ripe ovule is normally extruded from the ovary by the rupture of a Graafian follicle (Figs. 27 and 30), or occasionally two ovules, from two separate follicles : a process known as *ovulation*.   The ovule may be fertilised and develop normally into a child,

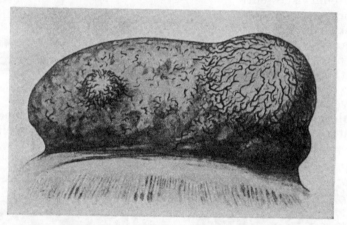

30.—Ovary of young woman with follicle ready to rupture.
(After Kollmann.)

or remain unfertilised and pass away.   In either case a series of phenomena result, of the utmost importance and corresponding to changes in the internal secretions. At the risk of anticipating the contents of some of our ensuing chapters we must consider them in some detail here, for during the decades of woman's sexual maturity there is an alternation of two cycles, or two possibilities.   Sellheim describes this as *functional duality*, the duality of the fertilised or unfertilised ovum.   If the ovum is fertilised, menstruation is replaced by pregnancy and birth.

The ovule is extruded from the ovarian follicle, whose rupture is the signal for the tendrils of the funnel-shaped mouth of the oviduct to touch or clasp the ovary at the site of the follicle ; and the ovule which has been released with some impetus, is caught and drawn into the tube—as a sea anemone captures a water-flea in Liepmann's striking comparison.   The ovule is carried along the oviduct by the capillary current and remains in the so-called *ampulla tubæ uterinæ* until the moment of fertilisation.*   If this is effected the fertilised ovum is further carried into the

* [Recent work is inclined to emphasise the muscular theory rather than the ciliary theory of the transport of the ova.   This point of view has been attained largely through the work of Corner and his colleagues in the United States.]

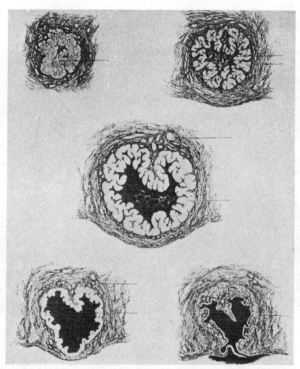

31.—Development and involution of a corpus luteum spurium.   (After Bumm.)
(a) Newly-ruptured follicle ;   (b) Corpus luteum of 10 days ;   (c) Corpus luteum of 3 weeks ;   (d) Corpus luteum of 5 weeks ;   (e) Corpus luteum of 8 weeks.

womb, whose mucous membrane has been prepared for its reception, and is there implanted for further development.   This is the initial functional stage of fertilisation or pregnancy.

   If the ovum does not meet and receive the sperm cell, it passes out of the body

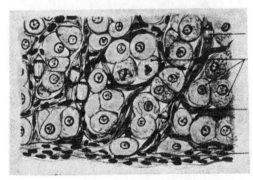

a. Mitosis of a connective tissue cell.

b. Lutein cells.

c Connective tissue cells.

d. Theca externa.

32.—Part of a corpus luteum of a rabbit, 52 hours after copulation.   (After Sobotta.)

together with the prepared uterine membrane, and this is *menstruation*, which might be termed the birth of an unfertilised ovum.   The respective durations of the two cycles are the 10 months (of 28 days each) of pregnancy and the four weeks of menstrual intervals.   Von Spee calculates that the unfertilised ovule takes between seven and nine days to traverse the complete length of the oviduct, which is 12 c.c.

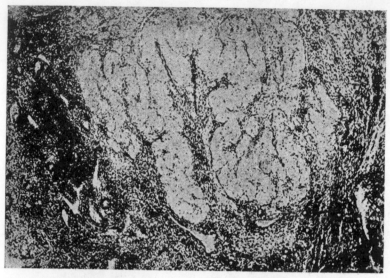

33.—Corpus albicans under low magnification.   (After Lindemann.)

What of the follicle meanwhile ? Its *theca*, or connective sheath becomes full of blood and the *membrana granulosa* swells and *proliferates* (Fig. 27).   It becomes

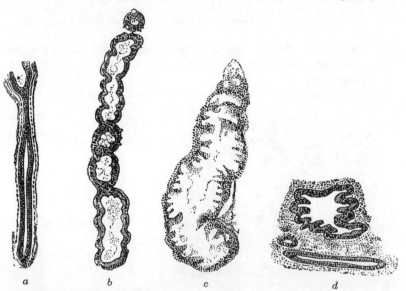

a   *b*   *c*   *d*

34.—Changes in single uterine glands during the menstrual cycle.   (*a*) Post-menstrual ; (*b*) Interval ; (*c*) Pre-natal ; (*d*) Menstrual.   (After Lindemann.)

full of blood clots and the cells show a distinct yellowish colour.   The colouring matter, which is full of fatty substance, is termed lutein (Fig. 31).   This yellow tint appears distinctively associated with reproduction : it is present in the pollen of flowers and the yolk of eggs. The enlarged granulous cells become interlaced with very minute capillaries and thus a kind of gland is formed. This is termed the stage of *vascularisation* of the *corpus luteum*, or yellow body, which acts as a source of internal secretion and these processes appear to be determined by the ovule itself, which exudes subtle chemical substances which stimulate its parent follicle. If the ovum should miss fertilisation its fate is shared by its chemical exudations and by its follicle, which cannot maintain itself, but disperses (Fig. 31) and makes way for a fresh follicle. But, if fertilisation takes place more powerful chemical stimulants arise and the corpus luteum remains active throughout most of the months of pregnancy. It inhibits the growth of fresh follicles and, in a sense, protects the

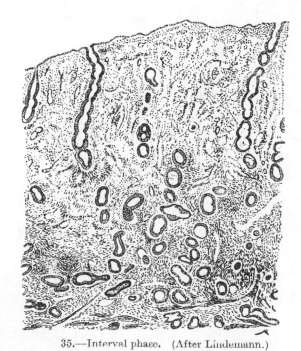

35.—Interval phase. (After Lindemann.)

developing embryo. If the preservation and development of the embryo are assured the so-called *corpus luteum graviditatis* also degenerates and disperses, as Novak has graphically shown. The cells of the *membrana granulosa* are almost free from fatty substances but the theca lutein cells have minute fatty particles even before the follicles burst. Later, the characteristic colour fades and the *corpus albicans* (Fig. 33) appears, these processes occurring more rapidly in the so-called spurious corpus luteum.

With regard to menstruation. Let us take, firstly, the *latent* stage (termed so by Hitschmann and Adler), otherwise the *interval* (Schröder), and the stage of *proliferation*. The outer surface of the uterine mucous membrane is an epithelium composed of cylindrical cells. The glands of this mucous membrane are tubular and of equal thickness. After 14 days changes begin ; the tissues have already become moist and now the mucous membrane swells, expands and forms a compact outer—or upper—layer over a spongy base. The glands expand and the connective tissue vanishes in the lower stratum more and more, but in the upper stratum it increases and its cells take a deciduous character. They become vascularised, and increase ; their volume is almost trebled. This is the *pre-menstrual* stage, the phase of secretion (Fig. 36). Thus the mucous membrane of the uterus prepares to receive the fertilised ovum ; it offers a "nest" for its adhesion and the establishment of gestation. If fertilisation fails, then this preparation is useless. The mucous membranes break down and disperse ; they are expelled together with the blood from the capillaries, in *menstruation* or *desquamation* (Fig. 37). The membrane returns to its normal or latent stage with cylindrical epithelial glands (*post-menstrual stage*, or *regeneration*) (Fig. 38).

The further question now arises as to *the relation between Ovulation and Men-*

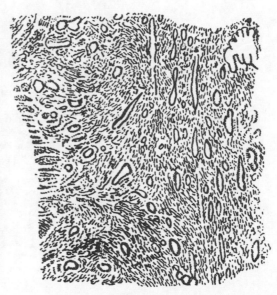

36.—Mucous membrane of a menstruating uterus. Through desquamation of the epithelium the sub-epithelial hæmatomata are emptied, the blood being discharged. (After Lindemann.)

37.—The upper layer of the uterine membrane in a menstruating woman has broken down. Regeneration follows quickly. (After Lindemann.)

struation. Are we able to determine at which precise moment of the monthly cycle the ovule is extruded from the ovarian follicle ? Obviously, this is highly important, and in various ways. The ovule, fresh from the follicle, is certainly ready for fertilisation ; moreover, if we knew the exact date of ovulation, both the real age of the embryo and the length of time before birth would be calculable. Unfortunately, the problem has not yet been fully elucidated. We know that menstruation without ovulation is very rare, but expulsion of ova without subsequent genital hæmorrhage is quite possible. Novak says : "Till now we have only ascertained that ovulation does not synchronise with the monthly flow, but precedes it. Also, we know that, during menstruation, the corpus luteum has already reached its degenerative stage. But we are not yet sure of the date of follicular rupture, nor the associated questions of the rate of maturation and development of the corpus luteum." Siegel, on the other hand, believes that his questionnaires to families of soldiers on furlough have proved the best time for fertilisation to be shortly after the menstrual period : that is to say, in the *phase of post-menstruation*. The aptitude decreases during the interval and in the pre-menstruation phase (some) women are almost sterile. The maximum of conceptions was between eight and nine days after menstruation.

It is impossible to be more precise in our present state of knowledge. As we do not know the exact duration of the ovum's existence, nor that of the spermatozoon, we are unable to calculate the exact age of the embryo. Triepel believes that fertilisation generally takes place between the 16th and 24th days of the cycle, as reckoned above, and that the maximum chances are on the 16th.

[The whole question of the relation of ovulation to menstruation and the time of ovulation has recently been given fresh impetus through important work among the higher primates and also as a result of current controversy on the so-called " safe period " from the point of view of the likelihood or not of conception. The belief that the mid-week or fortnight in the month is a " safe period " is now almost wholly discarded. Dr. Enid Charles, among others, has pointed out that the results of modern research point to two conclusions. Ovulation varies within wide limits in the human species, but the time at which it is most likely to occur is from the 7th to the 13th day, or as some think, midway between two menstrual periods. Thus the time of maximal fertility is in the mid-period, and this well accords with the Jewish interdiction of coitus in the seven days following menstruation.

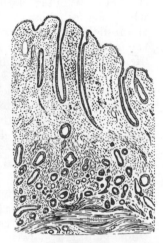

38.—Post-menstrual mucous membrane.

It is not yet known with any degree of certainty how long the sperm can live and be capable of fertilisation. Wide limits are probable, although the times previously accepted seem to be becoming less as research continues. However that may be, the week preceding menstruation is possibly the least likely period for fertilisation, unless, as has been thought, coitus itself may lead to a discharge of the ovum as is the case with certain animals, and as T. Bell seems to have believed in his *Kalogynomia*, p. 192.]

We shall now briefly consider the remaining endocrine organs. L. Fraenkel, in some of his papers, clearly demonstrated that the corpus luteum was a recurrently regenerative gland : its secretion is said to be a lipoid, and, according to Herrmann, a derivative of cholesterin. He has been able to compose it chemically as a thick, yellow, viscous, oily product. Seitz extracted two separate constituents from the corpus luteum : one, a luteolipoid, which slows down or suppresses menstruation ; and a lecithalbumin (Lipamin) which has the contrary effect. It increases the menstrual flow in women, or restores it again in conditions of amenorrhea, whence it may be an abortifacient. The secretions of the corpus luteum control the menstrual function, prepare the female organs to receive and nourish the product of conception and inhibit the growth of fresh follicles till pregnancy is over. But these luteal secretions are only a part of the endocrine apparatus. The corpus luteum has no power to determine the organic development of the female organs, or the psychic manifestations of emotion in women : these are under the domination of the interstitial cellular tissue of the ovaries.

These interstitial cells appear to consist mainly of follicles which have either reached the stage of *involution* or have not matured (latency). They are said to influence the special trend of the normal woman's erotic impulse, *i.e.*, towards man. Some authorities dispute their existence. but their arguments are not convincing. They do not explain which organs furnish the internal hormones previous to the first corpus luteum. Limon, on the other hand, describes the determinative ovarian parts in mammals as large cells grouped around the blood vessels and resembling those of liver and suprarenal capsules, but smaller in size than the distinctive cells of the corpus luteum ; and Seitz and Wallart have proved the same facts in human subjects. Wallart claims that these cells steadily proliferate until puberty, after which the follicular mechanism comes into play. This is as might be expected, for the follicles do not function in producing ova before puberty. During pregnancy the interstitial cells again proliferate and there are traces of them after the change of life. But, in human beings, these important cells are not concentrated into a separate gland. Seitz states that all the larger follicles are dispersed during pregnancy, forming a further reserve of fatty substance called by him *thecalutein* cells, as distinct from the lutein cells of the corpus luteum itself. Thus we must assume that the thecalutein cells regulate the psychic factors in the sexual life of the woman and promote the development of secondary sexual characteristics, in the bony structure of the skeleton, the amount of fat and its distribution, the hair on head and body, the throat and larynx, the breasts, and the actual genital organs in the earliest years of life.

The general working of the ovaries may be seen negatively as well as positively. Consider the effects of their total removal (castration). If castration occurs before puberty, growth is arrested : if afterwards, there is a general degeneration of the whole genital apparatus. If the ovaries are removed after a pregnancy has begun, its further stages are hindered. The specific degeneration following castration shrivels the genitalia and stops the monthly period. Von Franqué has shown that there are also nervous symptoms, like those which generally accompany the change of life and due to decrease in organic functions. They may include cardiac palpitations, rushes of blood to the head, sensations of fear and disquiet, profuse perspiration, vertigo and sleeplessness. They are ascribed to the extra activity of the suprarenal glands, which overpower the waning ovarian activity. The typical symptom of "the change " is, however, the cessation of the monthly periods. And there is a change in some or all of the secondary characteristics. There is a loss of the roundness of the hips, thighs and bust ; hair grows on throat or upper lip and the pubic hair approaches the masculine type ; the voice often changes noticeably and becomes both harsher in tone and deeper in pitch. In other words, the woman's body loses its special qualities and approaches an intermediate or asexual type.

We know already that the ovaries are not the only organs with specifically feminine internal secretions. It is possible that the epithelial cells of the oviducts also share in the endocrine flow after each follicular rupture, which would mean, in all probability, that they are also influenced by the corpus luteum. Bouin and Ancel state that in the second half of pregnancy a further endocrine organ appears in the wall of the womb : it consists of large, spindle-shaped or polygonal cells of darker plasm and they call it the myometrial gland. Fraenkel believes that it is not in evidence in every individual case, but agrees that it influences the secretion of milk. Guggisberg is of opinion that the main body of the pregnant uterus itself secretes substances which prepare its muscular structure, and here pituitary secretions might also be of influence.

Herrmann has investigated the placenta and states that a substance with similar properties to those of the corpus luteum may be extracted. Bouin and Ancel concur that this substance has endocrine action on the mammary glands after the fourth month of gestation. Basch demonstrated that injections, both of ovarian secretion and of placental extract, increased the size of the mammary glands in a pregnant bitch ; and Halban made the same observations. It has been stated that the typical effects of castration in doe rabbits has been obliterated by injections of placental extract ; and it has been shown that both the embryo and the more developed fœtus contribute this placental stimulant to the mother's blood stream and prepare her breasts to feed them. It has also been maintained that the breasts make an independent hormonic contribution which stimulates the genital organs in the same manner as the posterior pituitary. [Recent work on the placenta has shown that its secretions are of great importance ; and Aschheim and Zondek have demonstrated that the blood and urine of pregnant women contain theelin and also a certain amount of hormone from the anterior pituitary. By the injection of small amounts of female urine into test animals the nature of the reaction can be noted and a fairly reliable test for pregnancy can be established as early as the sixth week.] Thus the entire genital complex function in women is regulated by the joint activity of the endocrine glands.

Let us now consider the normal process of fertilisation in woman.

An ovarian follicle develops and swells and begins to secrete a substance which activates the oviducts, making them ready for the transport of the ovum. Then the uterine lining is altered and prepared for the reception of the ovum after fertilisation. This follicular product also prepares the genital organs for the reception of the sperm cells, and causes a rhythmic expansion of the breasts, but not, as yet, the secretion of milk. These manifestations steadily increase, while the follicle bursts, expelling the ovule, and they continue to increase if the ovule is fertilised. The fertilised ovule interacts on the corpus luteum of its parent follicle and inhibits the growth of a fresh follicle which would interrupt the process and bring on miscarriage. Meanwhile, the placenta has been formed, and, in a sense, has collaborated with the corpus luteum graviditatis in expanding the mammary glands and holding back their milk ; whilst the thyroid quickens metabolism in order to meet the increased demands of mother and child. During pregnancy a woman's weight increases by about a fifth and her heart expands by about a quarter. Towards the end of pregnancy the corpus luteum slowly degenerates, the suprarenal cortex increases in size and these glands exercise a tonic effect on the womb. The myometrial gland, placenta and, above all, the embryo, check further mammary growth while furthering the secretion of milk. Specific mammary secretions, together with those of the posterior pituitary, give the signal for the labour pains and finally the birth itself. The normal duration for pregnancy is 10 lunar months, that is to say, 10 times 28 days. The special structures and activities of the pregnant organism subside after birth, but lactation prolongs them. However, a new impregnation may easily occur before lactation ceases.

In the unfertilised functional cycle pregnancy does not occur. The ovule is not fertilised and its " yellow body " becomes a " corpus luteum spurium " which disperses and cannot check the development of a fresh follicle. This fresh follicle breaks down the proliferating uterine membranes and brings on *menstruation*—the birth of the unfertilised ovum—while extruding and preparing for its own ovule.

Thus, during the unfertilised functional cycle, the controlling body is the ovary and its secretions : but, when fertilisation occurs, this control is mainly taken over by the secretion of the other endocrine glands.

We shall deal with both the secondary characteristics and the instincts of sex in later chapters. But it is now appropriate to consider how sex is differentiated in the course of embryology : for this matter is closely connected with the properties and secretions of the essential gonads, *i.e.*, testes and ovaries, respectively.

THE EMBRYOLOGY OF SEX

We do not yet know how far there is sexual differentiation in the essential germ plasm. Some authorities uphold the view that there is differentiation of male and female in the spermatozoa ; others attribute this differentiation to the ovules ; others, again, believe that both sperm cells and egg cells may be either male or female, or, at least, disposed towards maleness or femaleness. But the most likely hypothesis attributes sex differentiation to phenomena of inheritance or determining genes, and admits that both spermatozoa and ova may contain male and female elements. In various forms of animal life sex differentiation certainly arises independently of the particular arrangement of the chromosomes, and it is possible that the same is true of our species as well.

We are able to distinguish special sex chromosomes and we know that in the course of formation the number of the chromosomes is reduced, one sex chromosome remaining in the egg. Half of all sperm cells has a sex chromosome but not the other half.* In the egg cell the sex chromosome is equally divided, so that each possesses this distinctive element. If an ovule is fertilised by a spermatozoon which does not contain the proper sex chromosome, the resulting product of conception develops as a male. If the fertilising spermatozoon has the sex chromosome, the resulting product evolves as a female. We may therefore conclude that there are spermatozoa which produce daughters and others which produce sons. Perhaps there are other factors as well : possibly some of the egg cells only react to—or attract—one kind of sperms, and others only to the other kind. This is, so far, unproved, but we do know that when fertilisation occurs it decides the sex—or the predominant sexual type—of the living creature to be born.

Fertilisation having occurred, we can now gradually trace the growth of the sex characteristics.†

The sex organs are contained within a portion of the urinary apparatus of the embryo which develops very early and is distinguishable before the actual genital structures. We, therefore, can speak of the *urogenital apparatus*.

It develops out of the *mesoderm* (as distinct from the *endoderm* and *ectoderm* respectively), or central layer of the germinal membrane, which separates along the rudimentary spinal site and forms the so-called *celom* or embryonic body cavity and the urogenital canal. Within the earliest weeks of embryonic growth, the so-called *pronephros* emerges, a duct runs from it, but, in the third week this

---

* [This statement requires modification.]

† The earliest human ovum (the Miller ovum) was about 11 days old. Of the older ones, the Teacher-Bryce I, Peters' and Florian's are representative. For three recent cases of interest see Ludwig.

structure has been superseded by the *mesonephros*, while the duct remains and develops. It is known as the *Wolffian* duct (Fig. 39). The mesonephros is differentiated from the urogenital sinus in the seventh week; the kidneys assume their typical form. And two weeks before, on either side of the rudimentary spine and on the inner dorsal surface of the embryo, two folds or pads appear, called the genital ridges.

Germ cells or distinctively sexual cells—which have, hitherto, been scattered —congregate within these regions and modify the epithelial germ plasm into glands, which are differentiated at about six weeks. They develop either as testes or as ovaries, and send their distinctive hormones into the blood stream, acting thus already as functional endocrines. Hirschfeld has suggested *Andrin* as a suitable name for the testicular hormone and *Gynæcin* for the ovarian. The germinal gonad

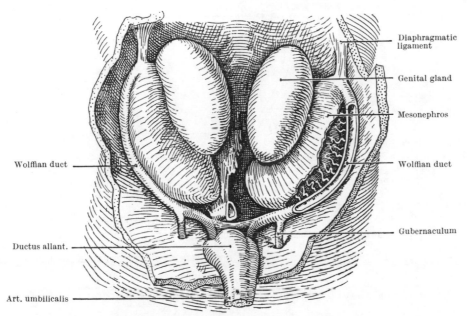

39.—Formation of the sex organs. (After Kollmann.)

is at first, however, undifferentiated sexually; it may therefore be modified in its male trend or its female; and it can be, and has been, maintained that there is no absolute organic male nor absolute organic female, but that the structures which show the greatest number of male characteristics are masculine and those with the greatest number of female characteristics feminine.

The range of sexual differentiation in human beings is like the keyboard of a musical instrument or a chart of colours, which runs the gamut from the palest to the deepest tints, even from black to white. There is an enormous diversity of *inter*-grades or intermediate types between the typically masculine and the typically feminine.*

* In the words of Professor F. A. E. Crew: "It is not the sex chromosomes that ultimately determine sex; it is the sex determining gene-complex, and disharmony among the elements of this may be such as must lead to the assumption of a totally inappropriate sexual characterisation . . . the sex chromosome constitution does not necessarily agree with the sexual characterisation" ("Sexuality and Intersexuality," B.S.S.S.P. Publication, No. 14, 1925).

Within the mesonephros is a network of minute tubules transversely arranged and opening into the Wolffian duct. In the further development of the sex organs both the mesonephros and the gonads collaborate and interlock. The mesonephros is gradually obliterated, but its upper portion evolves into the epididymis in the male, while the lower extremity atrophies until, finally, only the paradidymis (or Giraldes' Organ) remains.* In the female, even less is left of the primordial structure. The upper portion becomes the ep-oöphoron (or Rosenmüller's Organ) and the lower the par-oöphoron.

There is a double differentiation from the Wolffian and Müllerian ducts respec-

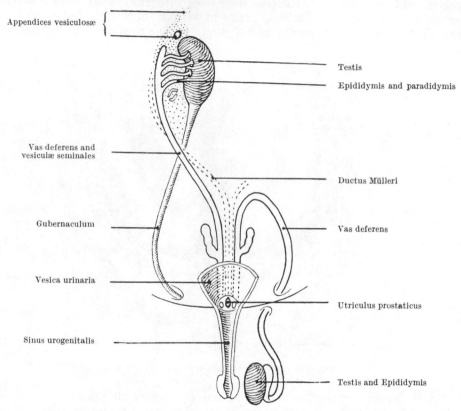

Appendices vesiculosæ

Testis

Epididymis and paradidymis

Vas deferens and vesiculæ seminales

Ductus Mülleri

Gubernaculum

Vas deferens

Vesica urinaria

Utriculus prostaticus

Sinus urogenitalis

Testis and Epididymis

40A.—Development of the inner sexual organ of the male.   (After Kollmann.)

tively. In the male, the *Müllerian* duct atrophies and the *Wolffian* is elaborated into seminal ducts or *vasa deferentia* (with the seminal vesicles and epididymis). Finally, nothing is left of the *Müllerian* duct but *Morgagni's hydatids* (*appendices vesiculosi*) and a small cul-de-sac, corresponding to the vagina in women.

In the female the two main ducts approach one another from either side and unite in a tube or canal : the Wolffian duct becomes obliterated and absorbed into this new structure, but its remains are sometimes found in the form of cysts in the internal genital tract of women. A conspicuous vestigial trace is known as *Gaitner's duct ;* others again, as hydatids. The upper extremity of the Müllerian duct becomes a funnel-mouthed cone and this further evolves into the oviducts or tubes,

* [This statement requires modification.]

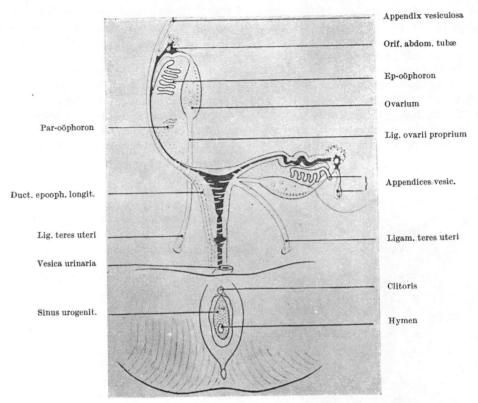

Appendix vesiculosa

Orif. abdom. tubæ

Ep-oöphoron

Ovarium

Lig. ovarii proprium

Par-oöphoron

Appendices vesic.

Duct. epooph. longit.

Lig. teres uteri

Ligam. teres uteri

Vesica urinaria

Clitoris

Sinus urogenit.

Hymen

40b.—Development of the inner sexual organs of the female.

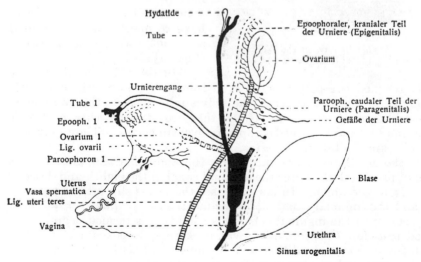

Hydatide

Tube

Epoophoraler, kranialer Teil
der Urniere (Epigenitalis)

Ovarium

Urnierengang

Tube 1

Parooph., caudaler Teil der
Urniere (Paragenitalis)

Epooph. 1

Gefäße der Urniere

Ovarium 1

Lig. ovarii

Paroophoron 1

Uterus

Blase

Vasa spermatica

Lig. uteri teres

Vagina

Urethra

Sinus urogenitalis

41.—Development of the female sexual organs from the indifferent anlage of the urogenital
system.

the uterus and vagina. If the union of the Müllerian and Wolffian ducts is not complete, there ensue malformations of womb and vagina, even bifid (double) forms. From Müller's eminence, at the lower extremity, develop the hymen and Skene's glands (Figs. 40A, 40B, 41 and 42).

In the first month both the Müllerian and Wolffian ducts and the allantois open into a common orifice, termed the cloaca. Part of the allantois becomes the bladder and part the urogenital canal into which the Müllerian and Wolffian ducts open. In the second month the exterior male organs emerge; there is a rudimentary penis and the perineum appears, separating the cloaca (which becomes the anus) from the urogenital aperture; and, as the perineum expands, so these two orifices grow more widely apart (Fig. 43).

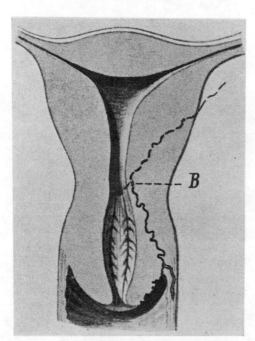

42.—Atypical course of the Wolffian duct. (After Schottländer.)

In the eighth week, definite external differentiation begins. In the female the general changes are not excessive; the distance between the apertures grows and the vestibulum vaginæ is formed; the genital cleft is developed into the labia minora and the genital eminence becomes the clitoris. The labio-scrotal folds become the fleshy labia majora, whilst in front the mons veneris is formed.

In the male the changes are more definite and extensive. The genital eminence becomes the penis and the genital sulcus or canal is formed in that organ in its middle portion (Fig. 44). The pads or folds become the scrotal sacs, which subsequently meet and unite in their median line, into the normal scrotum. But the scrotal sacs at first are empty, for testes, like ovaries, are concealed within the abdominal cavity. Both types of gonad have to make a descent into their future site, but the female gonads move first (Fig. 41).

In the third month the ovaries have already reached the pelvic cavity; in the sixth they are in line with the upper portion of the uterus and reach the pelvis minor, where they remain connected to the broad ligaments of the uterus. If they drop further, this must be regarded as an abnormality and is termed ectopia, or ovarian hernia. They may even protrude externally and be taken for testes.

In the male the testes approach the abdominal inguinal ring in the sixth month of pre-natal life, enter the inguinal canal in the eighth and descend or emerge externally in the ninth. In normal cases the testes slip into the sacs prepared for them and the inguinal canal closes behind them. If, however, either one or both testes remain in the inguinal canal this condition is termed cryptorchism or undescended testicle. Cryptorchism, ovarian hernia, hypospadia, etc., are all phases and stages of *hermaphroditism* and we must deal with them in somewhat closer detail for, morphologically, as well as mentally, the sexes may merge together in a series of intermediate steps.

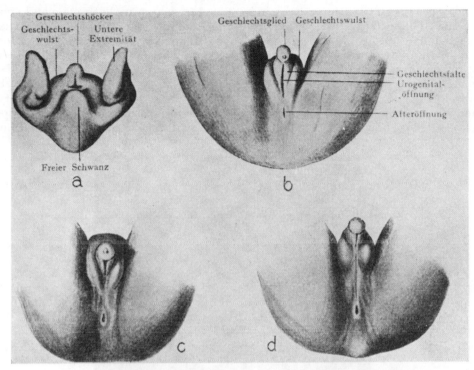

43.—Development of the external sexual organs. (*a*) Earliest stage ; (*b*) Indifferent stage (*c*) Female form ; (*d*) Male form. (After Merkel.)

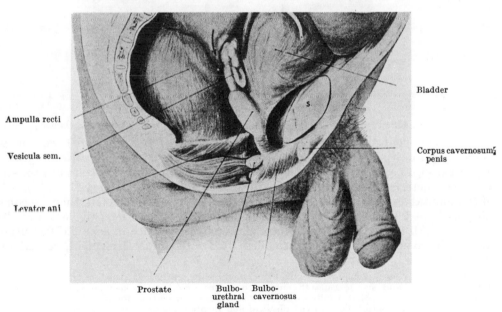

44.—Adult male sexual organs. (After Corning)

We have seen that the embryo, in its first stages, appears both male and female. But the differentiation is occasionally neither definite nor complete ; there is no " clean cut," but, while one sex may be dominant in physique and mind, of an individual, there are certain anomalies strongly suggestive of the opposite sex. If the endocrine secretions are abnormal either the actual gonads and genitalia, or the secondary characteristics (such as growth of hair, larynx and vocal pitch, bust development) or, finally, the direction of desire, will differ from the average type. Then we enter the far-reaching territory of hermaphroditism and intersexual types.* The possible permutations and combinations here are very numerous.   If the gonads

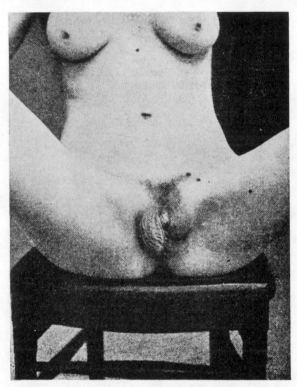

45.—Penoscrotal hypospadia with rudimentary penis.   (After Neugebauer.)

and external genitalia contain examples of both sexes (cf. Rutherford), we can speak of hermaphroditism, they are genuinely hermaphrodites (Hermaphroditismus genitalis) (cf. Figs. 45, 46 and 47).   If, on the other hand, the genitals are normal but the secondary characteristics atypical in structure, we speak of Androgyny (Fig. 48).   And, if the mental and emotional faculties and trends alone are affected, then we come to the fields of Transvestitism (Figs. 49 and 50), Homosexuality (Fig. 51) and Metatropism.   All these types, which arise through disturbance in sexual differentiation from whatever cause, have been called by Dr. Magnus Hirschfeld, sexual intermediate types.

* [In certain cases it may be possible by surgical means, partially at least, to transform a "man" into a " woman " and thereby cause the subject to assume a rôle more in keeping with his own feelings. It is unlikely, however, that a fully satisfactory solution could be thus found for such individuals, as a complete transformation both in the physical and mental spheres is far from easy to attain.   An account of such an attempt in the case of the Danish artist Wegener has recently been published.]

Hirschfeld, in his "Sexualpathologie," makes the following classification :

I. *Hermaphroditismus genitalis,* or true *Hermaphroditism.* Mixture of male and female genitalia in the same person

II. *Hermaphroditismus somaticus* or *Androgyny.* Mixture of other physical, secondary sex characteristics in the same person.

46.—Penoscrotal hypospadia in a 26-year-old cook. (After Neugebauer.)

III. *Hermaphroditismus psychicus.* (*Transvestitism.*) Mixture of psychic characteristics.

IV. *Hermaphroditismus psychosexualis.* (*Homosexuality,* "*Metatropism*".) Masculine direction of desire in woman ; feminine in man.

In certain forms of mollusca hermaphroditism is normal and typical. (*Cf. Handwörterbuch der Naturwissenschaft,* III. 26, IV. 320.)

In human beings we observe that bisexuality, to a more or less pronounced degree, tends to "run in families," and may be inherited or appear collaterally. In many pronounced cases malformations of hypophysis and/or suprarenal glands have been demonstrated. We have already mentioned the male defect of *cryptorchism.* In such cases there are no externally visible testicles and the undescended testicles are not normal in structure. There have even been cases of bisexuality in the gonads themselves : of glands containing both ovarian and

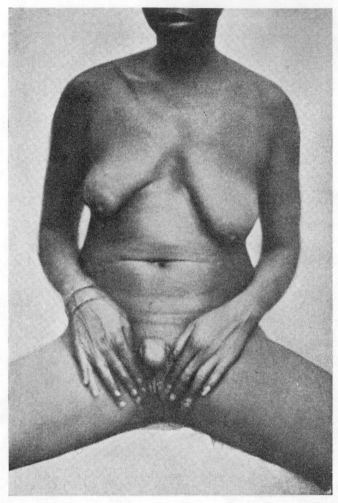

47.—" Hermaphrodite " from Loango.   (Anthrop. Society, Berlin.)

testicular tissue and secreting hormones of both types. These are termed *ovo-testes*.* We have seen that the primitive genital eminence can develop either as

---

* *Cf.* F. A. E. Crew, who states :

" Abnormality of the genital system, taking the form of an intimate mixture of male and female genitalia associated with some degree of imperfection of the external reproductive organs, is common in the pig and goat and is by no means unknown in the human subject.

" . . . . It was found, on examination, that the cases fell cleanly into one of two classes : (1) Those in which no morphological evidence of the previous or present existence of ovarian tissue could be found in the gonads, which were entirely composed of testicular tissue, with a histological structure varying with the position of the testis along the line between the primitive position and the scrotum, but always exhibiting some degree of degenerative change. And (2) those in which both ovarian and testicular tissues were present, the gonads being one an ovary, the other a testis ; one an ovary, the

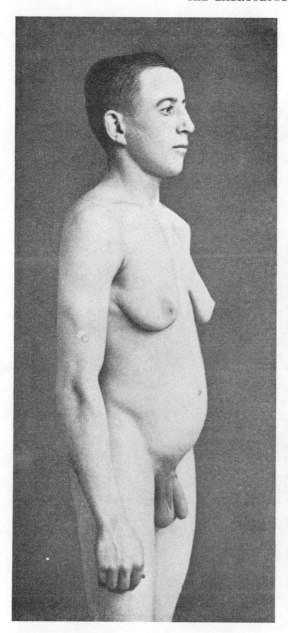

48.—Androgyny. (After Goldmann.)

49.—Homosexual female transvestite in male attire. (After Goldmann in *Gesch. u. Gesellschaft.*)

other an ovotestis ; or both being ovotestes. In one case, there were paired ovaries within the abdominal cavity and paired testes beneath the skin of the perineum.

"It was noted that, in the cases of class (2), in which one gonad was an ovary, this gonad was always the left one and that, in an ovotestis, the ovarian tissue was invariably cephalad to and sharply separated by a well-defined belt of connective tissue from the caudad testicular portion. The ovarian tissue was invariably of comparatively normal structure, histologically, whereas, in the testicular tissue, the spermatogenic was always degenerate to some degree and the interstitial plentiful " (*op. cit.*, pp. 16–17).

the penis (male member) or as the clitoris (Fig. 53) ; the female labia and the male scrotum also evolve from one primitive undifferentiated form.   If the labia develop the pudendal cleft remains between them ; but, in the male scrotum the cleft closes entirely.

If, however, the process of differentiation is disturbed or held up, the scrotal

50.—Two male homosexual transvestites in female attire.   (After Goldmann in *Gesch. u. Gesellschaft.*)

sac is not properly formed, even though there may be testes (whether normal or undescended), and the opening of the male urethra is either fully exposed or situated between the two sides of the scrotum—which may be either large or small, in comparison with average cases.   This genital anomaly is termed hypospadias.   (Fig. 52, 1–3.)   It makes the external genitalia indeterminate, *e.g.*, intermediate.   In women the clitoris may be so unusually large and cylindrical as to resemble the male organ.

In men afflicted with cryptorchism there are often effeminate traits of physique and features and, where there is hypospadias, there are generally a slight growth of beard, a high pitched voice, inadequate penile development and apathy or aversion towards women. Similarly, excessive clitoridal development often accompanies powerful bony structure, a deep or harsh voice and poorly developed breasts. In extreme cases of this anomaly there is atrophy of the uterus or excessive development of the labia or both ;

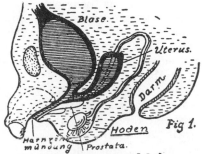

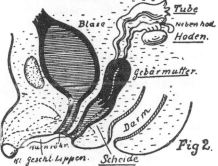

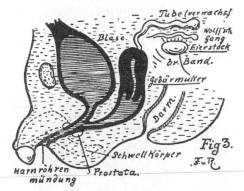

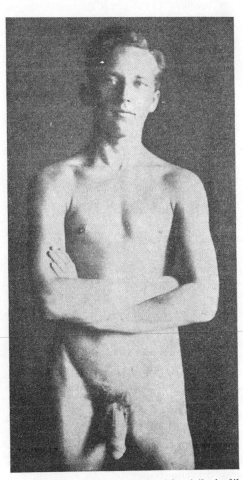

51.—Male homosexual with virile bodily development. (After Goldmann in *Gesch. u. Gesellschaft.*)

52.—Hypospadias. (After v. Reitzenstein.)

(1) Slight case of hypospadias with well-developed vagina (here called uterus). Male type.

(2) Perfectly formed case of hypospadias. Near the vaginal orifice open the labia minora. Oviducts and testes are present but ovaries are lacking. Male type.

(3) Slight case of hypospadias with fused labia majora. The vagina opens into the urethra near the prostate. Ovaries are under-developed and the oviducts imperfect. Female type.

and the characteristic differences are almost obliterated into an intermediate type. Steinach has been able to produce artificial examples by operative surgery.

To-day it is scarcely necessary to mention that Woman's specific nature, functions and qualities are as perfect in themselves as those of Man.

The founders of Classical Medicine and Natural Science — Hippocrates and Aristotle, for example—believed and taught the inferiority of women, physiologically and otherwise. They considered woman an incomplete, half-human being. Hippocrates stated that women were never able to use both hands simultaneously with equal skill (*Ambidexterity*). He further believed that the interior genital organs of woman

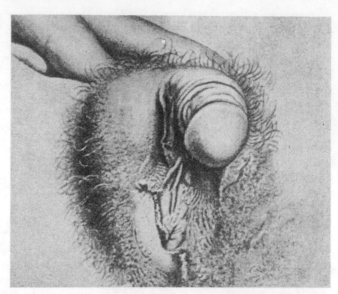

53.—Penoscrotal hypospadia ; 18-year-old male type brought up as a girl. (After Neugebauer.)

were exactly similar to the external genitals of men ; and that, in men, they were expanded and made visible by natural warmth and vigour but kept concealed in the body of the woman by the colder and feebler female constitution.

This ancient assumption has naturally no foundation in anatomical or biological fact. But it has had great influence on human history, through Christian dogma, closely connected as it is with certain later Greek (Hellenistic) schools of thought.

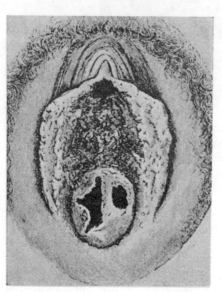

54.—Hymen septus with openings of different size. (After Kisch.)

Woman is, contrary to animals, as distinctively and specifically human as her mate : and this is the case both genitally and generally.

Nevertheless, many persons, even investigators, have failed to realise in what attributes this specific humanity consists. The structure of the mammary glands, the function of menstruation and the existence of the hymenal membrane have, for instance, all been cited as typically human as distinct from animal characteristics (Figs. 54–58). But this view is erroneous. Woman is not the only potential mother with two breasts ; not only the anthropoid apes, but most monkeys and many bats have the same number of nipples and situated in a corresponding position on the thorax. As regards the hymen, Blumenbach has already completely disproved Albrecht v. Haller's theory that this membrane has any special "moral purpose"; and Cuvier and other observers have found something analogous in other higher mammals.

This is specially pronounced in anthropoid apes. The existence of the variety known as *hymen fenestratus* has been shown in the gorilla and U. Gerhardt found the most frequent human form (the *hymen semilunaris* or crescent shape) in a second female gorilla (*cf.* Gellhorn). Again menstruation is

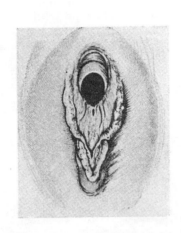

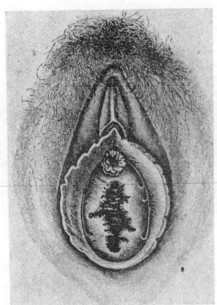

57.—Fimbriated hymen. (After Kisch.)   58.—Circular hymen. (After Kisch.)

hardly an adequate test, though Pliny termed woman "*animal menstruale.*" The differences between *œstrus* (heat) and the monthly period are not so wide and deep that they can serve to prove human difference. Here, too, the anthropoids approximate our species. A periodically regular change in the genitalia of the female chimpanzee has been proved by the observations of Heinrich

Bolau, Ehlers and Otto Hermes, and Robert Hartmann calls this phenomenon a sort of menstruation. The symptoms are, first of all, a dilation and congestion of the exterior genitalia ; then the outer lips (Labia majora), which are normally inconspicuous, fold outwards and protrude, and the inner lips and clitoris swell and become very noticeable. These symptoms are not peculiar to the chimpanzee among apes. The same swelling and reddening of the outer genital region and the buttocks as well have been observed in baboons and macaques during their times

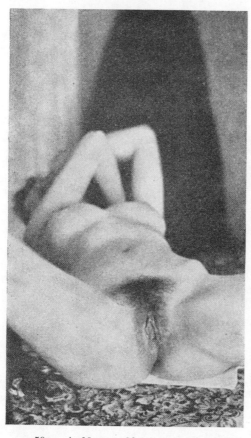 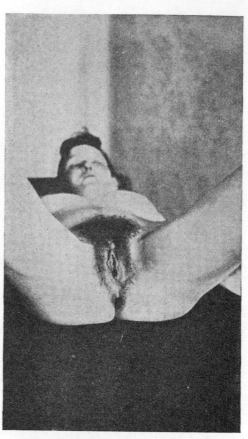

59A.—A 19-year-old virgin with visible hymen. (Hist. med. Mus., Pachinger.)

59B.—The same after defloration, taken over a month later.

of " heat," and there are researches by Pocock of great significance, for he was able to ascertain actual hæmorrhage from the vagina in the species *Papio porcarius*, the Chacma baboon, and *Papio cynocephalus*, the yellow baboon. These hæmorrhages appeared several times at more or less regular intervals, and lasted for four to five days. The loss of blood was quite appreciable. Grabovsky was able to ascertain an almost regular recurrence of sexual excitement at intervals of about four weeks in a female gorilla at the Zoological Gardens in Breslau, but was not certain whether these periodic maxima were accompanied by hæmorrhages from the vagina. We must, therefore, conclude that menstruation is not exclusively and distinctively a human attribute.

[A great deal of work has been done recently on ovulation and menstruation in the primates. Menstruation, or at least a discharge from the uterus, occurs without ovulation, and direct observation of monkeys has furnished a mass of important data. Those wishing to pursue the subject can consult the works of Zuckerman, Parkes and others, in whose contributions they will find lists of further references.]

We shall not detail the countless theoretical attempts which have been made

60.—Man and Woman (Adam and Eve) according to a Biblia Pauperum in the Tegernsee Monastery. About 1340. (Bayr. Landesbib. Munich. *c.l.* 19414.)

to degrade and depreciate the special anthropological characteristics of Woman, as compared with those of Man. Suffice it to say that there have been the most arrant misreadings of natural fact—according to the particular cultural climate and institutions in which these speculations took place, and to quote two startling examples—one from the sixteenth century, which abounded in bizarre metaphysical controversies and word spinning, and one from the nineteenth.

The first was anonymous, but attributed to Acidalius, and entitled *Women are not human beings* (*Mulieres homines non esse*), a question already debated at the Synod of Mâçon in A.D. 585.*

* Valens Acidalius was born in 1567 and died in 1595. Shortly before his death he was the centre of a literary sensation aroused by the dissertation *Disputatio perjucunda qua anonymus probare nititur mulieres homines non esse* . . . (Leipzig, 1595). The work has been translated into French in 1744 and again in 1766.

There is also an address by Paul Albrecht, delivered at an anthropological Congress at Breslau in the year 1884, in which he maintained the more pronounced animal traits as seen in female human anatomy.   He said :

" There are so many proofs that the female sex is the more persistently true to ancestral type, *i.e.*, the closer to our savage forbears.   These proofs include the following characteristics :

61.—Man and woman from the Missal of B. Furtmeyer, 1481.   (Bayr. Landesbib. Munich, *c.l.* 15709.)

" (1) The shorter stature of women.
" (2) The higher index of dolichocephaly, which is more frequent among women.
" (3) The more pronounced and frequent prognathism.
" (4) The greater size of the median incisors.
" (5) The *trochanter tertius*, which is specially developed in women.*

* *Cf.* the plaintive question by Dello as to why man has lost the third trochanter, and for other material see Waldeyer   and Fürst.

" (6) The less frequent synostosis of the first coccygeal and lowest sacral vertebræ in women.

" (7) The fact that five is the more frequent number of coccygeal vertebræ in women.

" (8) The greater frequency of hypertrichosis (excessive growth of hair) in women.

" (9) The corresponding infrequency of baldness among women."

The comparative variability of the sexes cannot be finally decided as yet; our knowledge of the effective range of variation in physical qualities alone is not

62.—Man and woman from a MS. of Boccaccio in the Bayr. Landesbib. Munich, *c.g.* 6.
French School.

sufficiently exact and detailed. The investigations of Giuffrida-Ruggieri suppose that women possess greater variability. Ranke is of opinion that deformities occur more often in women than in men; but, in certain organs, they are more frequent among men.

The æsthetic and ideal aspects of women's bodies have naturally been dealt with inexhaustibly. And again, many of the distinctive differences between women and men in physique are just those which appear especially desirable and lovely to men, when these are fully developed and delicately differentiated. What are these particularly typical and characteristic attributes? We must clear our minds on these points before studying their racial and ethnographical variations.

THE ACCESSORY SEXUAL CHARACTERISTICS

Figure and Build

In Figs. 60–72 we have reproduced certain typical representations of the " ideal man and ideal woman " as imagined and depicted in various ages and among different races ; these figures accentuate the typical, secondary sex characteristics very clearly.   Perhaps the most externally conspicuous and certainly one of the most

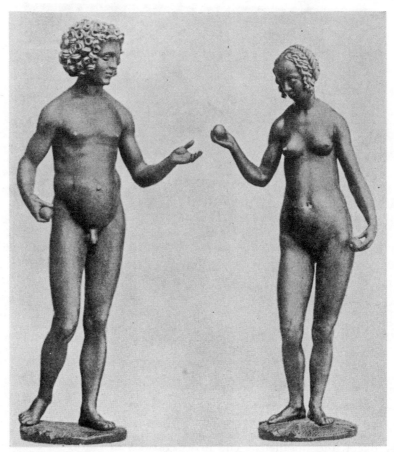

63.—Man and woman. Adam and Eve. Boxwood. K. Meit. *c.* 1520. Gotha Museum.

important of these secondary characteristics in woman is the bosom, concerning which we shall have to deal in detail in a later chapter.   But there are many other attributes, based on the greater fatty layer (adipose tissue) and the less pronounced muscular development, the position and influence of the internal organs and the skeletal framework, which is both less massive and less closely knit.

The once-famous Berlingy næcologist, Wilhelm Heinrich Busch, gave the following descriptive summary of the " secondary " differences in appearance between men and women.

64.—Man.   Aldegrever.   (c. 1502–1555.)

"The external appearance of woman is more conformable to harmony and beauty than that of man (in masculine eyes)—her proportions are at once rounder and more delicate; whereas the man's are angular and rough hewn (only not in feminine eyes). In women, the shape of the skull approaches the spherical; it has fewer and slighter ridges and protuberances

65.—Woman.   Aldegrever.   (c. 1502–1555.)

than the man's and the dense and often long growth of hair can be one of the chief charms of
women.   The length of the face, from brow to chin, is less—relatively as well as actually.   The

single features are less pronounced and the lines more flowing and less angular. The expression is apt to be less definite and even tends to insipidity. The forehead is lower, the nose and mouth smaller, the chin much smoother and, at the same time, less pointed, so that the whole face is at once smaller and rounder. In women, the neck is comparatively longer than in men and the lines of head, face and shoulders flow more gradually and softly into the neck than in the man; the 'Adam's apple' is less prominent. The trunk of the body is differently proportioned; the lower portion outweighs the thorax. Her shoulders and ribs are much narrower than the man's; her ribs are in a line with the pelvis, whereas the man's project beyond his. The female pelvis is very much wider than the male, and the muscles of lower abdomen, flanks and buttocks are sheathed in connective tissue and covered with flesh and fat, giving a much softer outline

66.—Man and woman. Matham. *c.* 1600.

and smoother surface. Ribs and hip bones are much less evident to the eye. The upper part of the trunk—the actual thorax—would appear disproportionately small in comparison with the dominant pelvis were it not for the development of the bust, with the mammary glands, and their sheaths of fatty tissue. Thus, in woman, a firm, symmetrical and adequate development of the bosom is necessary in order to balance the pelvis and is equally pleasing to the eyes and beneficial to the race. . . .

"The female abdomen in its lower portion is more rounded than the man's and slightly protrudes. The depression of the navel is deeper than in man, and, at the same time, further above the pubis. The thorax narrows gradually below the bosom and then the outline curves again into the pelvis, whereas, in man, the massive thorax narrows abruptly into hips and loins. The female form is most slender just above the loins, *i.e.*, at the waist. The collar-bone is shorter, the arms shorter, rounder and more plump, and the fingers narrower and more pointed. The beauty of the arms in women depends on a certain fleshy fullness and roundness. The breadth and flesh of the hips are continued into the thighs ; the muscles of the upper thighs are very strongly developed in comparison with the others ; the trochanters are widely separated and the thighs slope gradually inwards and downwards. The knees approach each

67.—Married couple from the Andaman Islands.   (After v. Reitzenstein.)

other and the inner surfaces nearly touch. The knees themselves are round and without the strongly marked masculine muscles. The calves are slenderer and taper more definitely towards the lower extremity. The ankles and bones of the feet are less prominent and the feet relatively, as well as actually, smaller and narrower than man's ; the whole body is supported on a frailer basis and legs are notably less long and straight than man's. In the male form, the pubic bone divides the body into equal halves ; in the female, the pubic bone is below the middle of the body. Thus, women take shorter steps in walking than men and their gait is apt to sway slightly. This may be able to give a peculiar grace of movement, but the normally built woman is not well adapted for running.'' *

There are two great differences in the whole organic life of women from that of men. First, women are primarily much more concerned with and specialised for

68.—Caroline Islanders from Fais.   (After Külz.)

reproduction than men; they have to deal with menstruation, pregnancy, childbirth, suckling and the care of children.   And, beyond this complex reproductive function, their whole nervous system is differently keyed; their emotions are predominant

* The Illustrations 73 to 77 show characteristic types of feminine physique, taken from women in various parts of the world.

and their mental and cerebral activity is less.   This difference shows in all movement and action : the women whose range of feeling is greatest and whose sensibilities are tenderest are those who—generally—appear to men as most completely women.

Accessory Sex Characteristics further considered, especially as shown in European Women

Perhaps the most obvious and constant difference here is *the relative size of the body* in the sexes.   Pfitzner made full measurements among Alsatian men and women

69.—Fuegians.   (Mission scient. du Cap Horn.)

between the ages of 20 and 50 years.   The ratio of *stature* was as 100 (in men) to 94 (in women) ; and the length of the trunk (as distinct from the lower limbs) was 100 (in men) to 94·4 (in women).*

Thus there is a typical difference not only in actual height and size, but in the

* The mean statures of certain racial groups represented in the United States and published by Martin in 1928 may be of interest.

Group	♂ cm.	♀ cm.	Group	♂ cm.	♀ cm.
Japanese . .	159·3	147·2	Germans . . .	169·2	158·0
Polish Jews .	161·0	150·6	Finns . . .	171·0	160·0
French . .	164·1	157·0	Norwegians . .	172·0	162·4
S. Russian Jews .	165·1	153·6	Sioux . . .	172·6	159·5
Danes . .	169·1	159·2	English (middle class) .	172·8	159·9

relative proportions of limbs and trunk ; a difference, not accidental, but primary. Johann Ranke says :

"The characteristic differences in the man are as follows : His trunk (thorax and abdomen) is slightly shorter in proportion to his whole stature than the woman's ; and his limbs and extremities, legs, arms, hands and feet are longer in proportion both to his whole height and his trunk. His lower limbs are distinctively longer in proportion to the upper half of his body and his shins, and arms from the elbow downwards, are longer compared with the thighs and upper arms, than hers. In proportion to his whole height, the horizontal circumference of his head

70.—Secondary sexual characteristics at puberty. (After Neugebauer.)

and face is somewhat less. In short, the distinctively masculine proportions are more those of the adult and the distinctively feminine more those of the infant.

"In this particular respect, the line of human anatomical evolution has advanced further in man ; woman has remained on a less differentiated level. There are, it is true, other typical feminine characteristics as well, but we may say, as the result of our investigations, that the far greater muscular and *motor* activity of the man in the white races of Western civilisation is based on and develops a more powerful and highly differentiated bodily mechanism than the woman's." And the same is true of the rural agriculturists of Europe, as was shown by two pupils of Stieda, who measured many Lettish and Lithuanian peasants. These Lettish and Lithuanian results showed the same tendencies, but, as might have been expected, to a somewhat less degree ; for there is no doubt that hard and continuous muscular exertion from childhood will develop a somewhat masculine texture of body and proportions approaching the masculine.

But the normal and typical feminine proportions are constant even among the most primitive peoples, and are the same as in European races, *i.e.*, there is a closer structural resemblance to children in women than in men.

Weissenberg does not attribute the typical womanly build either to "arrested

71.—Man and woman. German. (Photo, R. A. Giesecke.)

development " or to shorter stature and lesser bulk. but after exhaustive measurements he has concluded that both sexes follow their own specialised course of development.

The differences in the limbs affect arms as well as legs. Weisbach came to the following conclusions as regards the German women :

" The whole arm is shorter in women, so are the separate sections (from shoulder to elbow and elbow to wrist). But the hands and the back of the hand and middle finger are *comparatively* longer, though actually shorter and narrower than in men. The legs, shanks and feet are all shorter, but the thighs comparatively long ; the foot itself being wider."

Goenner declares that even at birth, girls have smaller feet than boys.

Sappey is of opinion that, in women, the trunk and lower extremities are about equal in length, but that, in men, the lower limbs are about 2·5 cm. longer than the trunk.   He further declares that men reach their maximum growth at 30 and their maximum weight at 40 years of age, the woman's maximum weight being reached at 50.   The average weight of men is given as 62·049 kg., and that of women as 54·877 kg.   Lapicque, quoting Vierordt, gives the averages as 66 kg. and 54 kg.

The bony framework of the chest shows sexual differences as well as the external

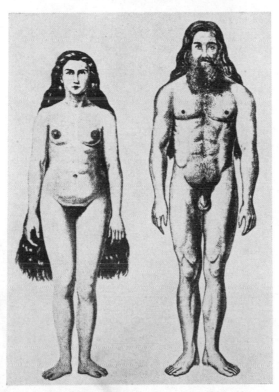

72.—" Ideal " figures in a man and woman of Caucasian race.   (After Friedenthal, *Haarkleid des Menschen.*)

contours (Fig. 78).   The thorax in women is less roomy and narrower and the respiration is less vigorous and expansive.

A century ago Ackermann described the main characteristics of the thorax in woman.   The cartilaginous portion of the lower ribs is comparatively larger than in man, according to this writer, and the lower extremity of her breast bone is either in a straight line with the bony portion of the fourth rib or extends somewhat further down, whilst the breast bone itself is actually smaller, on the whole, than in man.   In the famous work of Sömmering against the habit of tight lacing, he reproduced the statue of the Venus of Milo and drew a corset on it in order to show how harmful such a custom can be.

There is a general assumption that the extreme slenderness of the waist in woman is not only beautiful but natural.   Baelz shows the error here.   There is a certain degree of natural " waist " in human bodies above the arch of the hip bone (*cf*. Fig. 84). In some men this is quite pronounced, and there are a certain number

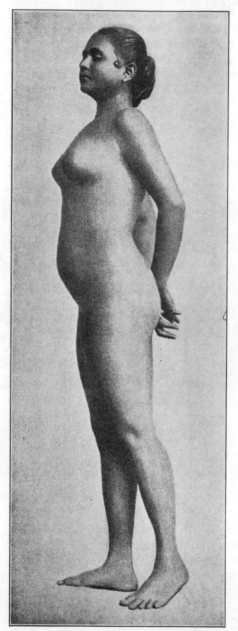

73.—Young Singhalese girl.   (After Stratz.)

of women whose shoulders are wider than their pelves.   Weil   has recently argued that both great pelvic breadth in men and great width of shoulder in women are caused by imbalance of the internal secretions, and may be associated with homosexuality. He declares that, in normal men, the ratio of shoulders to hips is as 100 to 93, and, in normal women, as 100 to 97. Whereas in the undoubtedly homosexual cases measured by him, the male inverts showed the ratio 100 to 95, and the women 100 to 94.

The natural waist is formed not only by the pelvic bones but by the tapering

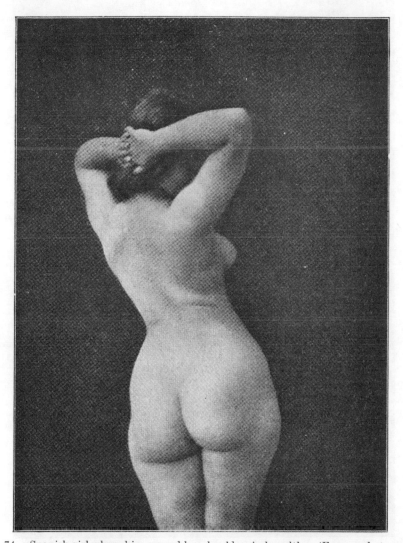

74.—Spanish girl whose hips exceed her shoulders in breadth. (From a photograph.)

of the lower thorax, and by the " floating " lowest rib. If the tenth rib on either side is not attached to the breast bone, so the lower portion of the thorax becomes more easily compressible and very sensitive to pressure. Baelz has emphasised the comparative rarity of this abnormality, and its existence in both men and women. Women with firm ribs and good bone development, even in the days of tight lacing, got off more lightly than their sisters with rachitic bones and floating lower ribs. It is said that the floating tenth rib is comparatively frequent in the Yellow Races. And we know, too, that there are women with virtually no percep- tible waist curve, as, for instance, in the photographs reproduced in this book of the Korean girls (Fig. 79), whereas the Japanese (Fig. 80) has a distinct natural

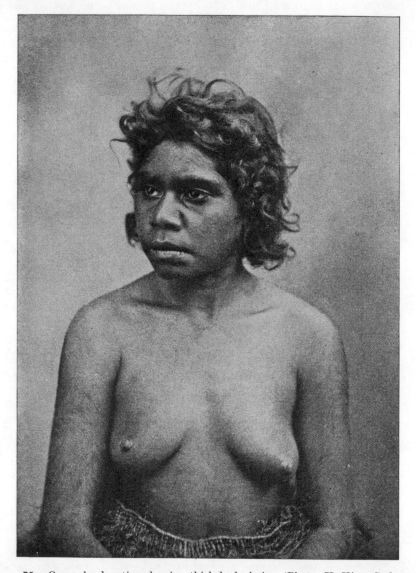

75.—Queensland native showing thick body hair. (Photo, H. King, Sydney.)

waist. Baelz points out that in the most artistic epochs known to us, the waist was not particularly accentuated nor admired, as is proved by the Greek statues of nymphs and goddesses and the women portrayed by Raphael and Titian. Even the Romanesque and Gothic sculpture of the Early Middle Ages sometimes showed no compression of the waist (see Figs. 81, 82, and *cf.* Figs. 83 and 84).

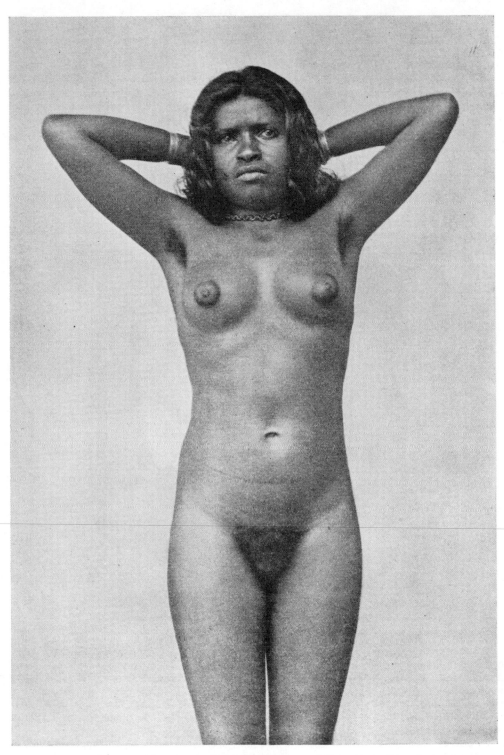

76.—Mixed blood.   Vedda and Singhalese.   (Photo, R. A. Giesecke.)

Further detailed measurements on the bodies of both men and women have been made by Liharczik.   He finds that, in general, the female body is shorter by about 1 cm.—that is, by the breadth of a rib—in the region of the thorax.   All the other distinctive differences in proportions may be deduced from this one (*e.g.*, the shorter trachea and higher vocal pitch of woman, her wider pelvis, and so on).

Wintrich measured the chest circumference of many persons of both sexes and in various

77.—German girl.   (Photo, R. A. Giesecke.)

usages and compared the results in three sets of measurements, *i.e.*, round the top of the chest, the middle and the base.   He found interesting results.   Until advanced age, the upper chest measurement exceeds the lower in both sexes.   After 60 years of age, these proportions are reversed.   In women, even in youth, the upper measurement exceeds the lower to a lesser degree, proportionately, than in men.   At about 14 years of age, the male ribs and thorax become much the wider and more massive.

We owe further facts to Lenhossek, who found the collar bone less strongly curved in women than in men.   Strauch investigated the sternum (breast bone) in greater detail and found that, in women, the manubrium or upper piece was relatively larger and the body smaller than in men. This difference influences both position and function of the lungs and heart, as Henke has shown. The feminine structure of the thorax in the region of the xiphoid cartilage may have been affected or accentuated by the pressure of stays and constriction of tight lacing. The general effect has been an inward pressure of the sternum and costal cartilages, while the

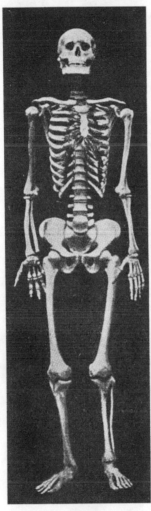 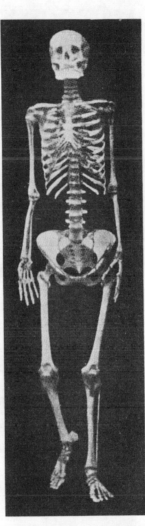

78A.—Male skeleton.   78B.—Female skeleton.
(After Stratz.)   (After Stratz.)

relative proportions of the thoracic cavity, containing lungs and heart, have not been greatly altered.

[Before passing on to a consideration of the skeleton a few words may be said on the general question of the bodily proportions of women. In 1924 a series of measurements were taken by Wilder and Pfeiffer of 100 students of Smith College in the United States, and the results tabulated and compared with other data from other countries where similar inquiries had been undertaken. The subjects were all young, ranging from 17 to 27 years of age, the mean being 20·4 years. The measurements were mainly of the kind usually taken by anthropometrists, and no attempt was made to examine other somatic features of interest to the physical

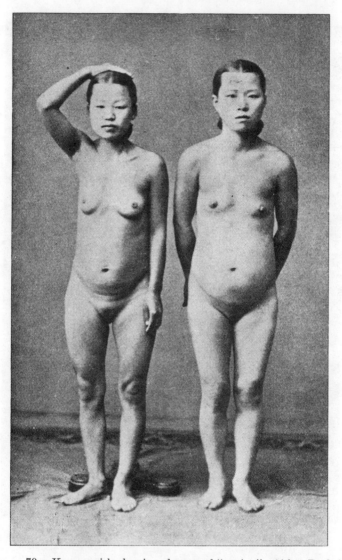

79.—Korean girls showing absence of "waist."   (After Baelz.)

anthropologists. Nevertheless, the work is valuable as far as it goes, and might be usefully consulted when more detailed examinations are undertaken.]

We will now consider the chief portions of the *bony structure*, and begin with the *skull*.

But certain general remarks, summaries, and reservations must here be borne in mind.

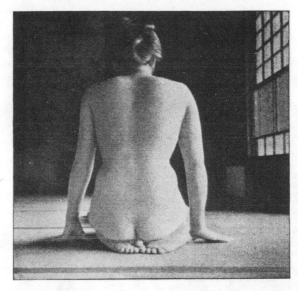

80.—Japanese girl showing natural " waist."   (After Baelz.)

81.—Adam and Eve.   From a MS. in the Landesbibliothek, Munich, 12th–13th century.

At one period in the development of anthropology and comparative anatomy, scientists were ready to set up standardisations and generalisations based both on measurement (Craniometry) and general description—often deductive description. Some are so still. And the processes of proof were often inadequate : for instance, measurements were taken on sets of male and female skulls respectively which were numerically insignificant and far too few to be representative. Again, some authors have ascribed skulls to whichever sex they thought

82.—Eve.   From B. Furtmeyer's Missal, 1481.   (Bayr. Landesbib., Munich, *c.l.* 15710.)

probable or suitable. Both the actual general differences between the skulls of men and women are, therefore, far from certain and the amount of such differences, even less so. There are, however, certain researches in this field, such as those of Welcker,   J. Ranke, Weisbach and A. Ecker,   whose results may be considered reliable, either wholly or in the main.

83.—Modern woman without corset.

84.—Modern woman without corset.   (Römmler & Jonass.)

Roundness of hip in artists' models.   (Verl. R. A. Giesecke.)

THE FEMALE GENITALIA
RACIAL AND ETHNOGRAPHICAL CHARACTERISTICS
GENERAL.

THE genital organs and the sexual and reproductive functions are of central importance for the whole life and personality of women. Moreover, they have structural differences in various peoples. Unfortunately the material at our disposal is slight, for it is not generally realised that here are important facts for investigation. All human manifestations are worthy of study, and sexual matters are, perhaps, most of all in need of honest and accurate investigation and discussion.

In order to understand these differences in the various races the external characteristics of the genitals must be examined. Special attention must be paid to the pelvic region in view of its importance for childbirth, and finally some consi-

85.—Schematic representation of the vulva (?), Musée de Périgord. (After Didon.)

deration will be given to the distribution of hair on the body and form and contour of the breasts.

Friedenthal has collected useful data bearing on the differences between human beings and the anthropoid apes. He shows that the female organs in our species are much more complicated in structure and more highly evolved; the vagina especially is deeply but delicately corrugated throughout its length in ridges and folds. Poech maintains that the Bushwomen have vertical rimae pudendi, and that, even among quite young persons, the inner labia protrude visibly. There can be no doubt that these organs have great anthropological significance. To give only one example, Professor K. Müller, of Dresden University, discovered and recorded 111 quite distinct names for the genital organ of woman in the written literature of the Old German tongue and its dialects. As Aigremont has shown, the most usual symbol in language is a shell or a snail. Luquet has collected a plastic and graphic record of the same type in "Anthropophyteia," and, moreover, he is of opinion that there was a sign for this in the Cretan (Minoan) alphabet, and it appears that this was certainly the case in other ancient alphabets as well (*cf.* Fig. 85).

[The symbol of a shell for the vulva is widely spread. In this connection the importance of the cowrie can hardly be exaggerated. The similarity of its opening to the genital cleft has led man to associate it with the same, and it became a " giver of life " and assumed a *rôle* in human culture which otherwise it might have never attained. Thus its significance for the position of woman is outstanding. Moreover, it has been suggested that the enormously developed lower extremities in early female figures are due to an attempt to combine a woman and a cowrie. For the whole theory see G. E. Smith and W. J. Perry.]

In considering feminine functions, we must include not only pregnancy, childbirth and lactation, but menstruation, coitus and conception ; and also practices such as excising the clitoris, lengthening of the nymphæ, sewing up the vulva, and manipulation of the breasts. All these have been customary in various parts of the world and certainly affect maternity, whether favourably or harmfully.

There are two currents of thought and emotion associated with the genital organs (especially those of the female) in folklore, tradition, religion and custom. One is depreciatory and contemptuous, expressing disgust, horror and ridicule. Sex is considered here equivalent to dirt and indecency. Among the common people in every so-called civilised country to-day sexual terms are also terms of insult. This is even the case in certain Oriental communities, and on some of the Malayan islands the exclamation : " By the genital organ of thy Mother ! " is one of the most flagrant affronts that can be uttered.

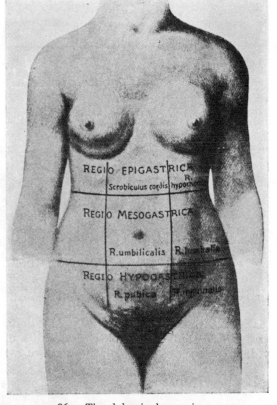

86.—The abdominal areas in woman.
(After Polano.)

87.—Schematic representation of the vulva for protective purposes on fruit trees (Amboina Islands). (After Riedel.)

Riedel, to whom we are indebted for many of these data, has recorded that in Amboina and neighbouring islands the natives cut rough symbols of the vulva into their kalapa and other fruit trees (Fig. 87). This is done with a double purpose, in order to make the trees more fruitful (a form of " sympathetic magic ") and as a spell to ward off robbers, for the symbols represent the parts through which the robbers were born.

Herodotus mentions similar figures carved on stone pillars set up by the Pharaoh Sesostris in Syrian Palestine to commemorate his victories over those peoples. Here there is not the sacred but the opprobrious significance and intention.

The ancient culture of Easter Island in the Pacific commemorated and depicted the vulva with reverence, according to Geiseler. There were many such sculptures and motive plaques, and the crew of the German vessel *Hyäne* brought several specimens with them.

It has been stated that these representations always accompany the figure of

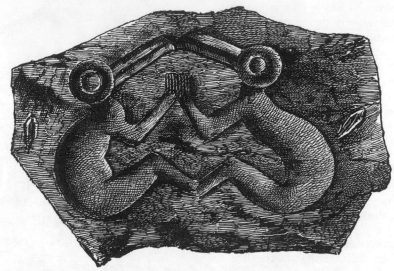

88 .—Representation of Make-Make, God of Eggs, with vulvæ.   Stone 0·45 m. high and 0·64 m. wide, Easter Island.   (After Geiseler.)

Make-Make, the duplex and bi-sexual deity who presides over eggs ; includes male and female ; and signifies the birth of a child when represented together with the vulva symbol, and, indeed, the birth of a child conceived in wedlock (Fig.   88)

89 .—Native of Easter Island with the sign of his marriage tattooed on his chest.   (After Viaud.)

The Easter Islanders preserved a further most interesting custom in their chieftain's families.   When a man of chieftain's rank married he had the vulva

symbol tattooed on his chest just under the collar bone, about 2 in. long, in order
to prove publicly that he was a husband (Fig. 89).

90 .—Linga-Yoni

In many parts of Hindustan, the feminine *Yoni* receives divine honours, like
the masculine *Linga* (*cf.* Dulaure, Foy, etc.). They are frequently represented

91 .—Linga-Yoni. Portable temple from near Rohilla. (Brit. Mus.)

together in Hindu art in the shape of an oval or rounded disc, in the centre of which
is a short blunt rod (*cf.* Figs. 90 and 91). The rod is the symbol of *Mahādeva*

or *Shiva*, the male principle throughout nature ; the *Yoni* portion is the symbol of *Bhavani* or *Kali*, his divine spouse, the mother of all living, and the female principle throughout nature.

There is, however, no doubt that the genital and phallic element in primitive art and archæology has been greatly over-estimated. At one time, especially, a phallic meaning was read into the most unlikely and impossible objects and monuments. In India this interpretation is, however, often justified, and sexual representations of a symbolic kind are distributed over wide areas.

In China there is also, according to some writers, widespread symbolism of the genital organs. They are represented as Yang (♂) and Yin (♀) and are, states Katscher, attached to the walls or doors of houses, or above the lintels

92.—Zulu girls. The one seated with her back to the observer exhibits two sacral dimples.

in order to avert ill-luck. Gray and Eng have cited striking examples of these customs and beliefs, but H. A. Giles states that he never saw them in 27 years in China.

Riedel has given a curious little instance of symbolism from the Island of Wetar (Wetta). If a Wetar woman is attracted to any man she sends him a little round box, full of tobacco and wrapped in a koli leaf, as a gift. But the gift implies more than tobacco ; by presenting a box she offers herself.

Hitherto, anthropologists have zealously enquired, collected and collated craniological and physiognomical data about all the races of mankind. But, in all probability there are not more ethnical and individual differences in heads and faces than in the whole genital region of women, internal and external. It is exceedingly difficult to obtain adequate and accurate statements and measurements on this subject, but such facts as are known to us are sufficiently important to be recorded in these pages.

LEGENDS AS TO THE ORIGIN OF THE FEMALE ORGANS

There are various explanations in primitive folklore of the origin of the sex organs. For instance, the Southern Slavs, according to Krauss, declare that St. Elias " clove the woman through the middle and the cleft remains to this day."

Pechuel-Loesche reports a legend of the Bakongo negroes on the Loango Coast as follows : Nzambi, the Creator, left a kola-nut about, and the first woman warned her partner not to eat of it.

" Nzambi praised the woman's steadfastness but he did not wish her to be stronger than the man, that did not please him. So he cut her open and took out some of her bones, making her smaller and softer to touch. Then he sewed her together again, but with too short a thread, so a piece remains open to this day."

There is a similar legend, states Krämer, obviously meant partly in jest, among the Samoans. In this story the girl, Popoto, and the three men who try to mate with her, have the names of mountains : Mangafolau, Tofua-upolu and Masa. Finally, Masa " cleaves through her with a shark's tooth " (the weapons, swords and spears of the islanders are decorated with shark's teeth). Krämer, who gives the story in full, is of opinion that " it symbolises the origin of the first woman."

Roth states that the Australian blacks on Tully River in Queensland believe that men and women " came out of " that river in the beginning of things and there was, at first, no special difference between them. Then the spear grass that grows on the banks became the male organ and the long wandering on the river banks gave the girls their *labia majora*.

The Queenslanders also believe that the Great Spirit Anje-a made little children out of the moist clay of the river banks, and before he put them inside their mother's bodies he " clove open " the girl children on a wooden fork.

Similarly, on Prosperpine River (Australia), the natives believe that in the beginning Kahara, the moon, made man and woman. He was formed of the metallic ore of meteor stones (thunderbolts) ;

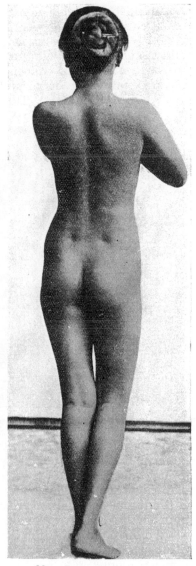

93.—Javanese girl with sacral dimples. (Anthrop. Ges., Berlin.)

she of the wood of the fruitful beech tree. The man was finished by being rubbed all over with black-and-white ashes and provided with a projecting piece of Pandanus root. The woman was made smooth and supple by being " oiled " with river slime and yam juice and a ripe pandanus fruit was placed inside her body, and finally, she was cleft open with a slice of pandanus root : " So that they could be told apart."

THE FEMALE PELVIS, ANTHROPOLOGICALLY CONSIDERED

In the bony system of mankind the two most important regions for anthropology are the skull and the pelvis.

In woman the pelvis not only contains and supports the abdominal viscera and trunk respectively, but encloses the uterus, tubes, ovaries and vagina, as well as the adjacent organs. When the woman becomes pregnant the structure of the pelvis is enormously important for the ante-natal development and the delivery of the new life within her. There are marked differences between the pelves of man

94.—Spanish woman showing area of the lozenge of Michaelis.

and woman ; and the distinctive characteristics of the female pelvis are based on the need to contain the child's body and to bring it forth. In a previous chapter we have discussed the chief anatomical sex differences (Chapter I., 3) and shall take these explanations as read. The special technique of pelvic measurements on the living body is somewhat complicated, and we refer those interested to the summary by Waldeyer and similar works.

We have discussed the bony structure of the pelvis and shall deal more fully with the genital zone : here we shall deal especially with two features particularly frequent among women : the sacral dimples and the so-called lozenge or rhomboid of Michaelis, who dealt fully with this area.

The illustrations (Figs. 92 and 93) appended, especially the Javanese girl, show clearly what is meant by the sacral dimples.

According to Waldeyer, these dimples are produced by a small oval plate of bone which is free from muscular tendons and just above the superior spina iliaca posterior. The dimples are apt to be much deeper in women. Waldeyer terms them *fossulæ lumbales laterales inferiores*. There is, occasionally, a third dimple, of which, however, Waldeyer has seen only *one* example among women. It lies higher on the iliac crest and corresponds to the point at which the sacrospinal muscle is attached. These lumbar or sacral dimples, according to Stratz, are normal in

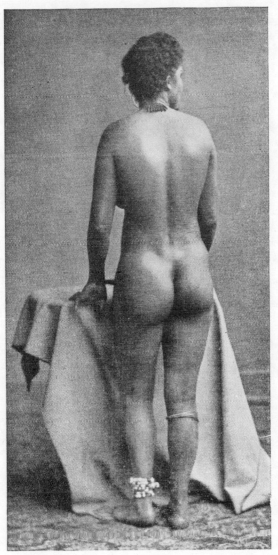

95 .—Mulatto girl showing sacral dimples. (Photo, C. Günther.)

women but are only visible in between 18 and 25 per cent. of men. In women they are deeper, more circular and more distinct.

Finally, it may be said that in the male four dimples may often be observed, the two additional ones being over the ordinary two and corresponding to posterior superior spines. Moreover, another distinct dimple is occasionally seen in both sexes. This is seated at the inferior apex of the rhomboid of Michaelis at the beginning of the gluteal cleft. In addition to the works already cited the notes by Müllerheim and Béna may be found useful, as also the illustrations in Black's "The Body Beautiful," Figs. 28, 118, 119–121.

96.—Spanish model showing convex type of lozenge of Michaelis.

The classic world knew them well and depicted them in their works of art. The poets also praised them, and under the same name as facial dimples, *i.e.*, γελασῖνοι. They are mentioned by Rufinus (Anth. G.) in his account of the judgment of Paris, and by the Greek, Alciphron (I., 39), in the contest of beauty between Myrrhine and Thryallis. [T. Bell, in his "Kalogynomia" declared that their absence was

97.—Austrian girl with lozenge of Michaelis.

a defect from the point of view of beauty, and Alexander Walker followed him in the same opinion. Boucher was a painter who specialised in dimples (see Laignel-Lavastine).]

The line between the two sacral dimples forms the base of a triangle, of which the apex is directed downwards just at the lowest extremity of the sacrum, and the sides are formed by the projecting contours of the buttocks. It is termed the sacral triangle, and there is another possible definite triangular area just above the first, with the same base, but apex in the opposite (upward) direction and sometimes marked by a dimple. This whole area is the lozenge of Michaelis, the size and prominence of which vary greatly in different individuals.*

This lumbar area, which is quadrilateral instead of triangular, is shown in the photograph (reproduced in Fig. 97.) representing a Viennese artist's model.

There. is also a recumbent figure of a Spanish woman (Fig. 94), which shows the sacral triangle, and the same is the case in another photograph of the same woman (Fig. 96) with quadrilateral area clearly defined and deep dimple at the superior apex. And she has another striking sacral characteristic : the strong convex curve of this whole area, a peculiarity also shown in the young mulatto girl depicted in Fig. 95 .

Stratz considers this sacral area very important as being combined with and symptomatic of various grades of pelvic development. He considers the ideal " sacral area " to be quadrilateral rather than triangular and to be always accompanied by a wide diagonal conjugate, quite independently of all the other exterior pelvic measurements. The longer the vertical axis of the sacral area, the less does the promontorium project internally ; and the longer the horizontal axis, the wider must the sacrum be. And there results a spacious, normally proportioned pelvis, apt for maternity. Stratz estimates the ideally desirable distance between the opposite points of the sacral quadrilateral, as (independently of other measurements and even of race) from 10 to 11 cm. He suggests that obstetricians as well as anthropologists should pay special heed to these proportions.

Without compass and measuring tape the unaided vision is able to distingish differences in the pelvic dimensions of various races. Sömmering was one of the first to make exact measurements here. Vrolik did important work in comparative anatomy, measuring the pelves of Negresses, Bushwomen and Javanese. M. J. Weber of Bonn tried, somewhat prematurely, and on insufficient material, to group pelvic types on an ethnical basis. He believed that the skull was the key to the pelvis and classified the types as oval (Caucasian), quadrilateral (Mongolian), round (Amerind) and wedge-shaped or triangular (African). Since then we have learnt much, but, as Ploss has elsewhere stressed, not yet enough. There is no agreed standard of measurement. Balandin, the Russian investigator, has pronounced the measurements hitherto adopted as insufficient, qualitatively and quantitatively, for the establishment of a standard of normality. He referred to European material alone and did not touch on ethnical differences throughout mankind. The most questionable measurement hitherto has been the habit of taking the transverse diameter of the pelvic inlet as the test of pelvic capacity. Contour, rather than actual capacity, is important. Zaaijer considered the typical difference was between the " round " and the " long oval " inlet and C. Martin suggested a grouping of :

(1) Pelves with round or circular inlet, said to be found among the American Indians, the Australian aborigines and the Oceanians of the South Seas and Malaysia.

(2) Pelves with oval inlets, found in African and European women.

These important measurements are not, however, the only racial characteristics, but the different regions of the pelvis are also typical ; especially the iliac fossæ, which are distinctly reminiscent of anthropoid pelves in some races (*cf*. Vrolik, Pruner, Carl Vogt, etc.). Other authorities think the sacral formation of primary

---

* Jarcho in his recent study of the pelvis has pointed out that the shape of the rhomboid varies considerably according to the type of pelvis. Thus in the masculine type or " funnel " pelvis, the rhomboid is narrowed, whilst in the rhachitic pelvis the reverse is the case.

importance.   Bacarisse estimates the width of the sacrum as greatest in the white race, then in the yellow race, and least in the black.   There is great variety in the vertical measurement here.   The African negroes have the greatest height among the sacra with six sacral vertebræ, the Europeans among those with five.   The sacral curvature is most marked in white races, especially Europeans, and the flattest in black races.

Radlauer declares that the European sacrum is both relatively and absolutely larger than that of coloured races.   W. Turner has suggested that the sacral region of various types be divided thus :

(1) Dolichohieric : with the index under 100.

(2) Sub-platyhieric : with index between 100 and 106.

(3) Platyhieric : with index over 106.

Radlauer reckons the Bushmen, Malays and Chinese in the first group ; the negroes, Ainu and some Japanese in the second, and the aboriginal women of Australia and Japan as well as the Europeans in the third.

He also points out that the curvature of the frontal surface of the sacral bone is much greater among the lower simian species than in anthropoids and human beings.

Le Damany measured the sacropelvic angles in some 1700 cases, and concluded that in all mammals, except the anthropoids, the angle was very constant at about 55°.

In gorillas and chimpanzees . .	60°
In the orang	70°
In the human embryo . . .	55° to 65°
In the human adult . . .	About 90°
In negroes	Males (♂) 90°, females (♀) 98°.
In the yellow races . . .	♂ 92°, ♀ 100°
In the white races . . .	♂ 100°, ♀ 104°

A later series of measurements gave a decreased sexual differentiation : 167 men were measured and the result was 107°, and in 120 women the result was 108°.   Riggs confirms the opinion that the pelvis of the white race is wide and shallow, compared with the narrow and relatively deep pelvis of the coloured people.

The Japanese, Ogata, made an interesting comparative study of the female pelvis in terms of the ratio of external pelvic measurements to height of stature. His results were as follows, based on the measurements of 725 Japanese women :

	In the Japanese Woman.	In the German Woman.
Conj. Ext. (lumbo-pubic depth)	12·314	12·66
Spinal breadth	15·723	15·83
Cristal breadth.	17·442	17·72
Bitrochanteric breadth	19·139	20·15
Diagonal diameter	13·782	13·93
Pelvic circumference.	52·555	56·44
Height	100	100

Thus the Japanese woman's pelvis is both relatively and absolutely smaller than the German.   Koganei and Osawa have also dealt in detail with the pelvis of both Japanese and Ainu.

There are also undoubtedly special racial differences in pelvic inclination, namely, the angle and position of the pelvis to the axis of the trunk.   Broca drew attention to them and suggested an instrument for their exact estimate.   Hennig also pursued such investigations on racial lines. But Prochownick, who had his own method, came to the conclusion that individual differences were so great that comparative ethnology could not do much with the material.

Even in different racial stocks living in the same territory, the pelvis shows appreciable differences. Schröter found the pelves of Esthonian and German women more powerfully developed than those of the Poles and Jewesses ; and he found the Jewish pelvic measurements the smallest of all. In the material he investigated he found the German women had the strongest pelvic inclination, the Poles the next, the Jewesses the next and the Esthonians the least. But the pelvic inclination is not always constant and invariable even in the same person, for position and attitude make much difference here. Up to the present time, we have no proof that the various attitudes during parturition customary in various races are, in any way, due to differences of pelvic inclination.

98.—Bedouin woman with child on her back.

For further facts the reader may be referred to the work of Vrolik, Zaaijer, A. Weisbach, Carl Martin, O. Franqué, Verneau, Wernich, H. and G. Fritsch, A. Filatoff, A. v. Schrenck, Minassian, H. Ellis, Derry, etc., who deal with ethnical differences common to both sexes.

With regard to children, Weissenberg made measurements of 2576 Russian citizens of Hebrew race : 1366 boys, 1210 girls. He found that, at birth, and till the eighth year, the boy had slightly wider hips than the girl ; after nine years, the female pelvis grows the wider. A fact that Konikoff has also confirmed. This is also the age at which girls take a sudden spurt in growth and often surpass the boys of the same age in height. At 15, the boys become and remain the taller, but the width of hip remains greater in woman through life. This measurement increases most of all in the first two years of infancy, and has its next spurt of growth in woman as mentioned above. Male width of hip grows steadily from 20 to 50 years, reaching its maximum of 280 mm. at that age. And the woman's again increases from 20 to 50, reaching its maximum of 289 mm. then. Thus, from 20 to 50, the feminine hip measurement grows thrice as vigorously as the masculine (increase ♀ 14 mm., ♂ 5 mm.). After 50, there is a slight decrease in both sexes. Le Damany found a remarkable sexual difference in the much greater diameter through the body from front to rear at the level of the spinæ iliacæ anteriores superiores in girls at birth.

There can be no doubt whatever that habits, customs and diet have great influence on pelvic structure individually and racially. The amount of bone-building nutriment obtained is crucial. G. Fritsch found the whole frame very undersized and the pelvic bones badly developed in the Bushwomen and Hottentots, and the sex differences were partly obliterated. There is confirmatory evidence that the pelves of negro women in the U.S.A., who have been accustomed to more abundant food and easier habits of life, have begun to approximate to the European type, owing to greater solidity and capacity of their bones.

Habitual and persistent positions and attitudes of the body and corresponding muscular effort or atrophy have also certainly some effect.   Thus Bertherand found

99.—Negress from Dahomey carrying her child, 1-year-old, on her back.   (Photo, C. Günther, Berlin.)

that the Arab women in Algeria had very widely opened pelves.   He concluded that this characteristic had three main reasons : (1) The habit of carrying the children on their mother's back (cf. Fig. 98) ; (2) much riding from childhood ; (3) The seated attitude with crossed legs.

Ogata took measurements of 725 Japanese women during life in order to compare results among the leisured and the wage-earners. He found that in all seven pelvic measurements the Japanese woman of the working classes was more robustly developed than in the leisured and wealthy strata. The differences were roughly equivalent to those between the Japanese working woman and the German.

Epp often found high and narrow pelves among Chinese women, which he attributes to their very sedentary way of life. Unfortunately, he is in complete disagreement with Mondiére who found the Chinese woman's pelvis exceptionally capacious in all its measurements. All these disputed details must be further elucidated, together with possible causes, such as the way young children are carried or allowed to crawl, or progress in a seated posture, while their bones are in a cartilaginous soft condition. Schliephake, among other authorities, dissents

100 .—Ancient Peruvian vase.   (Mus. d. Völkerk., Berlin.)

from the view that the tension of the muscles and weight of the trunk modify the pelvic form to any extent ; nor, so he thinks, have the thighs much effect through lateral pressure. He believes that the adult structure of the pelvis is constitutional and congenitally determined and can only be influenced by the factors above mentioned to a very slight degree.

In many parts of Africa the mothers carry their babies and little children riding on their backs, across the loins and slung to them for safety (cf. Fig. 99). This means that the buttocks are inclined and protruded backwards in order to support the child's weight and that the vertebral column is curved inwards at the loins and the pelvic angle increased : there is lordosis, or " saddleback."

Hennig, Bérenger-Féraud and others have discussed this peculiarity and its mechanism. Probably the whole bony structure of loins and pelvis are modified by this habit of carrying the children, possibly first acquired, and then with time and use, intensified.

The custom is not peculiar to Africa. It is found among other races, and depicted, *e.g.*, on a piece of pottery from Ancient Peru (Fig. 100). The child is clearly shown there, riding in a sling on its mother's buttocks. The same custom is found in Japan among women and young half-grown girls, and may be occasionally observed in England and the United States.

Does the accentuated curve of the lumbar vertebræ make birth more difficult and dangerous ? We can only say that many women of Africa are reported to take

101.—Grinding meal in Eritrea.   (After Schweinfurth.)

an attitude in which the lumbar curvature is stretched and evened out so that the child meets less resistance. But Riggs has put on record that births last longer among the black races than the white ; that they show fewer head presentations and fewer cases of easy labour. In white races, children at birth are, on the average, both longer (about 1½ cm.) and heavier (about 200 gm.), and with slightly larger heads than in black.

There is a further habit prevalent in the black race that probably accentuates both a tendency to lordosis and pelvic angle : that is the kneeling attitude in which the women grind corn on stone rolling mills by hand.   This is shown in Fig. 101, where a woman from Eritrea kneels, bending from the hips, and throws all her weight on her hands.   And as she grinds backwards and forwards the lifted hips and buttocks must move rhythmically up and down, keeping the lumbar muscles in deliberate tension and motion.   The South African girl from Natal (Fig. 102) is at the beginning of her forward stroke, so her body is upright and not in the quadrupedal posture.   Corn grinding means a rapid and vigorous alternation of stretching and contracting of the lumbar and pelvic muscles, and its effect is heightened if the women carry their babies on their backs while at the mill.

This way of grinding meal has been practised in Africa for thousands of years :

102.—South African girl from Natal grinding meal.

it is shown in many ancient Egyptian statuettes (*cf*. Fig. 103) of the Fourth Millennium B.C. (*circa* 3300).   The figurine represents a young woman and the stone base on which she grinds is worn away.   It is in the Museo Archeologico in Florence.

Le Damany's measurements tend towards the view that there are professional differences in pelvic angle in our race.   Certainly, carrying heavy weights on the head and shoulders throws the buttocks into greater prominence.   As to the influence on parturition, it will be necessary to enlist the observation and opinion of obstetricians as well as anthropologists, and obtain full material before we can form any estimate.

Moreover, head and shoulder measurements in the child, as well as pelvic angle and capacity in the mother, influence parturition, and should be taken into account in estimating anthropological and ethnical differences here.

The gluteal region and the thighs interact on the pelvis, and in the living body measurements round thighs, hips and groins help to indicate the bony measurements of the pelvis.

[Some simple external measurements of the latter are : (*a*) the distance between the anterior superior iliac spines ; (*b*) the intercristal distance ; (*c*) the distance between the heads of the trochanters ; and (*d*) the external conjugate measured from the small depression at the last lumbar vertebra to the anterior upper margin of the symphysis pubis. The use of radiograms for the purpose of measurement

103.—Grinding meal in ancient Egypt, 3300 B.C. (Mus. Arch., Florence.)

has certain disadvantages, but Thoms and H. Martius have shown that useful results can be obtained from their use in the earlier stages of pregnancy.]

Certain formations of the iliac bones make wide pelves look narrow because they are closer together than usual. This is said to be the case with the Loango Coast negresses, according to Falkenstein, who declares it is often difficult to distinguish the sexes when seen from the rear.

Paulitschke notes that the Somali and Galla women have very inclined pelves ; and Wolff says the same of the Congo women : " The pelvis seems turned on its horizontal axis so that the buttocks protrude greatly, while the hips, even in women, are comparatively narrow.

Rochebrune found the Wolof women had " very mediocre pelvic development," and while their abdomen was curved forward in the upper half, it was almost

104.—Viennese girl with short trunk and long legs.

straight in the lower without the slight outward undulant curve of the European woman.

Riedel has cited cases of racial differences among neighbouring stocks in the islands of the Malay Archipelago : wide pelves in the Babar Islands, narrow in Gorong and Ceram Laut.

There are also certain feminine figures which make an impression of almost fragile grace yet have great relative width of hip and posterior.   Wernich, who was in charge of a gynæcological ward at Yeddo for some time, found this was the case

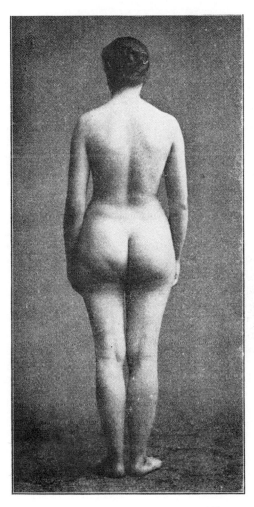 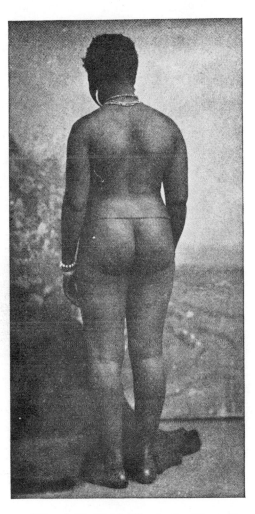

105.—European girl (25 years).   (Photo, Günther.)

106.—Ashanti girl (16 years).   The well-knit frame and firm buttocks are to be specially remarked (cf. Fig. 199 for view from in front).   (Photo, Günther.)

with the Japanese women patients.   Their pelves were capacious, and the angle of the symphysis pubis very wide and obtuse.   On the other hand, according to von Baelz, broad buttocks are considered hideous in Japan ; the smaller her pelvic region the more a woman is admired.

Again, Maurel ascribes to Cambodian women " very much developed buttocks and flat pubes."

J. L. de Lanessau says of the Agni in Dahomey : " The women have prominent buttocks even amounting to some degree of steatopygia, which is not ungraceful in its effect as they walk " (" *qui n'est pas sans ajouter une grace à leur tournure* ").

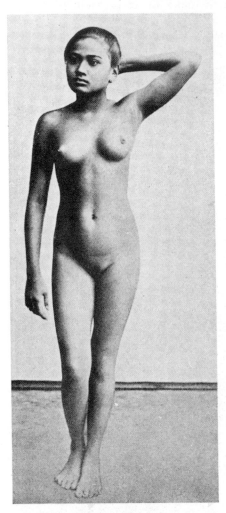

107.—Girl from Java seen from in front. Fig. **93** shows her from behind. (Anthrop. Ges., Berlin.)

THE GLUTEAL REGION, ANTHROPOLOGICALLY CONSIDERED

The hips in women are not only accentuated by bony structure but by their greater or lesser amount of adipose tissue. Here there are individual differences even in one racial stock. But even the camera shows greater differences between races, and, checking these results with the reports of eye witnesses, we can have no doubt of ethnical differences in the gluteal region.

Nevertheless, the most frequent proportions among European women are averages between the extremes of deficiency in adipose tissue and excess : between contours which appear to us either undeveloped or the reverse. Moreover, the size of the gluteal region is very important in its general effect : in the balance and symmetry it gives—or does not give—to the length of limb and trunk.

An example of a short trunk and unusually long legs and hips is shown in the photograph of a Viennese girl (Fig. 104 ; *cf.* also the various ethnical types in Figs. 105–114).

[Before considering various ethnical differences some account of the female buttocks in the white subject may not be without interest.

Before puberty differences in the sexes are not easily perceived. With the broadening of the pelvis occurs the accumulation of adipose tissue in the girl, and, generally speaking, the two sexes are fairly distinct. The buttocks of the girl are fuller, more rounded and softer than those of the boy. His are closer knit and firmer to the touch. The deposit of fat is more easily seen in the short than in the tall woman. In the fat woman there is a tendency to sag, but even here there is little backward growth such as is seen in Bushwomen and Hottentots.

Viewed from behind, with the subject upright, the main feature is the gluteal cleft, whilst below, the gluteo-femoral folds are characteristic. The former commences at the lowest point (sometimes a distinct dimple) of the rhomboid of Michaelis. The gluteo-crural folds (which are occasionally doubled) run across the thigh, are slightly curved with an upward concavity and unite with the genito-crural folds.

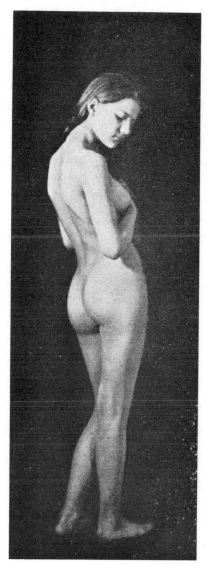

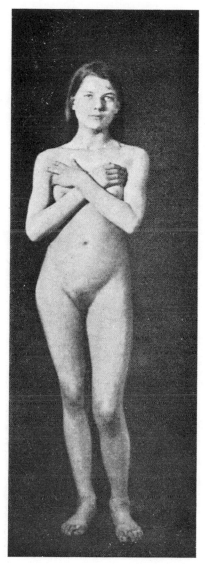

108 .—German girl.   109 .—German girl.
(Photo, R. A. Giesecke.)

With the subject in the dorsal position with flexed thighs the gluteo-crural folds
disappear and the same occurs in other positions.

At least six types of buttocks have been distinguished, but the variations are
not important.   The two main types are the rounded and the flat.   The first type
is characteristically *female*.   The pads are smooth, firm and elastic.   They can be
most often observed in short, well-nourished and active young women.   The flat
type is more *male* in appearance.   It is common in tall girls of slender figure and
has been much admired at various times.   In the case of certain rather plump,
full buttocks, a number of dimples and depressions are occasionally to be observed

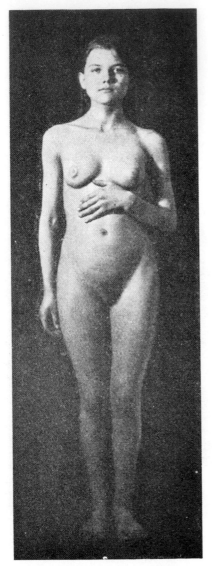 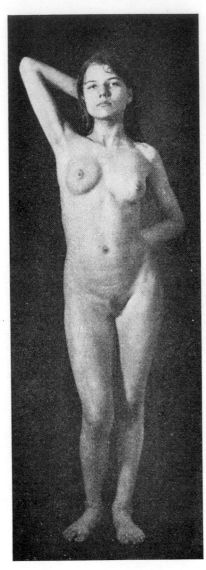

110.—German girl.   111.—German girl.
(Photo, R. A. Giesecke.)

in the skin.   These are said to be due to fibrous filaments between the skin and the gluteal aponeurosis.]

The buttocks of Papuan women are very much developed, according to Friedrich Müller, and he attributes this to the constant climbing of their steep hills.   Riedel made the same observation on Buru women.

Krämer noticed that Samoan girls and women had very slightly defined gluteal-crural folds : less, indeed, than their menfolk.

Steller, in describing the Kamchadale, said the women had " round, small and firm buttocks."

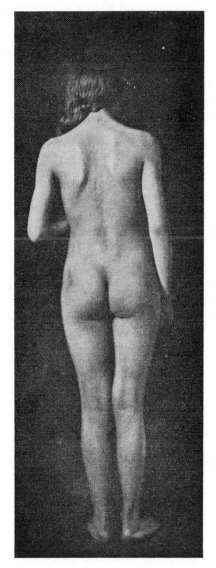 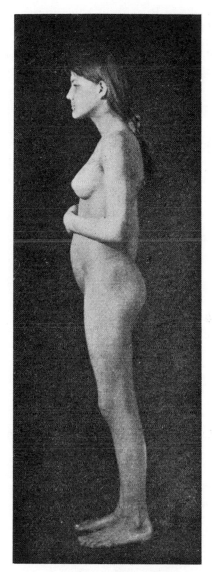

112.—German girl.   113.—German girl.
(Photo, R. A. Giesecke.)

Baelz reports that in those Japanese women whom he classifies as Korean-Manchurian in type :

"The hips are narrow and remarkably lacking in fat." He describes the women as slenderly built with long, slim throats and faces and aquiline noses, delicate limbs and extremities, narrow shoulders and hips.

There is a great contrast in the figure of the Ashanti girl (of 16 years old) (Fig. 106), which is much more powerfully developed than that of the young, mature and plump European girl beside her (Fig. 105).

A. T. de Rochebrune measured 150 Wolof women and found their gluteal and pelvic measurements half way between the European average and the peculiar Bushman type.

He found the following measurements between the trochanters over the maximum circumference below the hips :

Bushwoman	.	.	0·791 m.
Wolof woman	.	.	0·678 m.
Europeans	.	.	0·644 m.

Gustav Nachtigal found graceful figures with well-shaped pelves among the Tibu women of Lake Chad. But the Bornu women had both strong pelvic inclination and excessive fat, which had a repulsive effect to some European eyes.

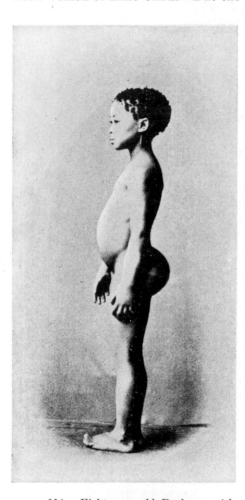

114.—Eight-years-old Bushman girl with beginning of steatopygia.

STEATOPYGIA

[Localised masses of fat on the body have long been of interest to medical science. Certain groups of animals possess these enlarged areas, and in the human species the example of the Bushmen of South Africa is of especial interest and importance. In this case there is an enormous accumulation upon the buttocks, mostly in females but sometimes in the males as well, only to a less extent. These elastic gluteal deposits are often present without any corresponding notable increase in the size of the thigh. The condition is known as steatopygia (,στέαρ fat, and πυγή rump).]

It has been observed to a peculiar degree among certain races in South Africa : the Bushmen, Koranna and Hottentots (very pronounced, according to E. H. L. Schwarz), whilst that of the Bornu, Wolof and Konde are, as it were, a transitional form. In steatopygous peoples the women are naturally the most conspicuous, and their peculiarity is said to begin at the earliest date—in childhood, not in puberty, as Blanchard, Le Vaillant and others have confirmed.

The males among Kalahari Bushmen, however, who were exhibited in Berlin under the name of "Farini's Troglodytes," had very large and prominent hindquarters, according to M. Bartels. In the females, one little girl, indeed, eight years of age, almost equalled the mature men in this respect, thus confirming the appearance of steatopygia at an early stage in individual growth (*cf.* Fig. 114).

It has been stated that steatopygia does not occur in persons of mixed European and Bushman or Hottentot blood. But apparently it is not universal even in apparently full-blooded Bush folk : for instance, among the Heikum and Kung, according to Werner. G. Fritsch states that the Hottentot woman is distinctly more steatopygous than the Bushwomen. But Livingstone maintained that there was a certain degree of steatopygia among some Boer woman. Thulié rejects this view so far as it refers to persons of unmixed blood and attributes any case that may occur to a streak of African or aboriginal blood.

The cause of steatopygy is not muscular but adipose, as has been demonstrated in many autopsies. The famous so-called " Hottentot Venus " described by Cuvier was steatopygous to a high degree ; the measurement is given as 16·2 cm.

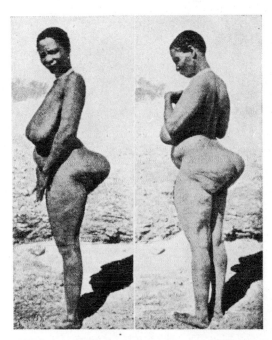

115.—Hottentot women from Berseba with prominent steatopygia.

Flower and Murie examined the body of a Bushwoman 21 years old who died in England. She had lost the adipose deposit and her skin was lax and wrinkled. Luschka and Görtz made an autopsy on the woman " *Afandy*," described as of Bushman origin. The thickness of her adipose cushion when preserved in spirits for a year was between 4 and 4½ cm. at its maximum point, and the disposition of this extra layer of fat was not on the European plan but particularly marked over the glutæus maximus, so that the sides were proportionately flatter and the posterior more prominent than in the European woman, apart from the larger dimensions.

It is out of the question that the phenomenon of steatopygia can be mainly due to bony structure or pelvic inclination. Theophil Hahn declares that the young Hottentot boys who were his playmates were steatopygous as well as the women ; and that their dimensions waxed and waned according to the season, becoming " almost incredible " when the rains brought an abundance of game and roots for food.

Sokolovsky believes that human steatopygia is analogous to the layers of fat on the hind-quarters and tails of the fat-tailed sheep (*Ovis aries steatopyga*).   He considers that they represent an adaptation to life on the African deserts, supplying

116.—Two Hottentots with steatopygia.

nutriment to the system when exhausted by lack of food, and that steatopygia is intrinsic in the Bushfolk but acquired by selective elimination in the Hottentots.

[The view that these adipose accumulations are analogous to such fat deposits as those of the camel, zebu, *Phascologale Macdonnellensis* and the fat and broad-tailed sheep is doubtless correct (see Shattock and R. Hartmann).   Here also we have to deal with a kind of food reserve which can be utilised in case of need: It must, however, be clearly understood that steatopygia is to be sharply distinguished from any form of crural obesity, lordosis, or the result of a general fattening treatment as is common in parts of Africa.]

Certainly the impression that steatopygia (in its pronounced forms) makes on an unaccustomed European observer is extraordinary and æsthetically repulsive. Even the slighter protuberance common in some Bushwomen is ugly in our eyes. But the Hottentots themselves consider their steatopygia, which they term " *aredi* " supremely beautiful (Figs. 115–123).

[Of the various groups of Bushmen the southern probably represent the purest type. The head is mesocephalic and the nose very flat. The figure generally is not fat, indeed rather the reverse. The limbs are slender and the hands and feet small. In girls the breasts are firm and conical with erect nipples, but later they become flaccid and shrivelled. Amongst the Northern Bushmen steatopygia seldom occurs, according to Schapera, who, in any case, does not regard it as a racial peculiarity. Among the Hottentots, the buttocks, considered in relation to stature, are small. Their prominence is due to the steatopygia which is found more commonly among them than among the Bushmen. It is curious that three unusual physical characters should be found in these people : the accumulation of fat on the buttocks and the elongated labia minora among the women, and the state of apparent semi-erection of the penis in men. L. Schultze-Jena has recently dealt with the physical characteristics of these people and the reader may be directed to his work, and to the earlier accounts, *e.g.*, Vincent].

In profile, this particular structure shows very clearly and a further peculiarity is occasionally revealed, namely, a second adipose cushion in the regions of the two trochanters. This is found in both Hottentot and Bushwomen, and has been described by Topinard and others as associated with steatopygia (Figs. 119 – 121).

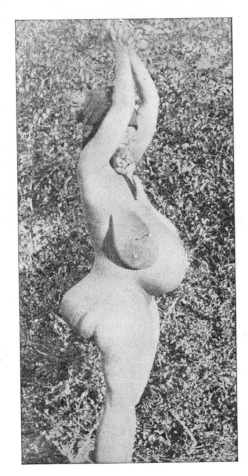

117.—Pregnant Hottentot woman with steatopygia. (Photo, Lotz.)

The maximum width of the pelvic region is thus much further down than in Europeans, even just below the gluteo-crural fold between thighs and buttocks. The increase in thigh circumferences is in the upper part only ; the lower thigh is not unusually thick.

This particular displacement of the maximum pelvic width from the area normal among Europeans is also found in many women of the white race (*cf.* Fig. 124). Thus the disposition of the gluteal cushion is of the same type, but the dimensions much less than in the primitive peoples we have described.

Revoil mentions cases of steatopygia in describing the Somali and Berber people. Stuhlmann observed "a certain tendency" in this direction among the Pygmies whom he discovered in the Ituri district. He brought back two young

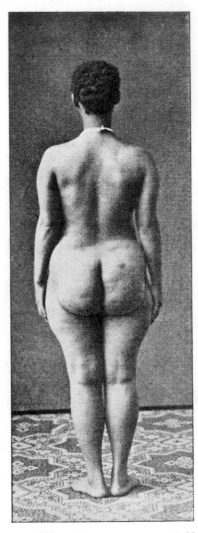

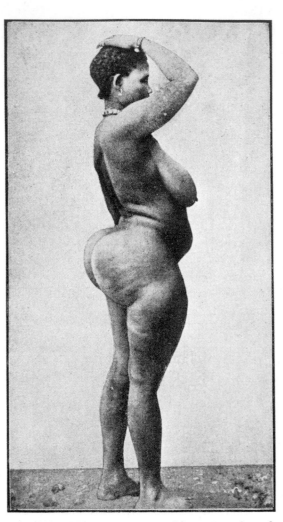

118.—Hottentot woman of 22 years with steatopygia and crural obesity. (Photo, Sander and Roeschke.)

119.—Hottentot woman with steatopygia and crural obesity. (Photo, Sander and Roeschke.)

Pygmy girls to Europe. On the one, Asmini, the buttocks were of very rounded proportions; the other, Shikanayo, was a genuine case of steatopygia.

There are in Europe cases of gluteal development so pronounced that they are almost steatopygous (*cf.* Fig. 128). But the structure is nothing like so extreme, though of great interest for comparative anthropology. In the early editions of this work, Bartels noted European cases. A. de Blasio has now pointed out that these semi-steatopygous cases occur in women of Mediterranean race.* Blasio recorded in detail the cases of two young women in their early 'twenties and practising prostitution in Naples ; their steatopygia was pronounced and well known among their acquaintances, so much so that they were nicknamed " *la culietta* " and " *la culacchiona* " respectively. Both girls said they had been steatopygous since childhood but specially since puberty. Blasio says one was a Neapolitan by birth : the nationality of the other is not recorded. Atgier and Ujfalvy have also called attention to French and Greek cases.

Prehistory, ethnology and anthropology have equal interest in the origin and purpose of certain primitive works of art which have been discovered and

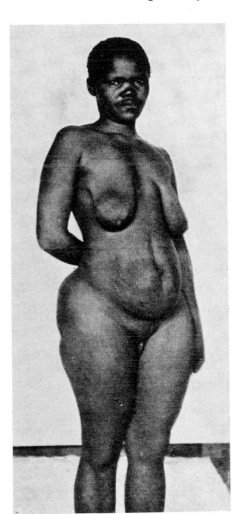

120.—Bushwoman. (Anthrop. Ges., Berlin.)

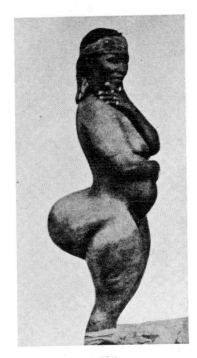

121.—Hottentot. (Anthrop. Ges., Berlin.)

recorded in increasing numbers and from various widely distant quarters. They are representations of the female figure, and they are likewise unmistakably steatopygous.

In the Thebian Temple of Dêr al-Baharî there was a relief of a Queen of Punt or Pevenet (Southern Arabia) which dates, according to E. Meyer, from c. 2000 B.C.

* [I have seen only two examples of steatopygia apart from Bushmen and Hottentots. One was an American girl of mixed blood and the other a West Indian half-breed.]

in the reign of Menthu-hetep.   Meyer believes the people of Punt were the ancestors of the Hamitic stocks (Somali, Galla, Masai, etc.) and the tribes of the Arabian desert and Lower Nubia (Fig. 126).   The corpulence and projecting posterior of the Arabian princess are very different from the extreme slenderness of the Egyptians. F. von Luschan, however, is of opinion that we have here a case of rachitic dwarfism combined with obesity, for rolls of fat are to be observed in arms and legs.

[Similarly in the reliefs at Shindî are to be seen processions in which women are represented who are extremely obese.   As has already been said, fat women are much admired in parts of Africa and, as we shall see later, they appear to have enjoyed similar admiration for many centuries.   The distinction, however, between

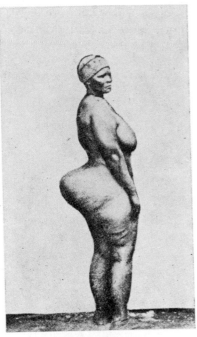

122.—Hottentot.   (Anthrop. Ges., Berlin.)

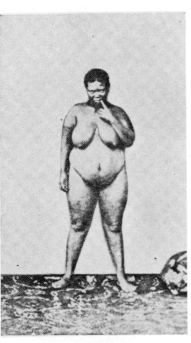

123.—Hottentot.   (Anthrop. Ges., Berlin.)

steatopygia and fat buttocks due to general obesity must be carefully borne in mind (see Budge, Ruffer, Slomann, Regnault, and for a modern discussion of fat women, *cf.* Wangen and Scheuer).]

Africa has not a monopoly of steatopygous statuettes.   They have been found both in Asia and Europe.   Some anthropologists have interpreted these statuettes as proof of the existence of a prehistoric population in Europe and Asia, which had the specific physique of the Bushfolk and Hottentots.   And the obvious conclusion has been drawn, but criticised by (*inter alia*) Cartailhac, who listed and compared the material available with valuable additions of his own discovery.   Moreover, Piette found three remarkable ivory figurines at Brassempouy (Landes), all repre-senting women, and all apparently dating from palæolithic times.   One of the three was said to be definitely steatopygous, one less so, and the third not at all. Three more, but very roughly executed, statuettes of the same Age, were described by Piette ; he found them at Baoussé-Roussé near Menton. Similar representations and statuettes are known from Malta (*cf.* A. Mayr and Zammit) and various parts

124 .—Excessive fat under the trochanters (Spanish girl).

of Thrace and Myria, from Butmir, Cucuteni and Sereth in Poland, from Greece and the Ægean Isles, especially Crete (see Macalister, Evans, Shattock, Dussaud). Among the hitherto uncatalogued and unexhibited treasures of the French National collections in the Musée du Louvre, Cartailhac was able to report several specimens from Lydia, which displayed all transitional stages from extreme steatopygia to complete absence of this peculiarity.   The same is the case in the collection brought by Morgan from Susa.   The " Great Goddess " is sometimes represented as unmistakably steatopygous and sometimes the posterior fullness is merely indicated, and here, too, there are transitional types.   Cartailhac concludes that we must not regard the statuettes as realistic representations, *i.e.*, as portraits, but that they are symbolic or typical, *i.e.*, more or less idealised or stereotyped, and that the artists who made them were attempting to emphasise the typically feminine roundness in an unmistakable fashion.   Szombathy agrees, and to him we owe the discovery and preservation of the so-called " Venus of Willendorf," an Aurignacian work of art found in Austria (Fig. 127).   He considers this figure to be an attempt at symbolic or æsthetic emphasis, not a portrait of any racial characteristic.   Mosso concurs, but Paribeni is of a different opinion.   In support of his view he reproduces a

125 .—Bongo woman
with steatopygia.

126 .—Steatopygia (?)
in an Arab Princess.

limestone figurine from *Adulis* (Eritrea, North-east Africa) which was found, together with a terra-cotta figurine of the same kind and a gold coin of King Israel of Axum, and is attributed to the sixth century B.C.   He points out that steatopygia and obesity are not identical with fertility and not necessarily associated therewith. Certainly, in some of his specimens there is strong evidence of actual steatopygia and an apparent effort to portray it faithfully.   Of course, it would be rash and premature to conclude that these statuettes represent a race allied to the Hottentots and Bushmen on their evidence alone, and, apart from human remains.   Further information on ancient specimens showing steatopygia and similar conditions will be found in the work of Royer, Myres, Saint Périer, and in the *Bull. Soc. préhist. française*, 1924, 81–88 ; 1926, 183, 187, 374.

THE VULVOANAL REGION IN WOMAN AND ITS ANTHROPOLOGICAL CHARACTERISTICS

Anthropological and medical knowledge is undeniably imperfect in some directions, and the feminine sex organs are one of these.   [The number of careful observations have been few and, in spite of much anecdotal material, our knowledge of the general characteristics and variations even in the white races is very meagre. Before, therefore, examining the different forms among coloured peoples it may be

127.—" Venus of Willendorf."

of some service if a brief account is given here of the external sexual organs of the white woman.*

The classical type is that described in anatomical text-books and usually represents the average vulva of the nullipara at full maturity. From the anthropological point of view, however, this is of little practical use. The female genitals vary enormously not only in different individuals but in the same individual at

* For a recent work see R. L. Dickinson.

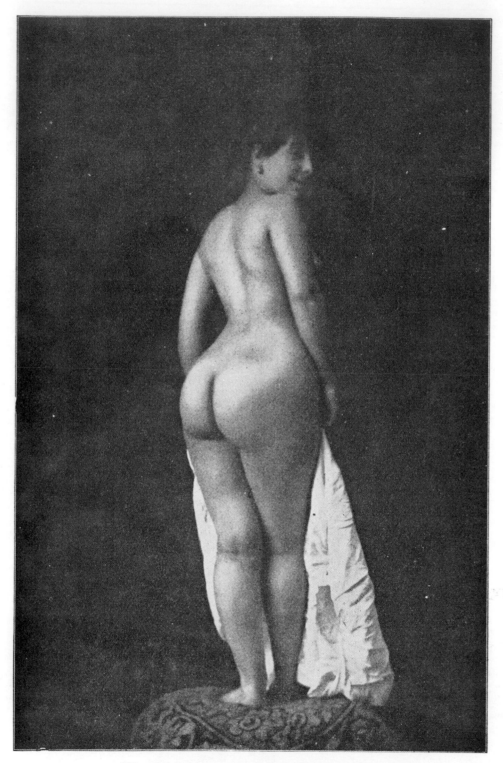

128 .—Spanish woman with slight steatopygia (Barcelona).

different times. The vulva of a young girl differs from that after puberty. The vulva at menstruation in a nullipara differs from the vulva of gestation in a multipara. Here it will be convenient merely to give an outline sketch in order to stimulate interest in medical anthropologists and suggest lines of further observation and research.

The most important general characteristic is the *position* of the vulva. If an adult woman is placed in the supine position with legs extended and thighs together (*cf.* Fig. 5) the degree of visibility depends on the anterior or posterior position of the vulva. Generally speaking, in this position about one-third is visible. In girls before puberty this appearance is often mistaken for an unduly anterior position, as the vulva is more easily open to inspection owing to the lack of fatty development and hair on the mons and the manner in which the labia and clitoris often protrude (*cf.* Fig. 168).

If we take a normal young woman of average height and weight the following measurements were found by Jayle to approach a fair approximation. In the dorsal position the total length from the summit of the mons to the centre of the anus was 12 cm. From the anterior limit to the clitoris, 4 cm. ; from clitoris to fourchette, 5 cm. ; from fourchette to anus, 3 cm. When the vulva is placed in a more posterior position visibility in front decreases and the perineum is often found to be somewhat narrowed.

The main difference in the various types of normal vulva are brought about by coitus and child-bearing. In the nullipara who has not had sexual intercourse or indulges but infrequently, the vulva is more contracted and elastic ; and the inner aspect can only be observed by separating the labia. In the multipara and in the vulva of age the parts are more open and lax, and the labia less resistant and elastic.

If, in the supine position, the legs are raised and the thighs separated, and either lightly flexed or strongly flexed on the abdomen the whole vulval and anal region becomes visible. Yet even in this position in the young nullipara the inner structures are not easily observable except by separating the labia. The difference between the two types is immediately apparent.

In woman the *pubic hair* does not attain full development till some considerable time has elapsed after the first menstruation. The character and distribution of the hair is quite different in various types, as might have been expected from a consideration of the pilous system generally. Thus the vulva and anus of the brunette differ from those of the blonde, not only in the amount and distribution of the pubic hair but in the pigmentation of the skin. On the mons the hair is usually curly or frizzly. Occasionally tufts are present ; but in very fair women the amount of hair in this region and below appears extremely sparse. The distribution varies according to the general condition. In some the hair extends upward towards the navel, some authorities putting 5 per cent. as the average figure. In the posterior direction, especially in brunettes, the hair thickly surrounds the vulva, extends to the anal margins and may be even found in the termination of the intergluteal fold. Jayle, among others, considers this posterior growth around the anus as unusual and suggestive of pseudo-hermaphroditism, whilst Waldeyer considers it far from rare. Similarly, the anterior extension upwards towards the navel has caused differences of opinion, due probably to the fact that the disputants were unaware of the practice of brunettes to remove hair from the abdomen and also from elsewhere.

In colour, pubic hair is often darker than the hair of the head in blondes ; lighter in brunettes. Red-haired women have red pubic hair, although the latter may be somewhat lighter. Few observations have been made on the average or individual length of the hair. In hirsuties exaggerated length has been reported, the hair sometimes reaching to the knees. The eyebrows are a useful guide to the paucity or otherwise of the pubic hair, a thick growth being very often accompanied by thick, curly pubic hair.

The *labia majora*, or outer lips, are of two types, the developed and the undeveloped. In the first they may be properly described as *lips* and conceal the inner structures almost entirely from view. In the second they are scarcely visible when the legs are strongly flexed and the clitoris and nymphæ are fully exposed.

The *labia minora*, or nymphæ, are of great importance to the anthropologist. We shall speak of the variations in different races in a later place. Even among white women these variations are considerable.* Normally they consist of two folds with an average length of 3 cm. and average height of from 10 to 16 mm. They lie in close approximation, concavity upwards, and possess a serrated or indented edge. They are rich in sebaceous glands and are highly pigmented in brunettes. Anteriorly they converge and divide into two lamellæ. The precise anatomical relation they bear to the frenulum and prepuce of the clitoris is still disputed. Posteriorly they fade away into the tissue, or fuse together, and in some cases extend almost to the anus. Four types may be distinguished, the short, the membranous, the aleate and the hypertrophic. The second can be called the normal, the others being variations of it. Secondary folds have been described by Jayle and others, but in certain cases these have probably been due to folds in well-developed nymphæ which would have been obliterated by traction. Their elasticity and erectile quality have caused much discussion, in view of the hypertrophy to be discussed later. It is possible that a woman with large sensitive nymphæ may increase their size by manipulation and masturbation (*cf.* Fig. 237) ; and this hypertrophy might result from such manipulations if these were commenced very early in life. Experimental evidence is lacking, and it is difficult to see how it could be obtained.

Before passing from the nymphæ it may be mentioned that occasionally there are found on these structures what have been termed *papillæ genitales*, which appear at puberty and show erectility and great richness in nerve endings. They have not yet been carefully examined, but it has been thought by some that they have a close connection with the stimulation arising from the rubbing movements of coitus, and thus may be compared with the artificial aids of primitive peoples and the devices which are sometimes attached to condoms in our own civilisation (*cf.* Lipschütz, Buschke and Gumpert).

On separating and folding back the nymphæ the inner structures are exposed. Above, the *clitoris* is visible, the glans covered or not by the prepuce, which slides over it. It is the chief organ of sensation, and is rich in vessels and nerves. The roots vary from 3 to 4 cm. in length ; when erect they are from 4·5 to 5 cm. long. Although it is capable of erection the clitoris cannot rise like its male homologue. It can merely swell and protrude under sexual excitement.

Marinelli declared that its sensitivity was so great that even the touch of an undergarment was sufficient to excite a woman to venereal ardour. The same view was expressed when the wearing of drawers became fashionable.

Between the glans and prepuce of the clitoris lies a small fold or pocket in which coagulates smegma. This, coupled with the other vulval secretions, gives the parts the peculiar *odour* which is of little anthropological interest, although of

* *Cf.* Kuligowska.

some importance in other directions.   Van de Velde has dealt with this question in his "Ideal Marriage."   More important to the anthropologist are the cases of hypertrophy of the clitoris and the relation of this condition to pseudo-hermaphroditism and nymphomania.   Becker and Kranz, among others, have dealt fully with clitoridectomy, and M. Buch has made a special study of the relation of the clitoris to erotic conditions.   The variations in coloured peoples will be considered later.

Below the clitoris lie the orifice of the *urethra* and the openings to *Skene's glands*.   A considerable number of varied forms of the former are to be distinguished. Bergh described several, and Jayle has dealt with some seventeen shapes, varying from a mere slit to a large pouting meatus.   Just inside and on either side of the urethral opening are the orifices of Skene's ducts.

Beneath the orifice of the urethra lies the *vaginal* opening, partially or wholly closed by the *hymen* in the virgin.   This structure, which has led to interminable discussion, can only be fully seen after the nymphæ have been widely separated.   Numerous forms are to be distinguished (*cf.* Figs. 54–58) of which more will be said later.   Here we may merely direct attention to the works of Budin, Devilliers, Gaullier, Geering, Ledru, Tolberg, Götzfried, Cullingworth, Gellhorn, Taussig, Dohrn, Chavernac, Volta, etc.

The vagina has considerable variations in length, according to the position in which it is measured among other factors.*   Normally it is about 3 in.   At the orifice there is a thin layer of muscular tissue which is of interest to the anthropologist for in certain persons constriction of this can

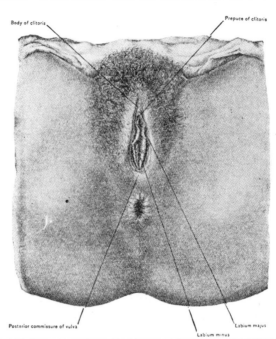

129 A.—The vulvoanal region.   (After Deaver).

be effected voluntarily, whereas in the majority action on this muscle is usually combined with powerful contractions of the levator ani.   The education of this group of muscles controlling the vagina and anus in order to perfect certain kinds of erotic technique has received attention in various quarters (E. Martin, Van de Velde, Liebenstein, etc.).   Their use and functions have long been known in erotic literature, and in Abyssinia such a woman is called "Kabbadah," a holder (see Fraxi, p. 291).†

Below the vaginal opening lies the so-called *fossa navicularis*, and at either side of the vagina close against the medial sides of the labia minora lie the openings of the greater vestibular glands or glands of Bartholin.   They are not easy to examine

* Kuligowska has compared the lengths in 400 Poles.   The average length of the anterior wall was 71 mm., and posterior wall 103 mm.
† *Cf.* also Brantôme, *Les vies*, etc., I., 251 ; Frank Harris, II., 409 ; and P. Couteau [M. Cotelli], who called this faculty " le charme secret de ces personnes dont les faveurs rédoublent l'amour de l'heureux amant qui les reçoit " (p. 197).

except under certain circumstances when inflammation is present. During sexual stimulation they serve as outlets for a slippery secretion which bathes the vaginal orifice and surrounding parts preparatory to coitus.

The *perineum* and *anus* are of slight interest for our present purposes. The condition of the former is highly important to the woman herself, since lacerations, occurring at childbirth and not properly sutured are apt to cause great lack of tone and control. The anus lies in a shallow depression and is characterised by folds which radiate from the centre. Its muscular control is of some considerable importance to woman, for by the conscious and deliberate control of its contractions a fuller erotic sensibility can be achieved. For this purpose special exercises have been devised (*cf.* Van de Velde *, Liebenstein, etc.).

[Many observations have been made on the various positions of the vulva.]

Columbato d'Isère, for example, made some deductions from his clinical observations and maintained that in southern climates these organs tended to be set higher in the body and nearer the pubes than in damp and cold regions. Thus, according to this authority the uterus is further down (nearer the introitus) and the vulva further backward in English, Scottish and Dutch women than in Frenchwomen of the south, Spaniards and Italians (Fig. 130). But there is no definite knowledge on this subject, and Buschan is probably justified in suggesting that, if Columbat d'Isère's remarks are correct, the reason is more due to pelvic structure and angle than to climate (Figs. 130–136).

Corpus (body) clitoridis
Glans clitoridis
Preputium clitoridis
External urinary meatus
Vestibule
Labium majus
Labium minus

Skin of labium majus elevated by tension on labium minus
Fossa navicularis
Fourchette (frenulum labiorum pudendi)
Anterior wall of vagina
Hymen

129 B.—External genitals of virgin.
(After Deaver).

There are certain existent studies of the variations in measurements of the external genitalia in European women. These treatises are of great anthropological value, not only in themselves but as suggesting a standard for comparison with the coloured races. There is a comparison by Götzfried (*cf.* also Tolberg) based on 111 observed cases of adult women and dealing with the varieties of structure in the hymen. The most frequent shape was found to be *annular* (62 cases = 55·8 per cent.) then *falciform crescentic* (25 cases = 22·5 per cent.), semilunar or crescent-shaped (4 cases—3·6 per cent.), and *labiiform* (7 cases—6·3 per cent.). This last-mentioned structural type is a modification of the crescent with more lateral development and less at front and rear. There were 13 further cases of rarer structures, *i.e.*, 11·7 per cent. There were only 7 cases of a perfectly smooth edge ; all the others

* "Sex Efficiency Through Exercises " by Th. H. Van de Velde (William Heinemann (Medical Books) Ltd., London).

had furrows and serrations which might almost suggest tears, owing to a certain slackness and looseness of the whole membrane (Figs. 54–59).

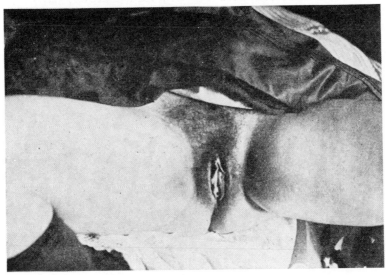

130.—Vulvoanal region (Italian).   The nymphæ have been separated.   (After Pachinger.)

Kisch follows Maschka in this classification :
(1) The circular or annular hymen, with round vaginal aperture.

131.—Vulvoanal region (Hungarian).   (After Pachinger.)

(2) The semilunar crescentic hymen with triangular aperture.
(3) The heart-shaped or cordiform.
(4) The infundibuliform hymen.

And there are other rarer formations, such as the rudimentary, in which there is no perceptible membrane at all : the *imperforate*, in which the aperture is either like a pin's head or quite non-existent (*cf.* Brindeau, McIlroy, Laporte); the sieve-shaped with several very minute apertures ; and the bipartus, which divides the orifice of the introitus into two equal or unequal parts by a very narrow bridge of membrane, and which may extend quite deeply into the vaginal passage, also called hymen septus. Finally, there is the loose, folded formation in which several (two to four) layers of membrane overlap one another.

In Kratter's treatise on forensic medicine he distinguishes the usual hymenal structures as :

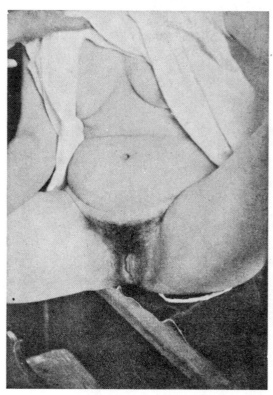

132 .—Vulva of a girl from Bohemia, 23 years. (After Pachinger.)

(1) Crescentic (hymen semilunaris).
(2) Annular (hymen annularis).
And the rarer formations as :
(3) Fringed or scalloped (hymen fimbriatus).
(4) Divided (hymen septus).
(5) Cribriform (hymen cribriformis).
(6) Infundibuliform (hymen labiiformis).*

Another detailed study of genital structure of women is by Jayle, who examined 500 individuals and collated his results in a monograph on the anatomy of the labia minora or nymphæ among European women. He found frequent asymmetry and either asymmetrical or bilateral excessive development or hypertrophy, an anomaly to be discussed in the following section. He found that the labia minora might either surround the introitus vagina completely with deep lateral folds or shelve abruptly away towards the rear. He also found cases of supplementary structures such as both Bischoff and Martin found in the natives of Tierra del Fuego. The extreme edge of the labia minora can divide into two, into the so-called *pli paranymphéal*, as Jayle has termed it ; and this modification or elaboration may be so pronounced as to merit the title of " *petites lèvres latérales secondaires,*" or, if the double fold is only developed behind the introitus in the rear portion towards the anus, then he terms the result : " *formation des petites lèvres postérieurs secondaires.*"

These investigations and recorded results are valuable anthropologically, but they are, of course, only the beginning of systematic study and are confined to cases taken from the white race. In view of the significance of the female organs juridi-

* [Tenbaum has also described various forms and Willette has collected material from the older authors.]

cally, anatomically and anthropologically, the small extent of our exact knowledge, absolute and relative, is to be regretted.

We are even very ignorant of conditions among the anthropoid apes in this

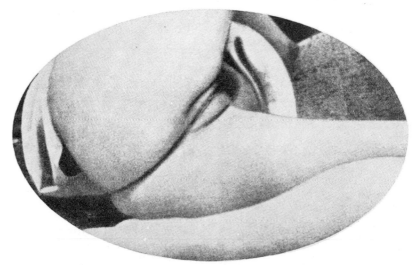

133 .—Vulval and gluteal region in a Japanese.   (After Stratz.)

respect.   Gerhardt says that the hymen exists in the gorilla and in certain ungulates but not in most mammalian species.   But Klaatsch maintains that the gorilla,

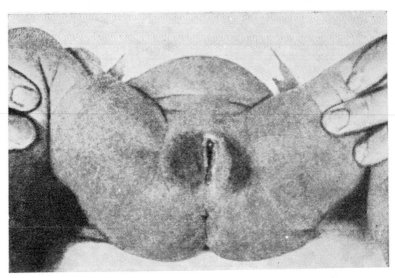

134 .—Vulvoanal region in a new-born infant.   (After Baisch.)

chimpanzee, zebu and gibbons have structures which may be classed under this heading, but that the orang and all other simians and mammals have not.   Thus there is direct conflict of statement and this is all the more unsatisfactory because

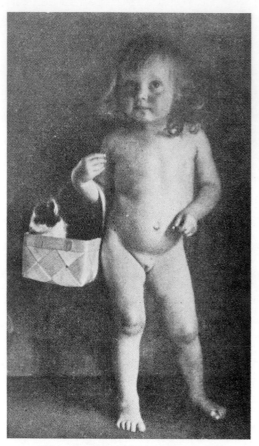

135 .—Anterior view of the vulva before puberty. (Photo, R. A. Giesecke.)

of the specifically human characteristics of the hymen. The form of the vulva differs in different races ; so further and more precise knowledge of sub-human species might be very instructive (*cf.* also Neuville).

We may assume as certain the non-existence of actual labia majora in orangs, gorillas and the gibbons, or at least, their very rudimentary size and shape. The interior labia minora are also comparatively slight, but appear larger than in the woman. In the chimpanzee the outer labia are some-what more conspicuous and swollen during the œstrus which corresponds to the menstrual period in human beings. (Hartmann and U. Gerhardt). Also, the chimpanzee has a prominent clitoris, but nothing corresponding to the mons veneris, or specially thick " pubic " hair (*cf.* v. Bischoff). The chimpanzee appears midway, anatomically, between the woman and the gorilla, orangs and gibbons, which resemble one another more closely.

We shall now collate and sum-marise what is known or reported on racial differences in the female genitals, with the proviso that many of these statements need corroboration.

According to Köler, the genital organs of the aboriginal Australian women are situated further towards the rear and away from the symphysis pubis than in Europeans ; and he adds that coitus *a tergo* is therefore customary among them. But this statement is directly contrary to the accounts furnished by Miklucho Maclay and Walter E. Roth ; the latter explicitly describes :

" The peculiar method of copulation in vogue throughout all these tribes does not prevent fertilisation, notwithstanding the mutilation of the male. The female lies on her back on the ground, while the male with open thighs sits on his heels close in front : he now pulls her towards him, and raising her buttocks drags them into the inner aspects of his own thighs, her legs clutching him round the flanks while he arranges with his hands the toilette of her perineum and the insertion of his penis."

This method can be compared with that prac-tised in the Trobriand Islands which Malinowski has described.

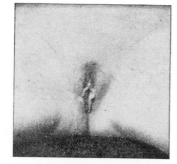

136 .—Vulva of a Korean. (After Baelz.)

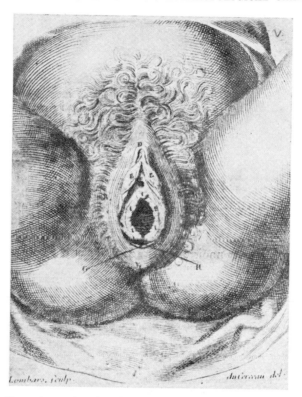

137 .—The vulvoanal region after a drawing by Lombars.   (French, *c.* 1740.)

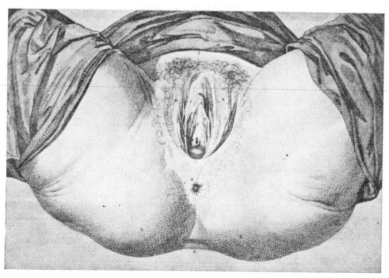

138 .—The vulvoanal region.   English, *c.* 1758.   (After Smellie.)

Riedel   has given some reports, hitherto uncorroborated, of the peculiarities of the inhabitants in the Molucca Islands.   He describes the women of Gorong and

Ceram Laut as having narrow vaginal orifices and with rudimentary inner labia. In the women of the Babar Islands the rima pudendi is reported as apparently shorter than in most of the women of Amboina. The islands Moa, Leti and Lakor are inhabited by two physically distinct stocks, one narrow headed, the other brachycephalic. The women of the former stock have the vulval cleft of oval shape ; among the brachycephalic tribes the labia minora are only slightly developed ; and the same is the case among the women on Buru, in whom the pudendal cleft is also narrow.

Riedel   also describes the genital organs of both sexes among the Aru islanders.

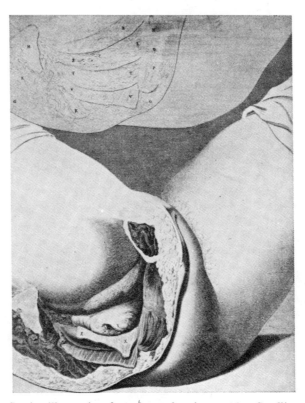

139 .—Section illustrating the vulvoanal region.   (After Smellie, c. 1758.)

He says the vagina is small, as is also the penis in men, and thus the people are mutually proportionate.

The New Caledonian women have a more decided backward slope of the vagina than is usual among Europeans, according to Dr. Jacobus X., and, if the hymen has been preserved, it is generally annular. The same authority gives the following particulars about a native woman of Tahiti : a well-developed clitoris of $1\frac{1}{2}$ to 2 in. in length. The hymen is only found intact in children. The vagina slopes less backward than among negresses, New Caledonians and Melanesians of the New Hebrides ; its position is more that of the European average.

Both Azara and Rengger mention the very large and thick labia of the Guarani women in South America.

The available material about the women of Tierra del Fuego is comparatively detailed. Two Fuegian women who travelled through Europe with their husbands some years ago died, and autopsies were performed on them. The French Ministères de la Marine and de l'Instruction publique sent a joint expedition to Cape Horn, and Hyades and Deniker have made anthropometrical reports about fifteen women of various ages. Moreover, R. Martin thoroughly examined and measured an anatomical specimen of the organs of a woman who died in Zürich. The accounts of post-mortems, plaster casts, anatomical specimens and observations on living women of that race (v. Bischoff, v. Meyer, Hyades, Deniker, Mondière and R. Martin) concur in ascribing the following peculiarities to their genital area, in the words of Martin : " almost total lack of hair, flat labia majora, rudimentary clitoris, medium-sized labia minora, with a few folds and a well marked urethral meatus."

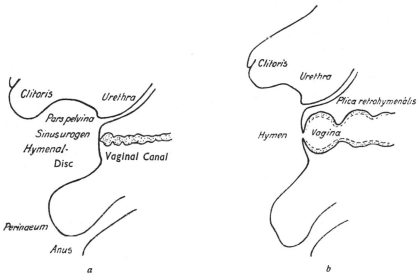

140.—Schematic representation of development of hymen.
(a) Early stage. Müller's tubercle. No hymenal opening. (b) Later stage.

It is significant that v. Bischoff, who independently examined the organs of a Fuegian woman (post-mortem), found both the folds or ridges in the labia minora—on one side at least—and a flap-like appearance of the urinary aperture.

Virey attributes great vaginal capacity to the Kamchadale, as they are accustomed to insert a cylinder of birch bark, but it is not certainly known whether they only do this during the monthly period, as is usual with some women of the Malay Peninsula and Archipelago, or habitually.

Steller also mentions their size in this region, and adds that they " preferred Cossacks and Foreigners to their own countrymen " in consequence.

According to Pallas there is a similar custom among the Ostiak women who " constantly wear a twisted roll of soft schappe silk pushed as far up as possible and frequently changed for the sake of cleanliness. And because this would fall out if it were not kept in place, the Ostiak women have invented a belt almost like the girdle of chastity inaugurated by the jealousy of Southern Europe, in this case, and a bandage passed between the thighs with a special shield of birch bark."

According to E. v. Baelz, the external genitalia of the Japanese women (Fig. 133) are not æsthetically pleasing to European eyes, either in form or colour ; and this is specially the case in the aristocratic type. The illustration (Fig. 136) shows clearly the formation frequent among the yellow races, *i.e.*, the slightest possible development of the outer labia and a strong protuberance of the inner. Wernich made the following observations in his work as a gynæcologist at Yeddo : " The labia majora have very little fatty tissue and are very loose and slack even in young persons. The urinary aperture protrudes appreciably, perhaps because of the habit prevalent among the poorer classes of micturition in the standing posture. The vagina is short ; Wernich found none over 7 cm. (3 in.) in length. He never saw one case of a hymen. The perineum appeared generally moderate in breadth. During the gynæcological examinations there were many more cases of congestion and turgescence of the portio vaginalis among the Japanese than the European women."

It is stated by Dr. Jacobus X. that in Japanese women the mucosa of vulva and vagina are much lighter in tint than in Chinese and Annamese and of the same reddish-yellow shade as in some Spaniards.

Morache has described the labia majora of Chinese women as " *plus developpées.*" The medical writer quoted above described the genital colouring of the Cantonese women as brilliantly carmine with a dash of ochre or orange.

There are various descriptions and comparisons between the women of various races of Cochin-China and Europeans. The Moi women are reported to be more developed than the Annamese and darker in colouring, being a reddish black or maroon. In Annamese little girls the vulva appears higher up than in the French, but there seems little difference between the adults of the two nations except that the Annamese vulva and vagina are smaller and shallower. The nymphæ are also small and are concealed by the labia majora, and the clitoris is only slightly developed. After the tenth year of life there was no trace of a hymen, according to Dr. Jacobus X.

Mondière gives further details. He describes the Annamese genital formation as different from the European, less wide and less curved and with a shorter perineum. The region bounded by os pubis, os ischii and os coccygis is more trapezoid in shape Neither perineum nor vulva is curved. There is a relative flattening of both inner and outer labia ; and the vagina appears very short so that the portio and os uteri are much closer to the introitus.

Maurel has the following details as regards the women of Cambodia :
" The labia majora are slight or medium in size and very slightly hairy. The inner lips medium or long and pigmented either evenly or in parts. Moderate clitoris, pink vagina with well marked rugæ."

It has been stated that women of certain Turkish tribes are very narrow vaginally even after they have borne children.

Pechuel Loesche mentions that the existence of the hymen is recognised and valued by the Bafióte (Bakongo) of Loango on the West Coast of Africa. The membrane is termed " *nkumbi* " or " *chikumbi,*" and the same word means a young girl from puberty till marriage.

De Rochebrune has studied another African people : the Wolof.

He describes the genitals of the women as " of moderate development." The outer labia form a fold only a few millimetres in height, the nymphæ are rudimentary, and thus the vulva appears as a flattish surface with two ellipsoid folds as its outer boundaries. These folds extend from the middle of the mons veneris to the anterior part of the perineum and their inner surfaces touch and appear merely as a slight wavy line, even in women above a certain age.   The genital colouring is paler than that of the rest of the body : the inner lips are slate blue in mature women, dark red in girls.   The clitoris always projects visibly ; the glans being exposed.

These dimensions and proportions differ much from those normal to European women.   The elongated nymphæ so frequently described in other African races are not found among Wolof women ; rather is there the reverse, i.e., some degree of atrophy.   De Rochebrune speaks of arrested development and compares the genital proportions—with the exception of the prominent clitoris and width of the pudendal surface—to those of a European girl between 8 and 10 years of age.   The perineal measurement is also distinctive : in the European woman the perineum averages 0·012 m.,* and in the Wolof woman, 0·025 m.

Conradt made medical examinations of certain Adeli hillwomen from the Togo hinterland : in one of 25 years old and two girls of 14 he described the genitals

141.—Young Hottentot girl.   (Photo, Speer.)

as small.   And he used the same expression about a woman of the Akapamé people from the same region, she being between 18 and 20 years old.   A woman of the same tribe between 20 and 23 years old, was said to have " normal " or " symmetrical " organs ; terms which are far from conveying a definite impression.

The body of a negress who died in Munich was examined post-mortem by v. Bischoff.   She was said to be of Sudanese origin.   Her labia majora were strongly developed and her hymenal membrane unmistakable ; the vulva, moreover, was widely open, exposing the everted, pigmented outer labia with their reddish inner surfaces.   V. Bischoff adds : " apart from these modifications—which may occur to an equal degree in Europeans, the genitalia showed no difference from the European racial type ; and the clitoris was certainly no larger."

The same authority states that the main characteristics of the external genitalia among Bushwomen and Hottentots (Figs. 141 and 142) appeared to be a flatter

* [This appears to be under estimated.]

142.—Young Hottentot girls. (Photo, Speer.)

mons veneris, slighter labia majora and thinner pubic hair which, however, was never wholly absent.

Bertherand has mentioned that the habits and way of life among Algerians favour " very pronounced genital development," and that the volume of the labia majora explains their excision in some neighbouring tribes. He describes the clitoris as large and prominent, the vagina as very wide.

Before dealing in greater detail with the " Hottentot Apron " we may refer to possible or probable differences in the vaginal flora among different races, a matter on which there is no precise information, although we are already aware that within our own racial and cultural conditions there are great individual differences such as between healthy women and those infected with certain diseases ; between healthy women who are and those who are not pregnant ; and even in the same woman in the different phases of the menstrual cycle, or in the tranquilly latent or turgescent states.

[The normal vaginal secretion is acid, which Zweifel, in 1908, showed to be due to lactic acid. Glycogen, glucose and a diastatic ferment is also found, but it is the presence of the acid which keeps the vagina relatively immune to harmful bacterial invasion. The germicidal power of the secretion both in non-pregnant and pregnant women is remarkable. Krönig found that a lysol douche materially lessened the power of the vaginal secretion to deal with injurious cultures which had been introduced, a considerable amount of time having to be added to that taken before the douche was interposed.]

Moncelon has furnished almost the only modern statement of this nature and he describes the women of New Caledonia as "extremely disagreeable " to European senses during intercourse in spite of frequent washing.

The ancient literature of Hindustan has been much preoccupied with the differences between the genital organs and erotic functions of women. In the " Kokkōkam " * (Kama-Shastra) four categories are enumerated : the Padmini or lotus scented, the Chitrini or bright coloured, the Shankhini and the Hastini, the latter being compared respectively to the snail and the elephant. And according to R. Schmidt's study of sex life in Hindustan, the Kāmasūtra of Vātsyāyana divided both sexes into three classes according to their genital proportions.† The women were designated respectively gazelles, mares and elephants ; the men hares, bulls and stallions.

An anthropologist with some knowledge of comparative anatomy who reads the highly ornate comparisons and metaphors of these four descriptions with careful attention, will conclude that there has been a good deal of careful observation. We know that among European women there are various well-defined types of genital formation and hair distribution, and we must suppose that the " *lotus scented*," " whose organ is like the blossom of the crimson water lily and even as a holy secret," has full, fleshy outer lips meeting closely over the nymphæ ; whereas the second group has much less prominent labia majora and a visible pudendal cleft. In the third group the labia majora are again prominent but thin and approximate to each other ; while, in the fourth and last, the median edges of the outer lips do not meet but are normally apart, thus allowing the highly developed, salient clitoris even in a sexually latent and tranquil state to project visibly between them. The peculiarities of these descriptions must not blind us to the importance of their subject, both scientifically and humanly.

* [Translated from Sanskrit into Tamil by Varakunarāma Paṇṭiyaṇ.]
† [For an account of the social life of the age of Vātsyāyana, see Chakladar.]

There are many similar descriptions in ancient Sanskrit literature. From the "Anaṅgaranga," it appears that clitoris, introitus, vagina and Bartholin's glands were well recognised and classified. [Every part of the genital region was known and developed and a breadth in these parts was much esteemed. Although in ancient India the waist, in order to be beautiful, had to be small, yet the breasts and buttocks had to be round and full to excite admiration. Rāvaṇa tells Sita that her breasts have a fair, firm fullness, for they are bold and swelling with erect nipples like the fruits of the wine-palm. He tells her, moreover, that her thighs are as the trunks of elephants, and that her secret parts are widely open and firmly swell (see J. J. Meyer, II., 432, etc.).]

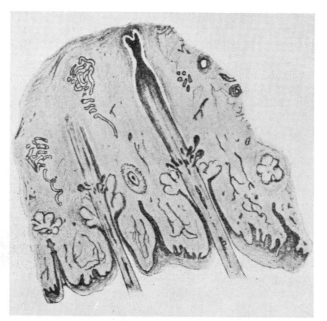

143.—Labium majus, hair, sebaceous glands, sweat glands, etc. (After Winter.)

In conclusion we may mention two anomalies of these organs not infrequent among women of the white race, and often fraught with disastrous consequences. In the first of these deviations from the normal, the vulva is placed farther backward and towards the anus than is usual. The perineum is very narrow in such cases so that in sexual intercourse, if the woman lies on her back, her introitus is directed downwards instead of forwards. This means corresponding adjustments for the male partner who often cannot achieve more than very superficial insertion and causes the woman acute pain by his efforts to penetrate deeply. This pain often causes complete failure of the sexual relation. The German common people have a curious vernacular expression (*hintervötzig*) for this peculiarity in women, which is frequent enough to be recognised among them. There is, however, a remedy, namely modification of the posture in coitus by means of cushions and pillows placed beneath the woman's pelvis and thighs till the axes of the two organs coincide or are congruent.

The opposite condition is less remediable. If the introitus is unusually far forward, *i.e.*, nearer the symphysis pubis, there is no difficulty in intromission for either partner. But when the culminating spasms of the local muscles begin, the male organ is forced against the rigid pubic bone, and this is so painful for the man that he relinquishes all attempts at union.

It may be added that many of the extraordinary postures and attitudes described by Indian and other erotic writers (*cf.* Forberg) and depicted in Indian art are impossible for average human beings to execute. They have, in many cases, been constructed and imagined on a theoretical basis only.

As is known, the genitals and the nipples are among the most highly pigmented regions of the human body. Solger considers this the result of natural selection and the extinction of less pigmented individuals because these organs are highly sensitive and important.

[However this may be (and there would appear little to recommend it) the amount of pigmentation varies to a very considerable extent. In European women the blondes show no great pigmentation either with regard to the nipples or genital region. The nymphæ are usually light coloured, and the perineum scarcely darker than the adjacent surfaces. In the brunettes, however, the nipples are often dark with highly pigmented areolæ ; the skin around the vulva is also dark, and the nymphæ slate-coloured or brown. The perineum, too, is much darker than the skin of the buttocks, and the anus also deeply pigmented.]

THE HOTTENTOT APRON

The inner lips or nymphæ in women of the Bushfolk and Hottentots are extremely and conspicuously long and pendant. There has been much description and discussion of this peculiarity, which is known as the *Hottentot Apron*, or in French, the *Tablier*.

The early travellers gave accounts of it. Thus W. ten Rhyne described the protuberant nymphæ as " *dactyliformes*." Blumenbach rejected this statement as an invention, but Lesueur, Sparrmann, Barrow, Péron and others confirmed ten Rhyne's account. It appeared from their testimony that the " apron " consisted in a typical hypertrophy of the inner lips up to 7 in. (18 cm.), and that the prepuce of the clitoris sometimes was involved in this excessive enlargement.

Le Vaillant was the first to propound the theory that the Hottentot Apron was not wholly " natural " in such extreme cases, but partly " acquired " or " artificial " ; a view to which we shall refer more fully.

Cuvier described the so-called " Hottentot Venus " and so did Johannes Müller. She was not a genuine Hottentot, but a Bushwoman, whom a Dutchman had brought to Paris with him and who died there in 1816. Cuvier found that the upper portions of the " apron " in her case were hypertrophied parts of both clitoris and inner labia, but the pendant elongated portions were labia alone. And Virey reported on the post-mortem on this woman, " The apron is nothing but the two nymphæ (inner lips) which are elongated and hang down on either side, protruding from the shrivelled and hardly perceptible labia majora. The nymphæ are about 2 in. long and hide the vagina and urethral orifice ; they do not disappear into the perineum, but hang freely and can be turned back like ear flaps."

There was also asymmetry A. de Quatrefages says of the model of the Hottentot Venus in a Paris museum : " The right labium internum is 55 mm. and the left 61 mm. long. The breadth is respectively 34 mm. and 32 mm. ; the thickness is equal on both sides, namely, 15 mm."

Similar descriptions have been furnished by Barrow, Damberger and others. Barrow mentions that the hypertrophy increased with age. The greatest elongation he was able to measure was 5 in. But there was a difference from European women in the smoothness of the Hottentot nymphæ : in the white race they are serrated and dentate (Fig. 156).

For some years a Bushwoman named Afandy had allowed herself to be exhibited in Central Europe, and when she died, Luschka made a careful autopsy and anatomical report on her with illustrations. There was complete correspondence with the cases described by Cuvier and J. Müller as regards the labia majora, which were very short and flat, leaving the nymphæ exposed throughout their entire length. These hung down and touched on their inner surfaces : they were shorter than those described by Cuvier and Barrow, measuring only 3½ cm., but even so they greatly exceeded the normal dimensions of these parts (Goertz). Another case was subjected to post-mortem examination and dissection by Flower and Murie

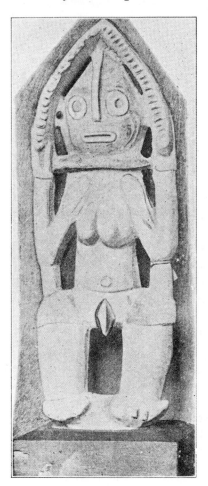

144.—Stone figure from the Bismarck Archipelago. (Mus. f. Völkerk., Berlin.)

in 1864. A Bushwoman, whose age was calculated to be 21 years, had died in London of tuberculosis. Here, too, they found very small labia majora, a clitoris of moderate size, which was only more conspicuous than in the average European because of the defective outer labia. But, although the clitoris was not large, it had a well developed prepuce which continued laterally till it merged into the nymphæ. These were pendant flaps nearly 2 inches in length and very elastic, of so dark a red as to be almost black.

Flower and Murie also cited the report of an anthropologist resident in Cape Colony, concerning the external genitalia of two Hottentots, mother and daughter, the latter 12 years of age. The girl had already the typical gluteal masses of adipose tissue and her nymphæ hung down in flaps 3½ in. long when she stood upright. The hymen was not intact. The mother was able to fold back her own nymphæ so that they met behind over her buttocks.

In the Berlin Anthropological Society a meeting was addressed by Waldeyer, who also exhibited an anatomical specimen from a Koranna woman. The Koranna live in South-east Africa and are Bechuana (Hottentots), but, according to Fritsch, with a strong infusion of Bushman blood. He reported as follows :

" Well-developed labia majora, the superior commissure is rounded, and there are a few hairs on the inner surface of the labia majora. The inferior commissure is non-existent, as the labia spread widely and merged into the perineum near the anus. Their breadth was 3 cm., in the middle 2 cm., and decreasing to 1 cm. at the rear. The pudendal cleft gaped somewhat throughout the entire length. This was due to a rounded projection set just under the superior commissure and developing into two rounded lateral flaps, like leaves, that protruded from the middle region of the cleft, hung down and covered the whole rear portion up to the perineum.

" In the present state of the anatomical specimen the rounded portion is not covered by the labia majora, but, if they are pressed together—as would be the case with the thighs closed in a living person—they cover the protuberance, which is, in fact, nothing else than the expanded, solidified and much elongated preputium clitoridis, with the inner labia as the two flaps. These flaps are 4 cm. long and help to delimit the vestibulum vaginæ merging, on their outer surface, into the roots of the labia majora just as in the case of normally proportioned nymphæ. Their width is from 2 to 2½ cm. They merge into two small folds of membrane, no larger than European nymphæ. At the rear, towards the anus, they are thicker and more prominent. Thus there are three distinct regions in these labia of distinctive and different shape. There is neither navicula nor fossa navicularis, but a furrow running from the vestibulum to the perineum. At the front there is a lateral frenulum on either side of the glans clitoridis. The latter is remarkably small without perceptible roundness and set deep inside the prepuce. The vestibulum is a deep hollow; the urethral meatus well below the clitoris and the carina vaginæ clearly visible. The ridges of the posterior vaginal wall protrude in a definite wedge-shaped formation, between the two thick posterior rolls of the nymphæ. The vaginal folds are well marked. The perineum is not quite 2 cm. in length."

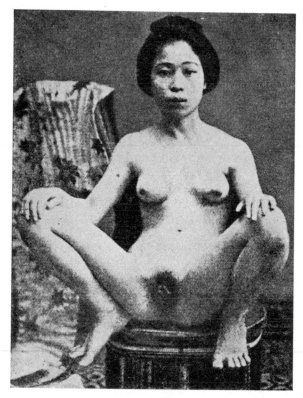

145.—Japanese woman with elongated nymphæ. (After Stratz.)

Duhousset has described a somewhat similar formation in a girl of 14 encountered at Beyrout, in whom the highly developed inner labia seemed continuations of the prepuce, the body of the clitoris being not perceptible.

The Museum of the Berlin Central Mission has a wooden figure representing a woman and carved in the most northern districts in the Transvaal. Its precise purpose is not certain, but it shows the elongation of the labia in an unmistakable manner.

The Wolof women in Senegal often have an early development of the labia to unusual proportions. The investigator (Jacobus X.) to whom these data are due, suggests that it may be either racial or the result of constant manipulations. And this elongation coincides with marriageable age. Kunike mentions that Weule observed a habit of pulling and fingering the labia minora as part of the ritual ceremonies introducing girls to adult nubility. These manipulations continue daily for a considerable time and the labia were sometimes elongated up to 6 cm.

In the South Sea Islands this anomaly is also not unknown, or so we must conclude from some carvings in wood, such as are made by the natives of New Britain. The illustration (Fig. 144) shows a stone image from the Bismarck Archipelago of very rough workmanship but extremely realistic, within the limits of its craftsmanship. The vulva is widely dilated and the nymphæ protrude with their inner surfaces closed so that they resemble a beak or one solid structure.   The whole figure is whitened all over with a chalky substance.

Steller mentions the long and pendant inner labia of the Kamchadale : he says these were characteristic of " some and indeed the greater number of them," and were " transparent like glass or parchment." " They called them *syrœtan* and often made merry about them among themselves."

Baelz observed and recorded the slightest possible development of the outer labia in certain types of Japanese women, whereas the long, strongly pigmented nymphæ protruded like flaps (*cf.* Figs. 136 – 145).

We have enumerated these statements and descriptions as fully and precisely as possible in view of their anatomical and anthropological importance.   But they show clearly that there is no unanimity as to the *cause* of the " apron."

Many authors have ascribed this elongation to manual stimulation, pulling, pinching and twisting, which result in thus deforming " normal " nymphæ ; in short, a singular kind of acquired malformation.

There are various points to be made in support of this view, for anomalies of the same kind appear sometimes among Europeans.   Broca, in controversy with Duhousset, at a meeting of the Paris Anthropological Society stated that he had found such elongations in France on various occasions, and that they were asymmetrical.   Robert Hartmann expressed himself in the same sense.   He pointed out, however, that there were no reliable particulars of measurements, maxima and minima, available.

Merensky, a Superintendent of Missions, who lived and worked for years among the natives of South Africa, also told the Berlin Anthropological Society that " The Basuto and other African tribes know how to produce artificially enlarged labia minora.   The necessary manipulations are performed by the older girls on the younger from their earliest years, as soon as they go together to gather wood or roots, *i.e.*, almost daily.   The parts are pulled and twisted and subsequently wrapped round little sticks and twigs." [Hartmann has also reported lengthened nymphæ in the Sudan, and Sarfert states that the labia minora are pulled by the women of Kusæ to make them long.]

Dr. M. Bartels was also inclined to take this view because of the particular portion of the labia minora which protruded the farthest.   He took part in the debate after Waldeyer's address and cited Merensky.   The same habit of genital manipulation has been recorded among the Bavenda people of the Northern Transvaal border.

He was also emphatically of opinion that Hartmann was right and that the Hottentot apron is not by any means such a rarity even in Central Europe as medical men have thought.*   He maintained, however, that these cases were all in women who were not averse from " masturbatory stimuli." Schröder, the famous Berlin gynæcologist, concurred in this view : in one asymmetrical case under his observation, in a lady in the thirties, one of the nymphæ expanded to thrice its previous size in the course of a year.   As he remarks, this is hardly a congenital condition or a racial sign.

[How far hypertrophies about the vulva can be produced by manipulations (for the purpose among others of masturbation) it is hard to say.   Few, if any, statistics are available, and the material is mainly anecdotal.   Moreover, methods of masturbation vary.   In the child, thigh compression is the most common : later, and before puberty, friction of the clitoris is the most usual method.   After puberty

* [Broca saw a French girl with nymphæ 5–6 cm. long, and such are not uncommon.]

pressure on the clitoris and vulva generally is practised, especially if this has been carried out by members of the opposite sex, as is commonly the case.   The vulva is

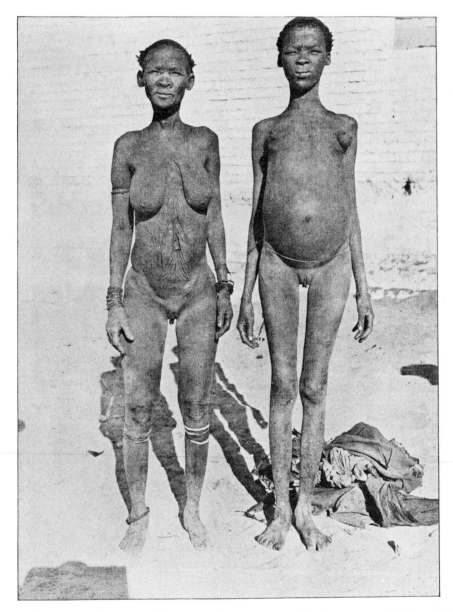

146.—Two Bushwomen with elongated labia minora.   The younger, aged 14, has had a baby.   (Photo, F. Seiner.)

pressed with the hands and the parts are caused to slide forward and backward over the symphysis.   When the clitoris and labia become turgid and swollen they are pressed and pulled, and it is here that some authorities aver that hypertrophies result, especially as regards the nymphæ.

Kelly, who had a large gynæcological practice, seems convinced that enlargements of the nymphæ can and do result from this traction.   He has described what

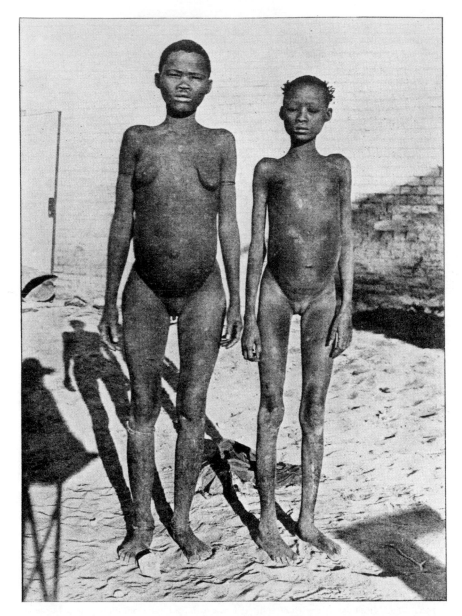

147.—Two Bushwomen.   The one on the observer's right does not appear to have elongated labia minora.   (Photo, F. Seiner.)

he calls a "typical case" in his "Medical Gynecology."   The patient was a well-developed brunette of 18, a virgin, and of excellent antecedents.   The breasts were large with prominent nipples and pigmented primary and secondary areolæ.   Thick hair surrounded the vulva, which was provided with rotund, coarse-skinned outer labia. "Between these outer labia," the account continues, "protrudes, in all postures, a corrugated roll of brown-black skin. Thickened, elongated, curled on themselves, thrown into tiny, close-set, irregular folds that cross at all angles as in a cockscomb, each lesser labium hangs in a double fold, its anterior projection partly concealing the rear portion. Unrolled, this little elephant ear, elastic and insensitive, reaches one inch, or even two, beyond the majora, and then drops back, wrinkling into deep furrows. . . . The prepuce, thickened and lying in rounded folds or wrinkling plaits, is continuous with these lesser labia [cf. Fig. 237]. They

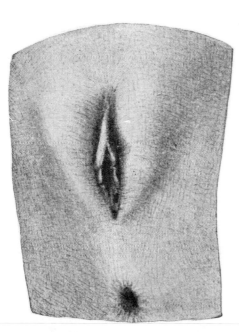

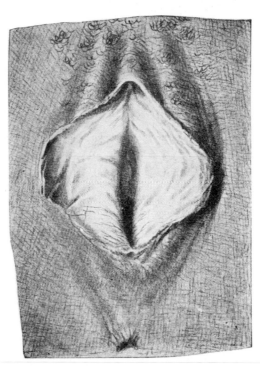

148.—External genitals of a Hottentot girl of 10 years, nearly natural size. From a prepared specimen. (After Bartels and Kaussmann.)

149.—Vulva of Hottentot woman of 30–40 years. (After Bartels and Kaussmann.)

unite in a sweep behind the vulva, so that the fourchette and the perineal raphe are as dark and corrugated as they. Laterally, from them, two bridges of the same fine-laid furrowed folds run across the shallow sulcus that lies between inner and outer labium on to the labia majora, like an accessory or intermediate pair of smaller labia ; and this duplicature hangs up or puckers the centre of each labium minus. The prepuce is partly adherent, and underneath it smegma lies hidden. The fully developed clitoris rounds its back and projects its tip under this thick cover nearly an inch in advance of the face of the symphysis. On each side a couple of prominent veins twist along the inner aspect of the labia majora. The wide meatus presents two curious ear-like flaps or tabs when drawn open. Into these ridges the forward edges of the hymen run. The openings of the vulvo-vaginal and urethral glands are reddened and gaping. The hymen is too small to admit the finger-tip.

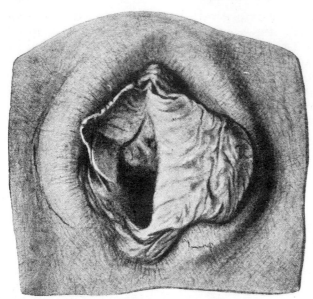

150.—Vulva of Hottentot woman of 30–40 years, showing asymmetry. (After Bartels and Kaussmann.)

The deeply pigmented anus with
its powerful sphincter is surrounded with small piles, and
finally, the pelvic floor muscles
are increased in vigor and
thickness and in susceptibility
to spasm. Vaginismus is not
uncommon."

In this account the development of the nymphæ is clearly
described. Moreover, Kelly
states that the little tabs or flaps
seen at the urethral orifice are
due to similar causes, an opinion
widely held by other observers.
The varied assortment of articles
(hair-pins, bits of pencil, etc.
(cf. Morand)) found in the female
bladder are too well known for
detailed description. Moreover,
the dilatability of hymens is
such that it is stated that occa-
sionally the orifices may be expanded from 6 to 9 in., yet when released they spring
back like closed puckered curtains. (Cf. for further details of hypertrophy in whites,
Broca and R. L. Dickinson.)]

In the previous chapter we have referred to Jayle's investigations of 500
European cases. He records
among this material " le plus
souvent " a protrusion of the
inner lips beyond the outer, often
to considerable degree and either
bilateral or asymmetric.

Nevertheless, there is also
considerable support for the view
of the " apron " as congenital.
Lichtenstein, and more especially
Vrolik (in a letter to Tiedemann)
testified that " in the new-born
child there was already the suggestion of this hypertrophy as a
congenital idiosyncrasy."

The photographs reproduced
here (Figs. 148 – 151) were sent
specially from South-West Africa
and come from the bodies of Hottentot women whose ages were
not stated. Mr. Franz Seiner
kindly also sent some photographs of Bushwomen and girls.
It is of some significance that

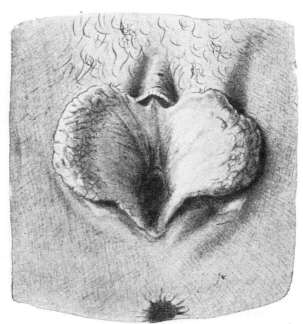

151.—Vulva of Hottentot woman of 30–40 years.
(After Bartels and Kaussmann.)

there is already a certain hypertrophy in a 10-year-old girl. Dr. Max Bartels is justified in protesting that he cannot believe in a wholly artificial (masturbatory) origin at that early age. Again, the younger girl who looks almost a child, has no visible enlargement of the nymphæ (see Fig. 147)

Max Bartels was further of opinion that artificial enlargements through manipulation never equalled the dimensions of the real "apron," though, of course, it is not disputed that this may owe something to the manipulations of the women. On the whole, the German editors are of the opinion—shared by G. Fritsch —that the Hottentot Apron is really a racial peculiarity. R. Hartmann, who disagrees, admits that we have no full and exact data of measurements, average, minimal and maximal, but it is these measurements which are the crux of the problem.

The question arises as to what could be the significance or purpose of the elongation in the terms of comparative anatomy? Is it an atavism, a symptom of primitive development?

Blanchard has voiced this opinion with emphasis. He places the Bushfolk on the most primitive rung of the whole human ladder. He points out that, while the nymphæ and clitoris are enlarged, the mons veneris and outer labia are subjected to "a veritable regression" which makes them rudimentary in comparison with other races. He declared it impossible to overlook "the remarkable resemblance between the vulva of the female chimpanzee and the local structure of the Bushwoman."

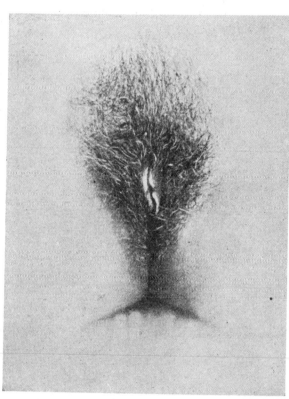

152.—Hottentot vulva. (Anthrop. Ges., Berlin.)

In his investigations, however, U. Gerhardt found a very slight development of the nymphæ in the anthropoid apes, although they were comparatively largest in chimpanzees. E. Fischer declared the same was true of the American spider-monkeys. And, indeed, the matter is far from simple. Not only actual but proportional dimensions must be considered. Not only general impressions, but exact and adequate details.

[From the earliest times this elongation of the labia minora among the natives of South Africa has excited the attention of travellers. In the early drawings (cf. Hooton) both the steatopygia and the "apron" are to be seen, and travellers such as Kolbe and Sparrmann have, as we have seen, remarked upon it. Drury, in discussing the vulva of the South African Bushwomen, states that the nymphæ attain the length of 1½–2 in., and can be tucked into the vagina. In the Cape women they hang down in front of the vulva like "two flesh finger-like pendants."

Occasionally they attain the length of 4 in., and the same elongation is to be found in Bechuanaland and among the Massarua. Drury does not believe that the elongation is due to intentional traction, and Schultze-Jena states that Bush girls, when isolated and brought up among the whites still show the elongation. He adds that the labia majora are as poorly developed as the nymphæ are fully developed. (For further details see R. Pöch, Peringuey, A. M. Wilson and Germann.)]

CONGENITAL HYPERTROPHY OF THE CLITORIS

Certain anatomists have maintained that the clitoris is larger among tropical races than in temperate and especially in cold climates. There is not sufficient

153.—Hottentot Apron.   (Anthrop. Ges., Berlin.)

material available for certainty about this view, but the reports of Hyades and Deniker respecting the women of Tierra del Fuego are in its favour. They found the clitoris " very rudimentary " in 15 of the cases they examined. But Mungo Park found persistent elongation of the clitoris in the Ibo and Mandingo tribes of Northern Africa ; and, according to Jacobs, the clitoris is very often highly developed in the women of Bali.

A negress, who was an inmate of Breslau Hospital, died there, and an autopsy was performed by Morgenstern. Otto describes the result and the curious conformation of the genitals.

" A thick flap drops before the vulva like a miniature curtain. There is nothing remarkable about the outer labia except that frontally they are somewhat far apart.

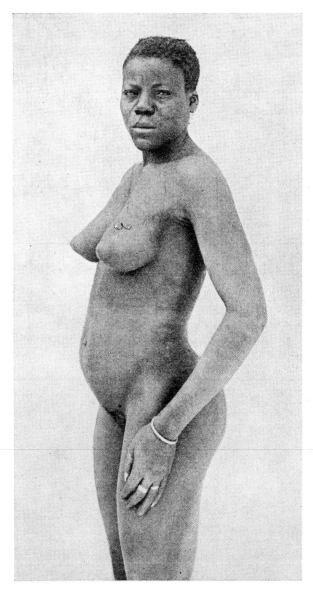

154.—Klip River " Kaffir." (After Speer.)

The nymphæ are much corrugated in places and reach backwards almost to the anus. The frontal flap is 4 in. long, 1½ in. wide and attached to a stem ½ in. long."

Johannes Müller was probably right in terming this remarkable anomaly a hypertrophied clitoris.

Bruce of Kinnaird has some details about the women of Abyssinia. He declares that their clitoris projects so far and is of such unusual size as to cause repugnance and discomfort, and even to militate against the purpose of marriage. And he suggests this racial anomaly as some explanation of the custom of clitoridal castration which prevails in those regions. Görtz comments on this in a doubtful sense,

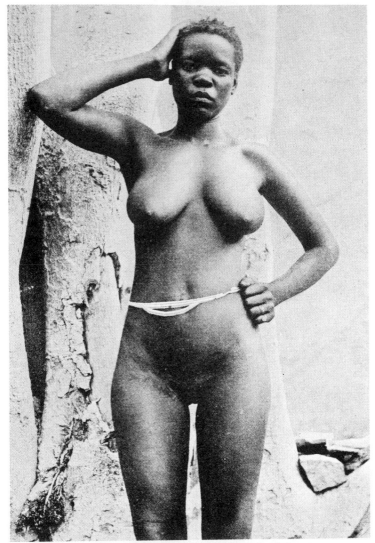

155.—Klip River " Kaffir." (After Speer.)

for he points out that the Kamchadale girls, though equally hypertrophied in the labia, and also the Bushwomen and Hottentots, are not subjected to this excision. But in making his objection, he obviously confuses clitoridal castration with excision of the labia ; and these are two perfectly distinct operations or mutilations.

The young Wolof woman is also credited with a large clitoris which also grows appreciably after puberty, according to Jacobus X.

The African races are themselves quite aware of their clitoridal hypertrophy and represent it in many native works of art : for example, in the wooden figure of a woman, from the sources of the Nile (Bongo) which Schweinfurth reproduced (Fig. 157). The little statuette commemorates one who has died. Her clitoris projects in a manner which cannot be overlooked.

But among women of one and the same racial stock at least in Europe, the clitoris has great individual variation. In any large group of women there is

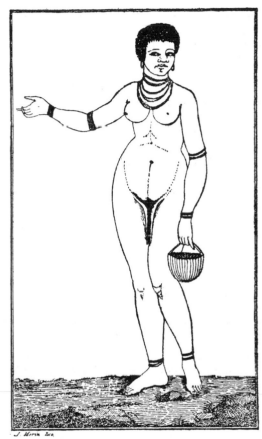

156.—" Hottentot Venus." (From an eighteenth-century drawing.)

157.—Female figurine. Source of the Nile. (After Schweinfurth.)

always a certain minority with much larger clitorides than the rest. This may, in certain circumstances, give occasion to abnormal sexual practices, to which we shall refer later. Parent-Duchâtelet, according to Lombroso, observed only 3 such cases among 3000 prostitutes whom he inspected. Lombroso himself recorded 6 cases. According to Lombroso, Ricciardi found clitoridal hypertrophy in 6·6 per cent. of his cases and Gurrieri as many as 13 per cent. among his.

ARTIFICIAL ENLARGEMENT OF LABIA AND CLITORIS

In dealing with congenital hypertrophy we have mentioned that the labia minora are sometimes specially manipulated in order to elongate them.

The exact purpose is not always the same. Some are admittedly a form of auto-erotism or sexual gratification by self-excitement. Others again, may be masturbatory but through another person, as in the behaviour of the elder Basuto and Bush girls to their juniors, as has been alluded to above. It is certainly hardly likely to be merely a conventional game. And in yet another category of cases there is no need to suspect masturbation : it is rather a form of " beauty culture," an attempt to meet the racial æsthetic standards by increasing a peculiarity which is considered attractive. Or, again, there may be the deliberate intention of heightening sexual stimulus in coition.

Le Vaillant has observed that Hottentot and Namaqua women, or at least some among them, pull and stretch their inner labia or attach small weights (?) to them to make them longer from motives of vanity. Adams made the same remark as regards the women of Dahomey and Uganda, and Corre has also discussed the matter. It has been stated that the women of Wahia on Lake Nyassa " know how to elongate the clitoris to the size of a finger " !

Among certain American Indians there would seem to be similar habits. The Mandan women are said to " deform their genitals artificially," and among the Hidatsa and Crows, both inner and outer labia are elongated in accordance with custom, according to Prince M. zu Wied.

Finsch gives an account of the elaborate sexual practices and preliminaries of the natives of Ponapé, one of the Caroline Group.

" Very long and pendulous labia minora are considered particularly attractive in women. They are deliberately produced and cultivated from early childhood by manipulations performed by elderly men who have become impotent. These manipulations are continued till the approach of puberty. At the same time and as part of the same training, the clitoris is not only subjected to prolonged friction, but also to suction, and a certain large kind of ant (native to the islands) is applied to this region in order that its sting may produce a brief but acute and not unpleasant stimulation.

" The cult of sexual pleasure is correspondingly ingenious. In order to rouse their mates to the highest pitch of excitement, the men use not only their tongues but their teeth as well."

Kubary testifies to the same custom on Sonsol, another of the Caroline Group. He found the labia minora in mature women " much stretched, owing to the habit of genital suction, which, so far as I know, prevails on every one of the Pacific Islands which I have visited." Moreover, Gudgeon mentions elongation of the clitoris on the Cook Islands.

THE INTENTIONAL DESTRUCTION OF THE HYMEN

Many of the customs already described appear strange to European traditions, and we find yet another, the intentional and deliberate destruction of the hymen. This is practised by peoples on different cultural levels, some relatively civilised and highly evolved. Most nations attach very high value to the hymen, especially in some oriental countries. But, in many parts of India and most of China, it is completely obliterated and removed in the earliest years amongst girls.

Thus even Chinese medical practitioners are unacquainted with its existence. According to Hureau de Villeneuve, the Chinese nurses wash and cleanse the private parts of the children they tend with such thoroughness that they always insert their finger into the introitus and thus gradually stretch the hymen till it wholly disappears, for in those climates cleanliness is necessary to remove the deposit of matter, which is constantly accumulating. M. Bartels examined a half-grown European girl, born and brought up in China, and found no trace of any hymen.

[How far these statements can be substantiated is uncertain. Professor H. A. Giles, who spent over 20 years in China, is of the opinion that there is little truth in the belief that the hymen (*ch'u nū mo*) is destroyed in China, and points out that in many parts of that country the young bride is given a piece of cloth on which to receive the blood shed at the first coitus. Moreover, in the " Hsi Yüan Lu," or " Instructions to Coroners " (*c.* 1250) are notes relating to the examination of virgins. To test virginity the finger is to be put within a piece of cloth and then inserted into the vagina. Should the cloth show signs of blood when withdrawn virginity is indicated.

It must be remembered that many fantastic beliefs about China and the Chinese are due to missionary propaganda.]

In British India and the Dutch Indies the *ayahs*, it is said, wash the children as vigorously as the Chinese *amahs* and with the same results

The same customs prevail in the Moluccan Archipelago and the Amboina Group, probably mainly for reasons of cleanliness.

In Brazil, among the Machacari, the mothers dilate the vaginæ of the little girls by introducing large folded leaves and then washing them with tepid water, according to v. Feldner's report. Here the original purpose is probably preparation for future sex relationships.

Mantegazza sent Ploss a written account of methods in Paraguay. When the midwives receive boy babies on their birth they proceed to pull and stretch the male member with their fingers ; and, indeed, according to report, the natives of Paraguay are very long in this part. But when the midwives deliver girl babies, they at once push their finger up the vaginal passage, saying, " This is a woman." Thus there are no maidens in the anatomical sense of the word in Paraguay, as the hymen is ruptured by these manipulations.

Riedel gives a description of further Malayan and Indonesian customs, such as the insertion of a roll of vegetable fibre like a cylinder in form, during menstruation, for cleanliness and convenience. And the procedure on the Sunda Islands of the Malay Archipelago is more direct and deliberate. On the first occurrence of menstruation, states Riedel, a koli leaf, folded together, is pushed into the passage and acts as a dilator. This recalls the custom of the Brazilian Machacari.

Both Virey and Steller state that the Kamchadale used vaginal tampons of grass or vegetable fibres at the period and wove special bandages to keep them in place. As for their hymenal membrane, that was not in existence after early childhood. It was considered humiliating and ridiculous to enter marriage as a virgin, so the mothers removed the hymen in the little girls by digital dilation and manipulation, and " taught them their business betimes," in Steller's phrase.

THE CIRCUMCISION OF GIRLS

Many races have a form of circumcision which is applied to women analogous to the preputial circumcision of men. This was at one time considered a specifically African custom, but we have learnt since then that there are similar practices in Kamchatka, in Indonesia, and among certain South American tribes in Peru. We must regard any imitation here as impossible for geographical reasons and because of ethnical differences.   Rather have we a further proof of the resemblances in the mental processes of primitive peoples throughout the world.*

Female circumcision† is generally termed excision.   It consists in the shearing of the inner lips and a portion of the clitoris with knives of metal or stone.   There are, however, great differences of procedure in different races ; sometimes both labia and clitoris are mutilated, sometimes only the labia, sometimes only the prepuce.   Variations of excision are practised in Egypt (Sonnini, etc.), Nubia (Kordofan), Abyssinia (see Abyssiniennes), in Sennar and its environs, in the Sudan (Sarrazin) and among many tribes, such as the Galla, Agau and Gonga.   Excision

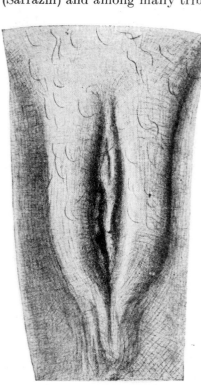

is also said to be customary in the smaller oases of the Libyan Desert, and among Arabs (*cf.* El Tebib) the exclamation : " Oh, Son of an uncircumcised woman ! " is one of the deepest affronts in their huge vocabulary of insult, according to Wilken.

Fig. 158 shows a specimen in the Berlin College of Anatomy which it owes to G. Fritsch. This specimen consists of the outer genitalia of a " circumcised " woman, a negress who had been a slave in Alexandria ; glans and prepuce have been removed, and, it appears, part of the inner labium on the right side.   But the mutilation is comparatively much less than in other examples.

Billharz presented Ecker with a specimen of the organs of a lower-class woman where the glans and prepuce of the clitoris and the labia minora had all been entirely ablated.   The bulbi vestibuli were lacking and also the corpora cavernosa of the clitoris—which seemed embedded in hard scars of connective tissue. Ecker concludes that when the mutilation was performed the glans and prepuce were caught, drawn outward and forward and chopped off near the root.

158.—Genitalia of a " circumcised " woman.   (After Fritsch, Berl. Anat. Mus., 1894, 168.)

Excision is not confined to Mohammedan East Africa.   In Central Africa it is practised among the Wasambara (Eichhorn) and Mahenge district (Hodgson) ; in the West (*cf.* Daniell) among the negroes of Benin, Sierra Leone (Thomas), Accra and the Congo (Torday) ; among the Fulah, Susu (Godel), and Mandingo ; in Bambuk, Old Calabar (Hewan ; Malcolm) and Loanda ; and in the South-east, among the Wa-Kuafi and Masai, as well as some Bechuana tribes of the south.   We have mentioned the Malays of the Archipelago and the Kamchadale. · And, finally, the custom has also been found among the South American Indians of Peru : the Omagua (*cf.* Tessmann), the Campa, and the Pano, and among those living on the Ucayali River.

Attempts have been made to attribute excision to the inventive powers, dogma and ritual of Islam, but Strabo mentions the excision of girls in Arabia centuries

* [This view is not held by anthropologists of the diffusionist school.]
† See Bryk.

before Mohammed. In one of the Greek Papyri in the British Museum (Forshall, XV.: Peyron: Greek Papyri Cat., I., Papyrus XXIV., 31) occurs a passage of some interest. The date of the document is attributed to about 163 B.C. It is concerned with the Serapeum and its recluses. Dionysius, strategus of Memphis, has a petition addressed to him by Harmais, a recluse and mendicant. It is said that there was a girl, Tathemis, also connected with the Serapeum, who earned money by begging. From this money she had saved 1300 drachms which she gave into the charge of Harmais. Her mother, however, named Nephoris, represented to Harmais that her daughter had now reached an age at which circumcision was usual and that as she was now entering womanhood she ought to be provided with dress and dowry. Accordingly she persuaded Harmais to hand over the money and trouble

159A.—Kenya girls about to be excised. Fort Hall, Izeri Areas. (Photo., A. Brown.)

is caused when Tathemis discovers what has happened and demands the return of her money.

This passage is of interest for it suggests that, though male circumcision was reserved for the priestly and military castes in Egypt, excision was practised on all women when they were of age to receive their dowries. Herodotus informs us that no woman held any priestly office in Egypt, so we must conclude that excision or female circumcision, was either practised on all girls at puberty, or was a privilege of those who were reared on the sacred precincts of the Temple of Serapis.

Early medical writers mention this Egyptian custom, among others, Paulus of Ægina, who lived in the seventh century. He describes (VI., 70) the excision of the clitoris or nymphæ when they are hypertrophied, and when the erection of the clitoris becomes objectionable. Barbes is of the same opinion.

Brehm, in discussion with Ploss,

159B.—The interlocked position for the operation of excision. Fort Hall, Izeri Areas, Kenya. (Photo., A. Brown.)

expressed the view that excision was intended to set bounds to the extremely active sexual impulse of the women of African race. Other authorities hold that the purpose was mainly *æsthetic* because, as already indicated, the labia minora and clitoris are apt to attain unpleasing and inconvenient proportions.

159c.—The operation of excision in progress. Fort Hall, Izeri Areas, Kenya. (Photo., A. Brown.)

We have already quoted the view held by Bruce of Kinnaird that the exceptional development of the clitoris among the Abyssinians was a positive obstacle to coitus and birth, and that, therefore, the clitoris was mutilated, since in Abyssinia and the adjacent lands the increase of the people has from early times been considered most essential. He adds that there was no definite date, but that the operation was always performed before marriageable age. He goes on to relate that Christian Missionaries forbade their converts to practise it as they thought it " a Jewish rite ! " But the result was that the natural structure of the girls so repelled the men that they would not marry and fewer children were begotten, or they married " heretics " and unbelievers who had been excised, rather than good Catholic Copts, and lost their faith. So the College of Cardinals *de propaganda fide* in Rome sent skilled surgeons to enquire into and report on the matter. On their return the surgeons declared that either climatic or other causes had so altered the genital anatomy of the women of Abyssinia and such parts that they were very unlike the women of other countries, and that their natural structure caused repugnance which prevented the purpose of marriage. Thereupon Rome gave way on this point, but the girls' mothers had to make a solemn repudiation of any " Jewish propaganda " in excision before it was agreed that this " obstacle to marriage " must not on any account be preserved. In the course of time all Abyssinian Christians adopted excision, which takes place by means of a knife or razor when the girl is eight years old. It is always performed by women. [C. K. Rein states that the operation is less common to-day. He adds that complete excision of the clitoris was never practised in Abyssinia, but only a part was removed. Sometimes, on the contrary, the clitoris is artificially lengthened.]

Mungo Park says that the *Mandingo* have no religious concepts about excision,

159d.—After the operation of excision. Fort Hall. Izera Areas, Kenya. (Photo., A. Brown.)

but think it " useful " in making marriages fruitful. But there are also apparently mystical and magical elements in the associations which have gathered round the practice. [Those dwelling between the Gold Coast and Nigeria are especially addicted to the practice. The clitoris seems here to be over-developed, according to a report received by the Editor. The medical officer, in his account, states that it is about an inch in length, although he does not say if by this he means the clitoris itself, erect or quiescent, or whether it is the glans only to which he refers. At any rate he says that the clitoris and parts of the labia minora are removed.

Among the Ibibo in Nigeria the clitoris is not reported to be in any way over-developed, but cases are known where this occurs. Indeed such a case featured in a local court where one woman accused another of rape, and it was discovered that the prisoner had a much hypertrophied clitoris, which when erect, was able to be used for the purposes of coitus. This case was discussed by an administrative officer with the Editor. For the northern part of Nigeria, see Meek, and for the south, see also Talbot.]

H. Krauss has vouched for a description of the conditions and customs among the Swahili. According to this, if all the children born to any particular woman should die, the woman's clitoris is cut off with a razor and " then the subsequent children live." But, it may be remarked that the Swahili native who was Velten's authority here, said the ablated part was " a little growth under the clitoris." We shall have occasion to refer again to this apparent case of so-called " sympathetic magic."

Velten's highly important account, as taken down from a native's speech, runs as follows :

" If a woman brings forth children that die soon, or if her husband has no long life with her but dies early, she is called *Mwanamke Uwenyi Kisukumi* (lit. woman possessing that which thrusts behind) and the men are in great fear of her. If her Kisukumi is one that kills children, wise women are sought and such as are skilled in magic. Her husband tells her parents that she is ill and must be treated with *dawa*. The parents reply : ' We agree to that.' The old wise women take her into the enclosed place, taking her clothing away and make her sit quite still with open legs for her children die because she has a little growth beneath the clitoris, which is called *Kigwara cha Kuma* and slays the children. Then the magic women search for this till they find it and cut it out and the woman, of course, feels pain ; women that feel pain resist this cure. As soon as the thing is cut out, some *dawa* is smeared on the place and behold there is no wound, nor any pain except for the moment. And her husband can sleep with her again the next day. And should it be God's will to give them another child, behold it lives."

The Comte de Cardi endeavoured to get explanations of the origin of and reasons for excision from the natives of the Niger Delta in Old Calabar and of the Cross River district (*cf.* also Partridge). The usual reply was simply that it was an old custom of their forefathers. One old man said that it kept the girls from having to do with men ; and old women told him that " many years ago " their tribeswomen had often been afflicted with a strange form of madness, and that this madness was much lessened after the operation, so it became generally customary. Russegger found and studied excision in Southern Nubia. He writes :

" In my opinion, this primitive custom is wholly a manifestation of tropical jealousy and its utilitarian merits are all the less because it must necessarily diminish pleasure in coitus on the woman's side, and thus react unfavourably to reproduction. Moreover, it does not by any means always effectually prevent premarital adventures. I know of several cases of girls who, having been treated in this manner, had themselves secretly re-opened and then subsequently scarified once more and scarred so that they were able to form marital alliances without fear ; their virginity was proof and immortal."

Russegger, however, has confused two distinct operations : excision of the clitoris is not the same as labial infibulation, of which we shall treat presently. Infibulation is much less widely spread than excision, and infibulation is probably an invention of male jealousy, whereas excision is by no means necessarily so. But the peoples who practise excision of the clitoris do not seem to know how or why this custom first arose.

Excision is attended by special ceremonies and is part of a festival. We can distinguish the groups among peoples practising excision ; those who operate on the young child and those who wait till puberty and the puberal initiation rites.

The customs in this respect may be illustrated from a few areas :

Age at which Excision is Performed

(a) *In Early Childhood :*
In Arabia, a few weeks after birth (Niebuhr). Among the Somali, between three and four years old (Paulitschke). In Nubia, in early childhood (Russegger). Among the Fulah in West Africa, soon after birth. In Sumatra (Groot), India (Gait).

(b) *At Puberty :*
Certain Malay tribes of the Archipelago, at the second dentition (Epp). Some Persian Nomad Tribes, at marriageable age (Chardin). In Southern Egypt, before puberty (9–10) (Werne). The Mandingo, at marriageable age (Mungo Park), in Kordofan, about eight (Rüppell), among Bechuana (Matchappi) at puberty (Delegorgue). Among the Chuncho Indians in Peru, at 10 years of age (Grandidier).

(c) *Before the Marriage Ceremony :*
The Omebi of Southern Ethiopia (Bieber), Balūchistān (Bray).

(d) *Uncertain Statements, too vague to classify :*
In Old Calabar, at puberty (Hewan). But Comte de Cardi states that there is no fixed age, but that the operation is generally performed in tender years. In Abyssinia, among the Galla and Agau, according to Bruce, at eight years, but according to others, 80 days after birth.

Bieber gives also the following particulars : among the Abyssinians, seven days after birth, among the Galla, eight days, among the Kaffitscho from four months to one year of age.

Duhousset gives this description of what is done in Egypt :

" Female circumcision consists merely in the removal of the clitoris and is performed on children between nine and 12 years old. The operator, who is generally a barber by profession, rubs ashes on his fingers, grips the clitoris, draws it to its full length forwards and shears it with a single razor stroke. Ashes are then sprinkled on the wound to staunch bleeding and it heals after some days of complete repose.

" I have both seen instances and heard statements from these barber-surgeons of their laxity and carelessness in operating. The full ritual limits of the mutilation should, strictly speaking, include the nymphæ from the level of the clitoris and almost to their junction with the inner fold of the labia majora. Their mutilated remnants then form a cicatrisation rigid and retracted round a gaping vulva in the circumcised Fellahwoman. The effect is singular."

Hartmann says that in Egypt and Abyssinia the prepuce is ablated more often than the shaft of the clitoris itself, or than a slice from the mons veneris.

[W. G. Browne describes the operation of excision which he apparently witnessed at Dar Fur. It is termed in Arabic *chafadh*, and consists of removing the clitoris a little before puberty or at the age of eight or nine. A woman operates, and some of the girls seen by Browne complained of great pain. They were prevented from walking after the operation, and the parts were washed every 12 hours to hinder suppuration. At the end of eight days most of them could walk, but some were kept in till the 13th day.

Infibulation also is mentioned by Browne as being performed on girls of eight to 16 years of age.

Among the Kikuyu, Kenya, the operations on girls have recently been described by Leakey and by local missionaries and are apparently of two kinds (see Bowie, Agnes Brown, H. B. A. Philip). Although the descriptions are not entirely clear it would seem that three main varieties can be distinguished. There is, firstly, an operation which consists in apparently " snipping the labia majora " (Bowie), but which is more likely to be a form of snipping the labia minora and perhaps a portion of the clitoris. The second form consists apparently of a general cutting and slicing of the entire vulva. Although some writers quoted above do not appear to distinguish between circumcision, excision and infibulation, it would seem from their accounts that the second form of the operation is a preparation for the stage of infibulation, in which the wounded surfaces are made to adhere through contact. The third operation is that of defibulation, or, in some cases, that of making an opening for the discharge of urine and menses if this has not been provided for after the second operation.

The ceremonies are of the well-recognised type and a large crowd assembles for the purpose of witnessing them. The operator is an old woman who passes from girl to girl and performs the operation with what Bowie describes as a " crude small knife not unlike a safety razor blade." (See Figs. 159 A, B, C, D, for which we are indebted to the kindness of Miss A. Brown.)

Various reasons of the usual kind are ascribed by the natives. It is said that unless the rite is performed sterility will ensue. Bowie, however, is of opinion that the infibulation is for the purpose of preventing sexual intercourse until marriage, as seems probable also in other parts of the world. From the reports of the medical missionaries sepsis is not uncommon, and suffering is also caused by the suppression and absorption of the urine and menses, for the escape of which no proper provision appears to be made by the natives, if we can judge from the reports. This is certainly unusual, and further investigation is desirable.

Attempts have recently been made by the missionaries to have these customs suppressed by law, although the documents they have kindly sent me do not suggest that they propose any relief for the boys who are also circumcised. The Kikuyu Association opposes any change in the custom and pays the fines of those who are occasionally dealt with by the District Commissioner. Leakey has recently discussed the matter with considerable clarity and common sense. The " infibulation " of the girls is, he thinks, if I understand him rightly, merely an accidental result of a too extensive an " excision " and is not in itself intentional.]

On the Upper Niger, as we have said, Mandingo and Bambara practise excision on girls in this manner, according to Gallieni :

" The young girls are generally between 12 and 15 years old, and the operation takes place at a season when the natives still possess great stores of millet, for the cereal is needed to make the succulent dishes consumed at the ceremonial feasts The operation is performed by the smiths (metal workers) on youths and by the wives of the smiths on maidens. Both use a plain iron knife, inadequately sharpened. Neither boys nor girls may give any signs of pain or fear during the mutilation. When we showed our surprise we were told that excision makes girls more faithful to their husbands. But the native women do not trouble at all to remain chaste.

"The families of the circumcised boys and girls celebrate the occasion with dance and song and with much more abundant food and drink than usual. The rich kill goats, fowls, and even sometimes, an ox. The poor folk pick up a stray dog or two in the village and put him into the pot with the rice or couscous. *Dolo* is brewed in every house and imbibed freely.

"After the operation, the circumcised persons are clothed in long robes with hoods over their faces and keep away from their homes till they are healed. The sexes are kept apart. . . . The girls carry little calabashes full of small pebbles like toys. In the morning early they return to their homes. The scars take long to heal, for the natives have nothing to hold the skin together. Convalescence, therefore, usually lasts from 40 to 50 days. When they return to their homes, there are prolonged rejoicings. The boys henceforward have the right to bear arms and to speak their mind in council and the girls may marry."

[Excision is well known in the Northern Territories of the Gold Coast. Among the Nankanse (Nankanni) the operation is performed about the age of puberty. It is considered better for the girl to be excised when still a virgin, so her mother warns her that to go with boys till she is "cut" is not desirable. Whether the girl is a virgin (*yab' pelego*) or not (*sulim*) the operation is the same. She sits on the outstretched legs of a man with her back to him. Her legs are widely separated and the *pukubega* (operator) squats in front of her. The clitoris and any other parts to be cut are seized and severed with a razor, the pieces being buried nearby. The women around utter shrill cries to drown the girl's shrieks. When it is over a woman binds her up with *biro* fibre, and for six days primitive treatment is continued. Nevertheless, some girls die as the result of the operation.

With the Nankanse, Builsa and the Kasena the rite is a preparation for marriage. Other tribes, such as the Kusase, Moshi, Isala, Lobi and Dagari perform it earlier. Amongst the Isala it is said, according to Rattray, that the reasons given are that if the clitoris is removed coitus and delivery are made easier and girls do not suffer ridicule.]

Baumstark mentions customary extirpation of the clitoris among the Warangi of East Africa in the Masai territory, when the girls are between six and eight years old. Expert women perform the ablation with little knives of special shape. The girls live apart for a while in a special building.

Merker writes of the Masai custom :

"As soon as the young girl perceives from certain physical signs that she is about to become a woman, she returns to her mother's hut though she has previously lived in the 'Bachelors' House' in complete and uncontrolled liberty If several girls of the village are in the same stage of growth, their mothers fix a day and summon the ancient woman skilled in the art of excision (the girls of the *El Kiboron* stock were always excised on the 24th day of the Masai month). But, otherwise, and if there is to be a circumcision of boys in the near future, both ceremonies take place on the same day. . . . No member of the opposite sex may approach the places where youths and maidens are respectively circumcised. On the previous day, the girl's mother crops her head and throws the hair under the skins of her couch. All the child's ornaments are removed and she is attired in a long loose garment made by her mother (*sol gela*, *pel gelani*). The mother calls on her child's courage and obedience and washes her genital organs in cold water to deaden the pain. The operation is a simple ablation or removal of the clitoris performed with a sharp piece of iron ore (*ol moronja*) such as is used for shaving.*
Then the little wound is washed with milk, which, with the blood, falls to the ground) ; no

---

* Among the Bushmen of the Kalahari Dornan states that a stone knife is used to perforate the clitoris.

styptics are used. The girl remains secluded in her mother's hut till she is healed ; she is termed : *es siboli* (plur. *es sibolio*) during this seclusion.

"The boys adorn themselves with bird's claws and ostrich plumes, while the girls wear wreaths of grass round their brow (*ol márisian*) and stick a single ostrich feather through the circlet in front. Both sexes smear their faces with white clay. The women of the village hold a feast among themselves. The girl's father slays an ox, her mother brews honey mead for them. The name for a circumcised girl and a young wife is the same : *es siëngiki* (plur. : *es siëngikin*), and, indeed, as soon as the girl's suitor learns that she has recovered, he hands over to her father the last instalment of the bride price and the wedding may then take place lawfully." (*Cf.* also Hallis, M. Weiss.)

Of the Wandorobbo, a related tribe, the same authority reports that among them the girls go to visit and say farewell to their playmates in the neighbouring camps some days before they are excised. On these visits they are entitled to take anything they fancy without the owner's permission, such as, *e.g.*, food, articles of clothing and ornaments.

The Comte de Cardi says of the negresses in the Niger Delta :

"The manner of performing the operation varies tribally. What happens in the Old Calabar region is this. The tip of the coconut shell is cut off carefully and rubbed thin and smooth. The 'eye' or knot of the coconut—through which the liquid milk flows—is scooped out and the rind rubbed smooth. The glans of the clitoris is then slipped through the hole and shorn off with a knife or sometimes with a sharp piece of bottle glass that serves as a knife."

[Similarly among the Ibo of the Niger Delta girls are excised on the fourth to seventh day after birth. The Abaw delay the operation till a girl is likely to become pregnant, whilst the Abuan, a semi-Bantu tribe, await the first menstruation. Amongst the Egabo-Sobo of Osua Konike at the junction of the Nun and Forcados branches of the Niger, and also elsewhere, the girls are excised before marriage " at the time of the coming of small breasts." The patients lie on reed mats and the oldest available woman is the operator. She performs her task with a small triangular blade and receives a bottle of gin from the mother of the girl, the other expenses being borne by the future husband (see Talbot).

In Dongola, where excision is apparently delayed till the girl is nubile, consummation of the marriage, according to Crowfoot, sometimes does not take place for 40 days after the ceremony if the results of the operation have been severe.]

The Wolof make a festival of circumcision. The whole village assembles, dressed in their best, to the sound of the drum and an ear-splitting orchestra. The girls are clothed with all available splendour and hung with all the family trinkets. They are led through the village in procession, then back again to the square or open space where a great dance is kept up for hours, all taking part. The girls are led into the blacksmith's hut by the old women of the tribe. For it is his wife's privilege to perform the rite, when dawn grows grey. Each young girl takes her seat on a block of wood set at a convenient distance from the wall of the hut, leans back so that her body is supported firmly, and spreads her thighs open so far as she can. The woman operator grips the inner labia between fingers and thumb of her left hand and slices them off with an old knife which strongly resembles a saw. A plaster is then applied. The girl remains in her father's hut for a week, then for another three or four weeks she goes to the stream, limping on crutches, to bathe herself in the ritual prescribed. At the expiration of this time the bandage is removed.

According to Dr. Jacobus X., who gives these facts, there does not seem to be any actual religious meaning in excision among these people.

[In the country of the Bavenda, in the northern part of the Transvaal, the excision of girls was introduced through Basuto influence. It is called *musevetho*, or *sungwi*, and is connected with ideas which link it to a secret society. Children may attend on paying two shillings. The function takes place in a hut in an enclosure outside the village. Various rites are performed and many people are attracted to the *musevetho* and persuaded to give gifts. Initiation into the various mysteries takes several months, but to-day less time is involved in the preparations. Finally the girls are taken down to the river, where an old woman awaits them. The clitoris is cut and a brand is placed on the outside of the thigh. After the ceremony Stayt declares that all the girls go to the kraal of the headman and join the boys who have been through the circumcision lodge. Festivities take place and continue for a fortnight. Boys and girls have sexual intercourse and then finally the girls are taken again to the river and smothered with red ochre and fat. After resting a few days they are washed and return home.]

According to Bieber circumcision (*girsett*) consists in the ablation of the clitoris (*ginter*) seven days after birth. The old women (*gerasch*) nip off the glans with a fingernail covered with a piece of cloth. Among the Galla the operation is eight days after birth. Here again the clitoris (*hadu*) is excised. The women who operate receive salt as a reward. Among the Kaffitscho the girls are excised between four months and one year of age. Having placed the girl on her back with the legs widely separated, the operating old woman seizes the clitoris and nips it off with her nails. Among the Omebi removal of the clitoris is accomplished before marriage.

[In Balūchistān female circumcision is well known. Two methods are practised, according to Bray. In the one an old woman cuts off the clitoris; in the other the labia are scarified. Among the Brāhūīs and Marī Balōch the first operation is considered a cure for sterility, and often it is a last resource. The Jaṭṭ have the custom of performing a certain operation at marriage although details are lacking even among themselves. An old woman, armed with a razor, performs some operation on the vulva of the bride. Whether it is cutting the hymen or the clitoris or merely snipping off the protuberant portions of the nymphæ is not known. Bray states that it prevails among the Balōch of the East, and also elsewhere.

Generally speaking, female circumcision is regarded as a religious ordinance in Balūchistān. It is supposed to be acceptable to God. The true reasons for the practice are hard to discover, and even if the original meaning be lost the modern reasons may be various and also conflicting. Bray surmises that the removal of possible obstacles may be one of the reasons, but little can be said until we have detailed accounts of the normal vulva of the girls of the district, and these records are lacking.

Regarded as a whole, the custom of female circumcision is not common in India, except where the influence of Islam is pronounced, as in Baroda, Bombay and the North-West Frontier Province. Even where formerly practised, as among the Dandi, Bohoras and other Shiahs, it is dying out. Sometimes the operation is performed in childhood and sometimes before marriage, as in Sind. Women are the operators and the clitoris is usually cut off and sometimes apparently the labia minora.]

We have already mentioned the custom in Indonesia. Riedel reports that it is practised on all the Molucca islands, especially by the Moslem population. There is generally a partial resection of the clitoris.

Riedel says of the people of Buru :

" Before the beginning of menstruation (and in boys before puberty) the teeth are filed down almost to the gums and circumcision is performed. The girls are bathed and placed across a stone and an old woman cuts away a portion of their *glans clitoridis*. It is said that this is done to suppress and limit their desires before marriage. Burnt and pulverised sago leaves (*ekbaa*) are applied as a styptic. Then the woman carries the girl in her arms into the hut which she must not leave till her wound is healed. She has a special diet till she is convalescent. The custom is said to be Mohammedan in origin."

On Ceram Laut and Gorong, Riedel found clitoridectomy practised between seven and 10 years of age with very festive ceremonial. Death from hæmorrhage afterwards was " not infrequent," but the victims had the satisfaction of entering Mohammed's Seventh Heaven. The operation was performed by the wife of the priest and the girls were bathed afterwards.

On the island of Celebes, states Riedel, in the districts of Gorontalo, Bone, Boalemo and Atinggola, the girls were circumcised at the ages of 9, 12 and 15 respectively. The term used was, *mopolihoe olimœ*, *i.e.*, " to be washed with Citrus histrix." There were great festivities although these involved less expense than for the boy's circumcision, and the operation was performed by women.

Wilken found that these ceremonies were usually performed at an earlier age in girls than the analogous rite in boys : J. L. van Hasselt states the same of the Menangkabau of Sumatra. The same is true of the Javanese, who excise the girls between six and seven years of age. The people of Macassar and the Bugi (Celebes) operate from three to seven, whilst around Gorontalo, 9, 12 and 15 are the preferred ages, but even this is earlier than the age for boys.

The exact extent of the mutilation is only known as regards the Javanese, the natives of Macassar and the Bugi. The Javanese cut off a piece of the clitoris— perhaps the glans—and bury it, wrapped in a cotton cloth with a piece of kurkuma wrapped in *kattun*, under a *kelor* tree (*Moringa pterygosperma*). The operation is termed *putingitil*, *i.e.*, the breaking of the *itil* or clitoris.

Among those in Macassar and the Bugi, according to Matthes, the mutilation is very slight, just enough to cause some slight bleeding. It is called *kattang* or *katta*, *i.e.*, scraping. The operation is performed by two women, of whom the assistant stands behind the girl and holds her in position so that the vulva is widely open and the clitoris exposed. (Epp seems to have erred in thinking the labia minora were also excised.) Excision, like male circumcision, has a certain religious character among the Mohammedans of the Malay Archipelago.

Riedel has a very similar report about the people of Sulu. He says only Mohammedans practise clitoridectomy among that people ; a small piece of the glans—*pokooti*—is cut away with a sharp knife. The girl sits on a woman's lap with thighs widely separated. Her legs are held by two other women. The wound is rubbed with the juice of *Curcuma longa*, and after the operation the child is bathed. There are also special dietetic rules till the girl has quite recovered.

This operation is performed between nine and ten years of age. Marriage and sexual intercourse alike are strictly forbidden to the uncircumcised girl.

Steller stated of the Kamchadale that their pendulous labia were considered a disgrace and were cropped, like a dog's ears, when young.

In Ecuador lived natives of the Pano linguistic stock. They were visited in the eighteenth century by the missionary, Francis Xavier Veigl. He learnt that they had been in the habit of circumcising their girls to make them, so it was said, more competent in fulfilling their natural duties.

The Chuncho and Campa tribes, on the Ucayali River, practise excision on girls at 10 years of age. There is a seven days' festival of all the neighbours, who assemble with dance and song and copious draughts of chicha, an intoxicant brewed from manioc. On the eighth day the girl is mercifully stupefied by a big drink of this powerful narcotic, and the operation is performed by a woman who staunches the bleeding with rinsing and pouring water on the wound.

Then the songs and dances recommence and the girl is laid in a hammock and borne in triumph from hut to hut. She is considered a grown woman after her operation, according to Grandidier.

Finally, we may refer to a *European* instance of this practice among the sect of the Skoptsi, who formerly flourished in Russia and Roumania (Lipovans). They mutilated themselves, making themselves eunuchs for the kingdom's sake, in the words of Matthew (xix. 12). The mutilations were performed on both sexes, and were more extensive in women, including both breasts and genitals. E. v. Pelikan has given a full and fully illustrated account. [*Cf.* also Grass, Leroy-Beaulieu, Pittard, F. v. Stein, Tandler and Grass, Teinturier, Tsakni, Wysozki, and *Le Seepit*, which deals with the Roumanian sect.]

The mutilations of the female genitalia may be either the excision of the nymphæ and/or of the clitoris or an ablation of the outer edges of the labia majora, together with both clitoris and nymphæ : this leads to a twisted scar which effectually bars the introitus.

Pelikan gives three sample illustrations of the mutilated organs of Skoptsi women. All three were young, and their hymens remained unruptured, nor was the frenulum of the outer labia injured :

In the first case, there is asymmetrical excision of the nymphæ. On the left side, in the central portion of the edge, there is a triangular jag. One side of the triangle is horizontal—measuring 0·7 cm., and an oblique side runs upward at an angle of 45° (acute). The lacuna in the inner labium is 1 cm. wide. The edges are curved and thickened. The right inner labium has apparently been cut away quite from the root in its lower third section, and there is only a sort of tip or cluster of fibres about as large as a hempseed on the lower extremity of the intact section.

The second of Pelikan's illustrations shows symmetrical ablation. In the upper (frontal) third of both nymphæ, there are diagonal cuts from above downwards, slicing away a broad tongue-shaped piece from either side. The breadth about 0·25 cm. A second excision slashes the middle section on both sides, removing triangular portions somewhat resembling that described in the first case ; the edges are curved and thickened. These two bilateral excisions leave a sort of flap about 0·3 cm. wide on either side, and both have grown into the adjacent mucous surfaces of the outer labia, leaving scars which indicate that this mucous surface was intentionally scraped or abraded at the same time and the free flaps of the nymphæ lightly grazed along their outer edge. For it is necessary to abrade both surfaces if their final coalescence is intended.

The third of this set of illustrations was, like the others, life size. It gave a *coup d'œil* of the mutilated organs of a female. There is no longer any pudendal cleft in the strict sense of the term. Instead there is an oval aperture of between 2 and 3 cm. in diameter, which appears to slope downwards, contracting as it slopes ; for the woman is lying on her back. The posterior surface of this orifice has a rather large meatus urinarius in its centre, and slightly below this, on either side, little *carunculæ* in the membrane which are probably all that remain of the excised inner labia. The mons veneris, with its covering of grey hair, bears a broad, irregular, roughly triangular scar 3 cm. wide at its base. The apex of this scar is downwards and a slightly jagged linear scar descends therefrom, down the centre to the meatus. There is no trace of any clitoris. There are also no outer labia in the true sense of the term. Their whole upper portion must have been cut away and the wounds drawn together, pulled upwards and together towards the centre with some force and then sutured tightly, as far as we can judge from certain regular pigmented spots. Thus the labia majora are no longer "lips," but tiny folds or ridges of skin which hardly break the level of the scarred surfaces around them ; while the furrow between labia and thigh has been almost obliterated.

[Removal of the clitoris has long been advocated by certain writers for masturbation in girls and for such female ailments as pruritus. In 1867 and 1868 the English medical world was convulsed by revelations concerning the opinions and practices of Isaac B. Brown who performed the operation at his London Surgical Home as a means of curing forms of insanity, epilepsy and hysteria, as well as masturbation. It appeared that not only was the clitoris excised but the nymphæ were clipped to their base, and the whole vulva cauterised. The case excited enormous interest and Mr. Brown was removed from the Obstetrical Society of London. However, many of his grateful patients, who believed that they had been saved from insanity by his ministrations, combined with others to present him with a silver dessert service in token of his " singular success in the treatment of female diseases " (see I. B. Brown).]

THE INFIBULATION OR OCCLUSION OF THE VULVA

The operation, which has been termed *infibulation* or " *sewing up*," or better, *occlusion*, stands in close association with *excision* of labia or clitoris, but the two are not identical.

Infibulation does not necessarily imply surgical sutures.

Moreover, infibulation appears to be really a specifically *African* practice, whereas excision is not limited to that Continent. North-Eastern and Central Africa are, so far, the only regions known to us in which infibulation has been commonly practised (*cf.* Freimark).

Linschoten certainly stated that he had found the practice in Pegu in India, but, as no other investigator has corroborated this, we may assume that his memory was slightly at fault.

[Yet this traveller describes the operation, stating that at first he himself did not credit the story. He states that the vulva is sewn up, leaving a small opening only for the purposes of urination. When the girl becomes nubile her husband opens the vulva himself.]

Excision does not necessarily imply infibulation, but infibulation (of one kind at least) must, in all circumstances, imply excision, and extensive excision, before there can be raw surfaces sufficiently large to form a solid scar. Either by surgical stitches or—as seems more frequent—by appropriate bandages and attitudes for days at a time, the raw surfaces are brought into close contact with one another and unite to form a solid scar.* The excision is so arranged that this hard scar of connective tissue occludes the whole vulva with the exception of the urinary opening. In India rings are passed through the labia majora (*cf.* Fig. 160) in some regions, to prevent sexual intercourse in the husband's absence, and as is well known, the Girdle of Chastity was used for this purpose.

In the Middle Ages of the Christian Era, Maqrizi related the customs of the Beja : he said that they cut off the inner lips in young girls and then sewed the

---

* [A similar method for uniting a torn perineum used to be employed by obstetricians. Beck states healing took under a week, even when the laceration extended to the anus.]

rimæ pudendi together.   And this practice still prevails among the tribes south of the Nile Cataracts, the Galla, Somali, Harari and women of Massowah.   Among the Bedouins of the Western Bayuda Steppe, north of Khartoum, the girls are infibulated between the ages of five and eight years.   In Kordofan, excision and stitching are inflicted at eight years ; among the Harari at seven.   Accounts differ about the Somali : some say from eight to ten, but Paulitschke says from three to four.   Lanzi specifies the third year as that which prevails for infibulation among the Danakil.

The method of executing this mutilation varies in different tribes.   The final results, however, appear fairly constant in all tribes.

160.—The warrior's return.   One woman (right) is infibulated.   Indo-Persian miniature.
(Mus. f. Völkerk., Berlin.)

Comte de Cardi relates that in the hinterland of Ekrika (Niger Delta), the interior surfaces of the labia majora are scraped till they bleed, and then drawn and pressed together so closely that they unite and close the vaginal orifice.

Among the Somali and Harari the preliminary excision removes a substantial part of the clitoris and abrades the labia majora or " outer vulva."   Probably the inner lips or nymphæ are cut away at the same time.   The operation is performed by skilled women and followed at once by a real " stitching " according to Paulitschke.   The materials used for the sutures are cotton thread, horse-hair or fibres.   Only a small part of the vulval cleft remains unstitched.   The girls have to rest for several days with bound feet and thus the abraded surfaces unite and are scarred over.

King says that the Somali operate on their girls at eight years old and sometimes earlier. There is always clitoridectomy as well as infibulation. The clitoris is drawn to its full length and cut off, and the membranes of the labia scraped raw with knives, leaving only a very minute section free, on either side, in the centre of the vulva. Then the labia are pressed together and sutured with two or three stitches. The girls' knees and thighs are firmly bound together. The healing process takes a month and is accompanied by fumigations. King states he has often seen little girls hopping painfully about with the help of a long stick just outside their huts. They were obviously crippled by bandages. He adds that the aperture left by the operation is no wider than the normal anus (*cf.* Fig. 164).

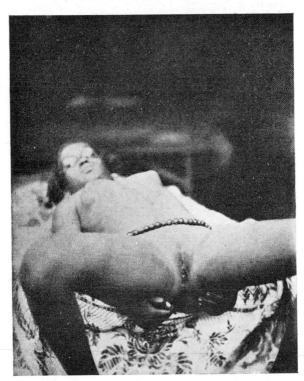

161.—Infibulation. First stage. The vulva is still partially open. Danakil. (Mus. f. Völkerk., Dresden.)

Burckhardt also mentions a literal *stitching*, known as " Mukhæyt " or " sewn up," and states that on inspection he found the vulva completely occluded with the exception of a small opening at the urethra. He adds that the operation is by no means rarely fatal.

Vita Hassan writes as follows about the Sudanese women, after mentioning that the female circumcision common to all Islam means excision of part of the clitoris :

" In the Sudan, most of the tribes extend this operation to a hideous mutilation. This is performed on children six years old with all the festivities customary at a wedding. Clitoris, labia majora and the most projecting edges of the inner lips are shorn off with a razor, leaving the pudendal region a bare flat wound. Then the raw edges are firmly sutured together, leaving one small slit into which a tiny tube of cane is slipped for urination. After some days have elapsed, the edges unite, the wound is cicatrised and closes and the tube can be removed.   The woman has become a monster and the sacred and accursed rite has been fulfilled."

[Professor and Mrs. C. G. Seligman have described the operation among the Kababish, one of the most powerful of the Arab tribes of the Anglo-Egyptian Sudan.

It is usually performed in early childhood between the third and sixth year. After healing has taken place the vaginal orifice is represented by a small opening at the posterior commissure.   Sometimes a small plug is inserted to prevent the

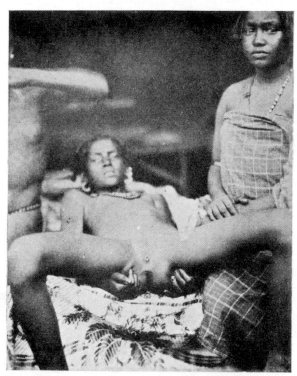

162.—Infibulation.   Second stage.   The vulva has closed with the exception of an opening at the urinary meatus.   Danakil.   (Mus. f. Völkerk., Dresden.)

urethra from becoming closed.   After the operation the legs are tied together for two or three weeks.

For the purposes of the operation the child is placed on her back with her legs flexed upon her abdomen, and the thighs separated as widely as possible.   The old woman who acts as operator then seizes the clitoris and cuts it off as closely as possible and then proceeds to carve away the whole of the vulva, leaving only a small portion just above the perineum.   Even part of the mons veneris was sliced away, a fact which explains the frequent absence of hair in this region.   The wound is then plastered with flour and the legs secured.   During the operation the child's cries are drowned by the spectators, who included several boys and girls.]

Bieber gives particulars about the Moslem Galla of Harai : they infibulate little girls from eight to ten years of age, and the process is termed *mutscha durba* or " stitching."   The mother of the child operates on her.   The inner lips are scraped raw, their edges sewn together with horse-hair and the feet tied together firmly for two days.   There is a festival with hospitality to friends and fellow tribespeople. Only a small orifice is left in the vulva for urination and menstruation.   Before she is given in marriage, women, specially expert in their business, cut open the genital cleft, according to measurements furnished by the prospective husband.

It appears that actual stitching is less frequent than pressure of the raw lateral surfaces together with tight bandaging of the lower limbs and resting recumbent till the wounds heal.   Dr. Peney, a Surgeon-in-Chief to the French Forces in the Sudan, writes as follows :

" Between the age of seven and eight years the girl is handed over to the matron

163.—Infibulation.   Third stage.   The operation is finished.   Compare the appearance of the normal vulva (left).   Danakil. (Mus. f. Völkerk., Dresden.)

whose office it is to perform the operation. Some days beforehand the mother of the family invites all her female relations and acquaintances to assemble in her abode, and the ceremony is preceded with food and merriment.

" When the hour comes, the child is laid on a bed and held down and in position by the assembled women, while the matron, kneeling between the patient's thighs, begins by slicing off the tip of the clitoris and the edges of the inner lips.   Then the razor shears along the rims of the outer lips, removing a ribbon of flesh about 2 cm. wide.   It lasts between four and five minutes. In order to drown the shrieks of the girl, the assembled guests and kin raise the loudest and shrillest din conceivable until the process is over.   Then, when the flowing blood has been staunched, the girl is laid flat on her back, her legs extended and tied firmly together so that she cannot walk, otherwise the desired effect would not be produced.   Before leaving the girl to the healing process of nature, the matron introduces a hollow cylinder of wood, about as thick as a goose's feather, into the lower portion of the vagina, between the bleeding edges of the wound, and this is kept in place until the scar is completely formed, for purposes of micturition and menstruation.   This tiny orifice is all that remains of the vaginal outlet."

Lanzi wrote that the Danakil girls have to lie still with tightly bound legs until the wounded region is fully cicatrised (Figs. 161 to 163). [Jousseaume, in his "Impressions," has given a long and vivid account of the operation and its results among the Danakil.] Cailliaud reports similarly of the women in the Sennaar country. He mentions the extremely small size of the artificial outlet : "hardly sufficient for natural needs."

Sir Samuel Baker gave a detailed account in Latin of the Nubian method to the *Lancet* in 1867. He describes how the girl is laid flat on her back on the ground. Her legs are then raised and flexed as far as possible, the thighs being widely separated. The lips of the vulva are then almost entirely cut off with a sharp knife, and a small tubular reed is introduced. This done, the edges are placed in close proximity so that finally healing takes place, leaving only the orifice in which the reed had been inserted. Healing is assisted by the fact that during the process the legs of the girl are tied together. When it is complete the vulva, "as nature designed it," is no longer visible. The parts are as smooth beneath as the mon veneris above and the girl resembles those examples of the sculptor's art where the genital organs are lacking. The aperture in which the reed was inserted fulfils the purposes of urination. [(*Cf.* Sir S. Baker ; Godard). Cadalvene and Breuvery describe the operation in Dongola. After the vulval lips have been clipped the parts are drawn together and the legs secured. The child of eight or nine remains thus for a couple of weeks, natural needs being met by the insertion of a tube.]

Panceri had the opportunity of examining a 20-year-old Sudanese girl who had been infibulated. He says :

164.—Vulvoanal region of a negress of 14 years. Alexandria. (After a prepared specimen by Kaussmann (Berl. Anat. Mus., 1894, 167) for Fritsch.)

"Instead of the pudendal cleft, there is only a linear scar, but it is possible to feel the clitoris moving under the mass of scarred connective tissue, which entirely encloses and hides it. Only when the knees were widely separated was it possible to see the slit which represented the vaginal orifice ; the ridged crest of the inner labia having coagulated with the outer. The superior commissure, the clitoris, the urethral orifice and the frontal section of the inner lips were invisible, for the outer labia had become united."

Finally, we may quote Werne, with reference to the tribes immediately south of the First Cataract of the Nile :

The older women lay the victim of custom down and graze and scrape along the surfaces of both the labia majora with a sharp knife till they are raw, leaving only a small intact strip towards the anus. Then they take a *ferda*—the long strip of cotton cloth with fringed and tasselled ends which both sexes wrap round them—and tie the girl's knees tightly together so that the raw surfaces agglutinate, or grow together with the exception of the small untouched strip on either side. A quill, or tube of cane is slipped into this portion for purposes of nature. The girl has to lie with fettered knees, except when nature calls, for the period of 40 days, and this time appears obligatory and in correspondence with what has been proved necessary in order to produce complete cicatrisation.

The illustration (Fig. 164) of an anatomical specimen brought by G. Fritsch from Alexandria, and presented by him to the Berlin College of Anatomy, shows part of the body of a negro slave girl of 14. The labia majora are tightly sutured in their anterior portion ; and the small round aperture which alone gives access to the inner genital tract is no larger than the anus. Labia minora, clitoris and urinary orifice are alike invisible and enclosed within the cicatrisation.

What is the purpose of this mutilation ? There can hardly be any doubt of the answer. Infibulation is performed simply and solely in order to enforce complete abstinence from sexual intercourse on the girls who are subjected to the operation.

Werne is quite correct in pointing out that infibulation and cicatrisation are indeed a more certain means of compulsion than any of the locks and springs of the " girdles of chastity " with which our knightly forefathers in Europe clothed their wives before they themselves rode forth on Crusade or other adventures. Werne quotes the rejoinder, half plea, half excuse, with which these native girls often reply to a stranger's caresses and attempts at approach : " El bab makful "—" The gate is locked ! "

King, however, states that this purpose is not invariably attained. Although slave traders often have the operation performed on their freshly captured " wares " in order to sell them more profitably, even they are sometimes subject to loss on that account.

He mentions that among the Somali, so far from infibulation always compelling abstinence, a form of incomplete intercourse is known to take place for money (12 dollars).

[Various other minor operations are reported. In Sind, Gait reports that the orifice of the vagina is occasionally treated in order to diminish its size, although details are not available. This contrasts with the further custom (reported by Fritsch) of sewing up the vagina completely so as to favour anal coitus. This is apparently performed in the East on certain prostitutes in whom the vagina has become too capacious to afford satisfaction to those clients who prefer even anal coitus with a girl rather than with the male prostitutes.

Moreover, Gait states that in Sind a ring is occasionally passed through the vulva of girls just above the vagina so as to afford protection against illicit affairs when suspicious husbands are away from home.

In 1885 Mr. W. T. Stead caused a sensation by publishing an account of the trade in virgins in England, in which he stated that means were employed to simulate virginity in girls who had previously been deflowered.]

DEFIBULATION OF WOMEN

The almost complete occlusion of the genital cleft in women who have been infibulated makes normal sexual intercourse quite impossible, as has already been fully explained.

Impregnation, however, may sometimes occur as the result of attempted approach and accident. But such impregnation and gestation cannot lead to a normal delivery without further operative interference. So, in order to make both functional intercourse and motherhood possible, the girls whose genital organs have been closed and cicatrised, must be defibulated—in King's expressive phrase, or we might say, ripped open.

Let us see what various authorities say of these further operations.

Cailliaud, whom we have already cited, writes of the Sennaar women :

" Before the consummation of marriage, the unnatural adhesions must be removed. If peril to life ensues, razor and red hot irons are to hand. The sensibilities of these races seem too much obliterated, too primitive for them to attach any weight to the exquisite suffering and the serious and inevitable injuries of such procedures—procedures invented and imposed by the dominant sex, in order to guarantee for themselves the enjoyment of that virginity which is apt in other lands to be so evanescent. However that may be, it is a serious enough affair to put the girl in a fit stage to fulfil her conjugal duties. If there is a woman, who, through lack of means, has been unable to prepare herself, then the husband must do what he can. If he succeeds in impregnating her, which is difficult enough, then she has the right to insist on the services of one of the older women, well versed in the cruel trade, who may be able to break down those obstacles which hinder the processes of childbirth. Moreover, the young widow who cherishes a desire to marry again, does not hesitate to submit a second time to the operation, although such cases are not common."

Vita Hassan says of the Sudanese natives :

" This procedure is customary among all the Mohammedan tribes of the south from Berber to Sennaar, including Khartoum, Metemma, Shendi, Wâd, Madani, Haraz, Sennaar and their environs.

" It is said that the operation is not only part of a religious ritual, but also has the purpose of prophylaxis against a certain disease, which afflicts women not so mutilated. The expectant mother has to face further mutilation. The child at birth cannot pass the cicatrisations in the normal way, so the muscles from groin to reins are severed in order to liberate the infant. And then this laceration is sewn together like the pre-marital wound, and the woman is once more impenetrable. Some time after delivery, a new *ssehāma* (the name of this mutilation) makes the wife and mother available once more."

Peney, whose account of the Sudanese we have already quoted, describes defibulation as follows :

" When the Nubian maiden marries, she has recourse to the wise woman, in order to have her vulva prepared and enlarged, for the infibulated aperture is far too small and too inelastic— because of the scars of connective tissue which surround it on every side—to admit even the roughest and most merciless husband. So the expert matron intervenes and makes a longitudinal slash, and intercourse takes place ; but first the matron introduces a fresh tube or cylinder of wood or vegetable fibre and far bulkier than the first, into the vagina, to the distance of 3 or 4 inches. This remains *in situ* for a fortnight until the new wound has healed and scarred when its presence becomes unnecessary.

" Nor is this all. If the woman conceives—and she generally does so—she is again put through the ordeal of the knife ; for the same rigid circlet of scars that locked the vulva against copulation from the outside is equally a barrier against the dilation of that part through which the baby emerges. So what will not stretch must be slashed open with wide and deep strokes. Often the child at the moment of passing the genital cleft is grievously injured. I have myself seen cases of mortal wounds inflicted on infants as they entered the world, by careless or clumsy operators. . . ." " But," he adds, " the young girls seem more attached to it than their husbands, for they say that those who have not been infibulated would not find a husband."

Baker and Burckhardt corroborate these accounts in detailed descriptions. Burckhardt maintains that no sooner is the defibulatory mutilation performed than it is followed by copulation " Unde illa Arabum sententia : Post diem aperturæ, dies initus."

Werne says of the tribes immediately south of the First Cataract of the Nile :

" When the girl whose virginity has been preserved in such a revolting manner becomes a bride, further indecent cruelties are practised. One of the women who perform infibulation visits the bridegroom immediately before the marriage in order to obtain exact measurements of his member. She then makes to measurement, a sort of phallus of clay or wood and by its aid she incises the scar for a certain distance and leaves the instrument wrapped round with a rag—in the wound in order to keep the edges from adhering again. Then the wedding feast is celebrated with hideous din, the man leads his bride home—every step she takes means pain—and without giving the fresh wounds time to heal or scar, he exercises his marital privileges.

"Before a child can be born, the vulva has to be opened again throughout its length, but, after delivery, infibulation is again inflicted, according to the husband's orders, either to the original or other dimensions : and so the process continues."

Brehm fully corroborates Werne and other authorities :

"Before marriage, the bridegroom sends the bride's family a wooden replica of his membrum and the slit in the girl's organs is made carefully to this exact measurement. If she

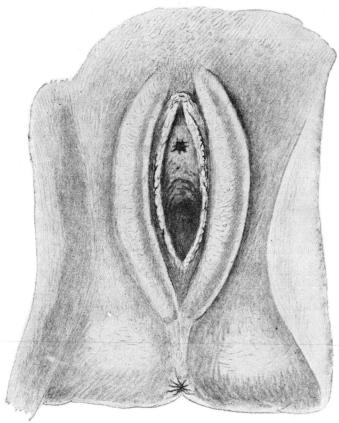

165.—Vulva of a negress from Old Dongola, who had been infibulated and then opened. Notice the stump of the clitoris and clipped nymphæ.   (From a drawing by R. Hartmann.)

becomes pregnant, there is a further mutilation before delivery, namely, a slash from rear to front, towards the mons veneris."

Lanzi reports exactly the same of the Danakil. He adds that the barbarous custom has become so ingrained that some women voluntarily request re-infibulation after childbirth.

King gives further particulars about the exact procedure among the Somali :

"In the town of Zayla, an elderly and expert woman of a strange tribe—*midg'an*—accompanies the bridal pair to their chamber. This woman performs the operation on the bride, who is held fast by the husband, so that her convulsive struggles are in vain.   Then the woman leaves the room or tent and the kinsfolk and acquaintances outside the door dance, sing, scream and clap their hands in order to drown the bride's shrieks of pain.   And in the interior of Somaliland, the young husband himself generally makes the necessary incision while two of his near male relatives hold down the bride."

The young negresses of Ekrika, in the delta of the Niger River, are operated on for a second time by an aged woman in the depths of the woods.   When sexual maturity begins they repair to the forest, and the woman perforates the cicatrisation with a rounded ivory stick about as thick as a pencil.

Hartmann was able to make a drawing from life of a Sudanese woman about 30 years of age from Old Dongola.   She had been infibulated and then defibulated. The drawing (Fig. 165) shows the stump of the clitoris and the hard vestiges of the inner labia.   The urethral aperture is just under the clitoris.   The cicatrisation following these mutilations is most unfavourable to maternity, as is indeed obvious.

Beurmann told Ploss that among the tribes who infibulate, very difficult labour often occurs ;   whereas other African women generally have remarkably easy deliveries.

There are also further dangers and disasters.   Egyptian hospitals contain syphilitically infected women who in spite of the operation suffer from extensive ulcerations.   Uhle saw many negresses who had been slaves with severe lesions. They had been infibulated, sold as slaves, dragged in an interminable march from their homes in Central Africa.   Then a syphilitic slave dealer had picked them out of the chain-gang, cut open their scars and raped them.   Their open wounds soon became extensive syphilitic sores which they had neither means to cleanse nor to disinfect.   For weeks they marched under the merciless glare of the sun till the hospitals offered them a refuge.

It often occurs that after childbirth the young mothers are re-infibulated. Hartmann, Brehm, Werne and Vita Hassan concur as to this.   And Hartmann adds :

"Slaves, too, are infibulated thus.   There are cruel masters—and some of them are Europeans !—who have had this thing done even twice or thrice to the same women who have been their mistresses—and then they have sold them."

Werne became acquainted with a young widow in the Berber district who bore hideous and loathsome mementoes in the shape of scars.   Her husband had subjected her to infibulation seven times in succession within a brief period of time.

Linschoten briefly confirms the fact of defibulation according to the husband's wish and instructions.

Ignaz Pallme states that in Kordofan most tribes inflict a second incision on betrothed girls 20 days before marriage is consummated.   This " second excision " must, it appears, be defibulation.

Rüppel writes :

" The defibulation of the bride, that is to say, the opening up of the infibulated parts, is not performed until the whole bridal price, so long haggled over, has been paid.   The extent of the incision depends on the husband's wishes : it may be large or small.   When the date of a birth approaches, there is a further incision to permit delivery.   Then, after childbirth, the whole area is once more abraded and cicatrised, so that the conditions prevalent after the first operation are restored.   The woman remains in this state while she nurses her baby at the breast. Then the mutilations recommence and, if the husband so desires, they may be repeated till after the third or fourth confinement. But they are often omitted after the first. I have known young widows whose husbands died shortly after their confinement when their wounds had closed and 'adhered.' They were in a grievous state and forced to remain so by their parents and kindred. For, if they had been defibulated on their own initiative, they would voluntarily have become public prostitutes."

Paulitschke says that among the Somali the primitive woman-surgeons above mentioned, or the girls themselves, slit open the infibulated vulva ; but that it is generally only fully opened up before childbirth.

Such are the possible results of pathological jealousy reinforced by superstition.

THE MONS VENERIS IN COMPARATIVE ANTHROPOLOGY

The formation, proportions and appearance of the mons veneris depend on three factors. The first is the general bony framework of the pelvis, especially the precise width of the angle formed by the two rami of the pubic bone. The second important factor is the amount of adipose tissue or fat ; and the third the density, disposition and colour of the pubic hair. And as all these characteristics show wide ethnical differences there must obviously be definite characteristics in the mons veneris, according to race. We are, however, far from being able to formulate these differences ; for the available material is very slight and imperfect. We are even far from well informed about the different types of structure and pigmentation in this region among women of the civilised white races. For, though there are hospitals and clinics and infirmaries, public and private, throughout Europe, and doctors in attendance therein, there are very few qualified observers who have taken the trouble to note or record these anatomical features. M. Bartels has emphasised the lacunæ in our knowledge of this portion of anatomy and anthropology and not wholly without result. In the scheme of investigation suggested by the special (1884) Commission for the Study of the Human Pilous System (selected by the German Anthropological Society), the hair of the body has also been listed as worthy of study. But, so far, there has been no appreciable result.

The lower portion of the mons veneris meets the labia majora ; their upper or anterior commissure forms the boundary of the mons on its lower extremity. At the sides the mons reaches to the groins, and above it is bounded by the lower of the two curved lines which cross the hypogastric area from side to side, with their concavity below the navel.

In women of Central Europe the generous amount of adipose tissue raises the mons veneris somewhat above the level of the surrounding regions in a softly curving mound. Moreover—in most cases—after puberty, it is covered with a more or less abundant growth of hair, which shows many variations.

The general pelvic angle, or inclination, also affects the relative prominence or the reverse of the mons veneris, and, moreover, there are also apparently distinct differences in the amount of pigmentation in the mons, for it would seem that, in some cases there is increased pigmentation. But, so far, nothing definite can be stated about this.

As we have said, anthropological investigation among primitive races is very imperfect in this respect, both for subjective and for objective reasons, as can easily be understood.

We have, however, a few reliable photographs which show representatives of various ethnic stocks, but so far very few.

In the portraits of negresses from Loango and district furnished by Falkenstein, the mons veneris seems in every case only slightly prominent and poor in adipose tissue.   The same may be said of the Abyssinians from Colonia Eritrea and near Massaua, photographed by G. Schweinfurth.

Through the courtesy of Herr Knypers, the Berlin Anthropological Society has some photographic studies of Javanese girls.   In all of these the mons veneris is well developed and rounded with the exception of one very young person in whom there is not yet any actual mons, though there seems a slight increase of local fat.

The Samoans and a Caroline Islander depicted in Godeffroy's album, are well developed in that region.

Riedel   makes special mention of the fact that in the Islands Lakor, Moa and Leti, the brachycephalic women had well developed adipose tissue in this region. In this respect they would appear to differ from the other cranial type among the island population as well as from the other women of the Molucca Archipelago.

According to Jacobus X., often cited already, the Tahitian women have, in some cases, " very highly developed " montes veneris.

Hyades and Deniker found the women of Tierra del Fuego under-developed in this respect.

Lockhart and Morache both mention a peculiar local characteristic in Chinese women and these authorities associate the enlarged mons veneris with the crippling of the lower extremities already fully described.

Morache writes :

" Many people have assured me that in the Chinese women, the whole lower or frontal portion of the pelvis, i.e., the mons veneris, forms a massive mound, separated from the abdomen by a deep fold, and that the labia majora are proportionately enlarged and developed.

"The Chinese find it natural and obvious that the voluntary and deliberate atrophy elsewhere should be compensated through a natural equilibrium by this abnormal expansion."

C. G. Seligman made further enquiries about this, but he has not obtained any corroborative evidence.

Both the Berlin Museum of Ethnology and other collections in European Museums possess a number of highly intricate Chinese works of art, which are known as spring-leaves (tch'üntch'eh) or secret sports (Pi-hi).   They represent erotic scenes to which we shall have occasion to refer later on.   All the women depicted in these works of art have crippled feet and all have also very high development of the mons veneris, and thick protuberant labia majora.   So it is not impossible that Morache's informants spoke the truth and that we have here a highly ingenious and indirect method of plastic alteration of the female form, or accentuation of the genital zone.

THE GROWTH OF HAIR ON THE BODY : DENSITY, DISPOSITION AND COLOUR

The growth of hair on the mons veneris occurs in girls at puberty ; the pubic hair in boys appears at the corresponding age.   In the summary of the main secondary and tertiary sexual differences, M. Bartels pointed out that there are characteristic and different dispositions or arrangements of hair on the body in men and women respectively.   On another occasion (Bartels), in a study of the subject, he wrote :

" On the lower abdomen in women, there are two clear, parallel, curved lines or folds in the skin, with their convex surface downwards.   The upper line begins slightly above the

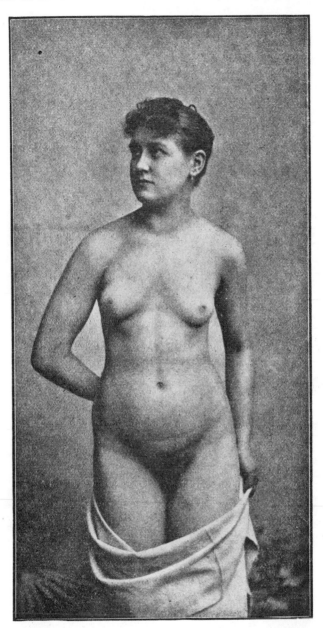

166.—The semicircular and suprapubic folds in a girl.   The lower fold forms the upper margin
of the pubic hair in woman.

anterior superior iliac spine and cuts through the linea alba about the point dividing its middle
and lower third section.   The lower line is less shallow and more sharply curved.   It begins
slightly below the anterior superior spine and runs in the approximate direction of Poupart's
ligament, the two lower lines from right to left meet slightly above the upper rim of the symphysis
pubis.   The mid-section of this lower line forms the upper limit of the normal female genital
hair.

167.—The suprapubic fold seen laterally. The upper limit of hair on the mons veneris is clearly shown at the lower border of this fold.

" The lower line is simply the external sign of the place where the abdominal wall merges into Poupart's ligaments and the symphysis respectively. All the skin above this lower line must be reckoned in the abdominal area, while below the epidermis is part of the outer covering of the pelvis, and its central portion consists of the skin of the mons veneris.

" In men, whose chest and abdomen have an appreciable hirsute covering, these hairs mingle with the pubic growth in a longitudinal arrangement.   But in women, chest and abdomen are normally free from hair, and only the mons veneris is covered with a cluster of hair ; thus the lower of the two furrows or lines must form its upper boundary, for anything above the line would be really abdominal."

Two Viennese artists' models (Figs. 166 and 167) show the disposition of the pubic hair and the two folds very clearly.   In one, the pubic hair does not extend to its normal upper limit.   In the other the pubic hair reaches the lower line but has not spread to its normal extent at the sides.   A third young girl, still a child, has these folds clearly defined (Fig. 168).

In certain exceptional cases we find that the pubic hair in women extends above its normal boundary, even to the mid-section of the abdomen so far as the navel.   This is a heterogeny, namely, a symptom or characteristic abnormal or anomalous to the sex of the person displaying it.   Similarly, it is an heterogeny for a male person to have smooth glabrous chest and belly with a thick tuft of hair of female type just above the genitals.

The lateral limits of the genital hair in normal women are the two inguinal furrows, or groins ; normally, woman's hair does not spread to the inner surface of her thighs.   This occasionally occurs, but it is undoubtedly exceptional, and, in fact, heterogenous.   The lower and rear boundaries of the hirsute zone may also be exceeded if there is a growth of hair over the posterior or inferior commissure of the labia minora, the perineum and around the anal orifice.   Hair round the latter region is considered a definitely male secondary characteristic.

[Although a posterior growth of pubic hair is, as stated in the text, a male characteristic, the absence of the same in women is by no means a constant feature. As stated earlier,   the vulvoanal region in blondes is quite different from that in brunettes ; and the brunette of Alpine stock cannot be compared with the Nordic blonde except to illustrate profound differences.*

The pubic hair in brunettes sometimes extends upward to the navel and in a posterior direction it is often found encircling the anus.   Moreover, the dorsal region of the thigh is often covered with hair and the growth of hair on the legs is sometimes so great that, when shaving or depilatories are not used, the hairs may be seen protruding through thin stockings.   It is only in cases where a thick pilous system is associated with other characteristics that heterogeny can be usefully discussed, although it is true that these are often found associated with general hypertrichosis.]

As excessive growth of hair may be found in women in more than one direction, so also may lack of the normal amount of pubic hair ; many women have only a very slight growth.   This may be considered an arrested development, a semi-infantilism.   We shall refer to these anomalies in a later chapter.

Our speculative forefathers were much puzzled to account for the purpose of the pubic hair in both sexes.   Opinions varied from that of Galen, who considered their purpose ornamental, " Jam vero et circum pudenda pili quoque necessario provenerunt (calida enim ac humida sunt haec loca) operimentumque ac ornamentum ejus loci partibus præbent, non aliter quam nates quidem ano, præputium autem pudendo " (Tom. III., 910)—to those of Burkard Eble and the great Danish anatomist Caspar Bartholin, who both preferred the view that the hairs were put there for.

* [Amongst German blonde women Bartels himself found the posterior extension around the anus far from rare, and Rothe came to the same conclusion.]

168.—The semicircular and suprapubic folds in a girl before puberty. Note the apparent anterior position of the vulva due to lack of adipose tissue and absence of pubic hair.

modest concealment ! The same teleological point of view in which human views of morals are attributed to the processes of evolution was expressed by Gerdy. The hair is, he says, modesty's veil, and he notes that it is a remarkable thing that this region should be covered just at the time when, " si j'ose parler ainsi," the genitals awaken and emerge from their chastity. By thus covering them nature inflames the imagination and rouses to a higher pitch " la plus impérieuse de toutes les passions." [T. Bell seems to have held a similar view.]

Blanchard taught that the purpose was wholly utilitarian : that of protection of the sensitive mucosa from cold and accident. Fabricius thought the hairs absorbed perspiration and relieved pressure in coitus by acting as pads.

Eble had a fuller and more logical opinion on the pubic hair, which he thought served, after all, several purposes :

(1) To dissipate the perspiration imperceptibly, and receive that flowing down from the abdominal regions ;
(2) To prevent excessive coital friction ;
(3) To afford a sign of sexual maturity ; and
(4) To " facilitate the accumulation and mutual interchange of electricity between the two individual opposite poles in copulation."

He continued :

" At least there is proof of the connection between these hairs and the generative function in this, that, in human beings, the thickness and crispness of pubic and genital hair is generally in exact ratio to the potency of the individual, and that the most libidinous people are, as a rule, very hirsute in that region. It would be interesting to ascertain whether there is the same relation between hirsuties and fertility or fecundity in women. If it is really true, as Jahn maintains, that no women with absolutely hairless mons veneris and genitalia ever became pregnant, it would be impossible to deny this interaction."

There is, of course, an association between extreme hairiness and sexuality. Both are based on and modified by endocrine factors. Natural and sexual selection may have helped to develop pubic hair, for it could also serve for protection. There is, however, another purpose, served also by the hair of the head and of the armpits ; namely, the collection, concentration and emanation of personal odours. (*Cf.* Schifferdecken, *Archiv. für Menschenkunde*, 1925, 35 ff.)

The first authority to tabulate such facts as are here available was the late Berlin gynæcologist, Eggel, who left his work to Max Bartels [1] to be continued and completed.

Analysis of Eggel's tabulated data resulted in the conclusion that the coloration of the pubic hair has a certain tendency to association with the colour of the hair on the head ; but that this is a tendency, not an absolute rule. Moreover, there is no such tendency to definite association with the colour of the eyes :

One thousand adult women were examined and the results tabulated :

Dark eyes	239
Dark hair on head	333
Dark hair on mons veneris and genitals .	329
Light eyes	761
Light hair on head	667
Light hair on genitals	671

Many dark-eyed women had light genital hair ; the same light genital hair was even sometimes found in women whose head hair was dark. Texture, amount and arrangement of pubic hair varied greatly from short to long, sparse to dense, straight and soft to wiry and curly.

We have mentioned and defined the condition known as *heterogeny* with special reference to hair. This, according to Bartels, seems indeed to be frequent among fair-haired women in Germany as well as among brunettes.

On Max Bartel's suggestion, Rothe* made an exact comparison and tabulation of his results in another group of 1000 women, studied in his Berlin practice. He found that among the North Germans there was an overwhelming preponderance of fair hair, especially medium fair or dark flaxen.

Women with red hair on the head had invariably either red or light genital hair, never dark. Women with black hair on the head had red genital hair in one-third of the cases ; in almost two-thirds they had brown, and in two cases, dark flaxen. The Jewish women had generally brown pubic hair. Among 52 out of 977 North German women the hairs on the labia majora were perceptibly paler than on the mons.

Rothe stressed the amount of individual variation in amount and arrangement of the genital and pubic hair in women :

" The extreme diversity in this respect would appear hardly to admit of formulated rules. . . . In almost every case, there are individual characteristics which distinguish it from all the rest. Nevertheless, two main types of pubic hair growth may be recognised together with many intermediate and transitional grades."

Later he adds :

" Among a group of 490 women, 477 were North Germans, 11 Jewesses and 2 Poles. There were two main types on the mons veneris. In one main type, the hairs grew mainly in a longitudinal strip down the middle of the mons and along the rims of the labia majora ; and, secondly, they covered the whole of the mons and the outer lips equally. About half the cases were either (a) longitudinal or (b) triangular. In both main groups, there were several sub-types " (p. 103).

He adds further details, for which we must refer students to his own work. However, it may be mentioned that in 420 North German cases he found curly hair most often, and straight least, and that both amount and length were more often moderate than excessive. He only found complete pubic hairlessness in one case : the woman was fair in colouring. He found several cases of heterogeny in the group of 1000 cases ; in 42 cases the hair grew above the normal boundary on to the abdomen, and in 146 (p. 73), it grew sideways out on to the thighs and backwards on to the perineum. Among the first heterogenous group was one Jewess ; among the second, three Jewesses. Rothe also found that blonde women incline more to heterogeny than brunettes [although in his statistics he does not distinguish the lateral from the posterior growth (see p. 74)].

We will now consider what little is known to us of this subject in women of coloured races.

We have already alluded to the Chinese representations of nude women in their " Bridal Books " or " Spring Scenes." In these the genital and pubic hair is depicted as black, and appears short, straight and not thick, but rather sparse, nor does it by any means cover the whole of the strongly developed mons veneris, but forms a somewhat narrow triangle with apex upwards.

Wernich says of the Japanese women that their genital and pubic hair was very sparse in comparison with the abundance of their head hair and the strong, coarse

*[*Cf.* also Rodecurt.]

texture of the single hairs ; moreover, the growth on the mons veneris was very seldom triangular in the area it covered but generally oval, " as though to indicate the contour of the vulva." Baelz states that the montes veneris of Japanese women are flat and covered with sparse and coarse pubic hair. Doenitz found absolute hairlessness in a surprisingly large number of cases. But this is not considered an attraction by the Japanese, for one of their most offensive terms of insult is " *kawaragé*," or " hair like a brick," *i.e.*, with a vulva as bald and hard as any brick.

The Japanese women of the Manchurian Korean type (*cf.* Baelz) had also very flat, glabrous montes veneris, and sparse, stiff hairs bordering the labia majora.

[In the erotic literature and illustrations of all countries may be found much material both for the anthropologist and social historian. The erotic " Picture books " of the East (of which the British Museum contains an admirable collection) illustrate the various forms of sexual allurements and criteria of " charm " which cannot be obtained elsewhere. Thus Japanese drawings show the distribution of pubic hair in women very clearly and confirm the gynaecological data. The hair shows the sparse, coarse growth mentioned by Wernich evenly distributed on the well-developed mons veneris and uniformly absent in the posterior direction (*cf.* F. S. Krauss).]

Jacobus X., already cited, says the Moi women in Cochin China have fairly thick, crisp pubic hair of the deepest black, whilst the Annamese women have only sparse hair on the mons. The same authority reports of the women of Cambodia that they also have sparse hair on the mons : it is dark brown in colour and slightly curly.

In the seventeenth century, the traveller and explorer Tavernier maintained that " after leaving Lahore and the Kingdom of Kashmir . . . all the women are naturally unprovided with hair on any part of the body."

Some photographs of Javanese girls are described as follows by M. Bartels :

" There are eight young women of whom only one is so completely hairless that there must have been deliberate epilation. The other seven are somewhat hirsute ; their well-developed montes veneris are thickly covered with long curly hair which grows closely. In some of them, the lateral portions of the mons are hairless. The hair extends downwards along the labia majora for some considerable distance so as to conceal the vulval cleft."

Stratz had the opportunity of examining over 2300 native women of Java. He wrote :

" The body has generally very little hair. Eyebrows are thin and narrow. The genital and axillary hair is apt to be artificially plucked out, as can be told from the hard surface of the parts. A hirsute mons veneris is rare. In cases where the genital hair has not been removed, it is apt to curl slightly and be lighter in tint than the hair of the head."

Roth reports abundant hair of the Sea-Dyak women on Borneo. Jacobs states of the Achinese on N.W. Sumatra, after mentioning individual variations and the effect of crossing with other ethnic stocks, that his informants told him that the labia majora were hairier as a rule than the mons itself, " a condition that seems to be typical of the people of Indonesia."

Steller states that the Kamchadale have thin black tufts of hair on the mons, and Schliephake found very slight pilous development among the Eskimo of Cumberland Sound.

There have been various statements as to Tierra del Fuego. v. Meyer mentions very flat mons with slight adipose deposit in an elderly Fuegian woman whose symphysis pubis projected in such a way that the outline was clearly visible. The hair was a mere down, fine in texture, and composed of hair $\frac{1}{2}$ cm. in length. The younger of the two Fuegian women, according to v. Bischoff, had only moderate development of the mons. The same results are recorded by R. Martin of another Fuegian woman, who had a flat mons with sparse hair.

Hyades and Deniker reported of their 15 cases :

" Only two had a few hairs on the mons, the other thirteen were quite glabrous."

Their detailed accounts, however, modify this statement, for they corroborate " very short and sparse hairs " or "a few stray hairs" in exactly half of 12 cases.

Among African and Oceanian women we find different characteristics.

Jacobus X. describes the women of negro descent in French Guiana as characterised by a strongly marked mons and a few hard and coarse genital hairs.

v. Bischoff performed an autopsy on a Sudanese Negress who had a strongly developed mons, abundantly covered with crisp black hair ; whilst Waldeyer says of a Koranna woman :

" The mons veneris is well developed with a layer of fatty tissue of between 2 and $2\frac{1}{2}$ cm. thickness and covered with short black curly hair, which forms single little spiral curls. The hair continues along the labia majora and thins out towards the perineum which shows a few strong and coarse single hairs on either side."

The Bushwoman who was celebrated and depicted as the " Hottentot Venus " had short, woolly tufts ; and the same was the case with Afandi, a Bushwoman on whom Luschka and Görtz made a post-mortem and reported fully.

Conradt gave accounts of nine Adeli negresses from the Ashanti Mandated Territory (Togoland). Here, too, there were apparently great individual differences from " rather profuse " to " sparse " and " patchy."

Hutter described the Bali negroes in the grasslands of the Cameroon hinterland as " in both sexes more hirsute than the forest folk. The hair of their heads is dense and thick as in all negroes. The armpits are slightly hairy, but the pubes have thick hair, especially in the women." He adds that he does not know whether this profusion is due to their habit of shaving the parts on certain occasions.

In New Britain Finsch noticed quite fair hair among the native women, although black was more frequent. But this fair hair may have been due to bleaching by strong acids in the preparations used for epilation.

Bässler referred to the genital hair of the native women of the Bismarck Archipelago in an address to the Anthropological Society of Berlin ; he stated that the heavy growth was extremely conspicuous, as the hair was usually dyed red like the locks round their faces. The women wiped their hands on their pubic hair whenever they were soiled or damp, as we are accustomed to use towels.

Jacobus X. has recorded the abundance of pubic hair in the women of Tahiti and New Caledonia, but, according to Riedel, the reverse is the case among the natives of the Aru, Luang and Sermata Islands. The same is the case in the women of Tenimber and Timor Laut but their head hair is reported to be long.

Riedel also quotes a term of opprobrium and insult among the Ceram Laut and Gorong Islanders, which indicates that thick genital hair was considered repulsive by these people.

Our comparative knowledge of the pilous system of other regions of the body is even slighter and more fragmentary. The hair of the armpits is the next in extent and importance to head and genitals. It usually appears at puberty, as does the pubic hair, and in males, the beard. We shall speak in greater detail of the course of puberty in a later chapter.

There has been much discussion as to the purpose and function of the axillary hair. Eble pointed out that the armpits contain not only hair follicles but abundant sweat glands and exude perspiration very freely. Friedenthal suggests that the main purpose of the hair is to promote the evaporation of the odorous secretions of the glands which exercise, as is well known, a strong sexual effect.* (Cf. Veit and Stoeckel, V., 1, p. 65.)

Rothe investigated the colour of the axillary hair in 1000 persons of adult age. All were women, and four nationalities were represented. He obtained the following results :

1000 CASES : TABULATION OF COLOURS OF AXILLARY HAIR

Colour.	In North Germans.	Jewesses.	Poles.	Dutchwomen.
Black	7	—	—	—
Brown	151	12	1	—
Dark flaxen	393	2	—	1
Yellow flaxen	383	3	4	—
Ashen fair (blonde cendré)	14	—	—	—
Red brown	1	—	—	—
Bright red	8	—	—	—
Reddish fair	3	—	—	—
No axillary hair	17	—	—	—
Number examined	977	17	5	1

These results show a strong prevalence of yellowish and light flaxen hair in the axillæ of North German women and girls. The darker tints of flaxen are only a little more frequent than the brighter. Brown hair is much rarer and ash blond rarer still ; then comes red hair and rarest of all, black, in 7 cases. Among the Jewish women, the axillary hair was brown in over half the cases, blond in 5, and black in none. The Poles had yellow hair in 4 cases, brown in 1. The only Dutchwoman had dark flaxen hair in her armpits. The axillary hair is lighter in tint than the hair of the head, and in many cases than eyebrows and pubes ; and it is much rarer to find darker axillary hair than dark eyebrows and pubes.

In 16 of these cases (one Pole, 15 Germans) Rothe found different coloured hair in the armpits on left and right respectively.

* [The odour of the perspiration from the armpits is undoubtedly a factor in the widespread habit of shaving this region among white people. The " deodorisers " of commerce are largely employed also for this purpose, and male opinion appears divided as to the desirability or not of the practice. In some the odour has a powerful and stimulating effect ; in others disgust is awakened instead of approval. (See Van de Velde, " Ideal Marriage," pp. 28 etc.). The following verse from Mirza Rahchan Kayil (Husain Izzat Rafi, nineteenth century) after the version of E. P. Mathers, illustrates the matter from one point of view.

" Oh, this scent floating from your neck, your breasts, your arms ;
That circles about your thighs and your little belly ;
This scent that is fed for ever and for ever
From two shady flasks under your bright arms,
I carry the scent of your body about with me."]

Among the nine Adeli negresses examined and reported on by Conradt, he mentions axillary hair in only one case. She was a girl of 16, and the hair was very sparse. But the Attakpami girl, who was between 18 and 20, had thick axillary hair.

Riedel says that on the Babar Islands many women have bare, glabrous armpits, and that the Aru, Luang and Sermata Islanders have thin axillary hair. The women of Tenimber and Timor Laut have thin but long axillary hair.

The Javanese girls depicted in photographs have apparently very little hair in this region. But they are all quite young, which may account for its absence.

Baelz found only slight development of axillary hair in Japanese women. The same seems the case in Tierra del Fuego, according to the reports of Hyades and Deniker.

The hair on the other bodily areas is seldom mentioned. Conradt speaks of a fine and slight down on the body of one Adeli negress of 25 years. He found the body covered with downy hair in 5 cases, the arms and legs in 3 and the legs alone in 2.

F. v. Luschan introduced six Pygmies from Ituri to the Berlin Anthropological Society some years ago. All showed fairly considerable pilosity. For example, the two women had just as much hair on their shins below the knee as rather hairy European males. And among all of them, if the light fell diagonally across their bodies, a very fine pale *down* became visible over the whole body.

The Ainu are, as is well known, very hairy. Baelz says :

" Their women share this quality so far as I could observe, but they are very modest and timid. In girls and women between 20 and 25, in whom only the feet just above the ankles were exposed, the ankles were as hairy as in extremely hirsute European men ; and the disposition of the hair was somewhat different, stopping abruptly at the ankles. Perhaps this is due to the long drawers they wear bound tightly at the ankles. One never sees an Ainu woman with much facial hair, though they deny attempts to shave it off. In Italy and Southern France, women with pronounced dark moustaches are quite commonly seen."

Koganei describes the Ainu women thus :

" They are, of course, much less hairy than their menfolk, but, in comparison with Japanese or European women, the relative hirsutism is as much greater as between Ainu, Japanese and white men. At some little distance, their legs look quite swarthy, because of the profuse hairy growth."

In Ancient India young maidens must sometimes have been afflicted with hirsutism, for among the signs which are mentioned as contra-indications to wooing and marriage in girls, we find : " She who is bearded," " whose shins and legs are hairy," " who is black with hairs all over her body," or " who has hairs on her hands, her sides and flanks, the slopes of her breasts, her back and below her knees " (Schmidt).

[Hair on the chest is not so uncommon as is usually supposed. In Rothe's 1000 cases 176 had hair on the areolæ and 29 had hair between the breasts. In the same series 17 had hair on the breasts themselves excluding the areolæ.]

PUBIC HAIR IN FOLKLORE AND LEGEND

We have already dealt with speculation and superstition relative to the exact purpose of the pubic hair. Traditional opinion has always accepted profuse hair in these regions as a sign of strong sexual instincts and functions, and lack of hair as a sign of sterility in women. These opinions can be contrasted with those expressed in folklore and legend. Scientific observations were not always of value in the past !

Burkard Eble has the following curious note :

"Women's hair is straight as a rule ; even their genital hair becomes straight as life proceeds, whereas, in the prime of life from 30 to 40, they are crisper and curlier than even in young maidens."

Among the Siberian Tungus, according to Georgi, thick pubic hair is considered a " monstrous growth," and attributed to evil spirits. And the husband of a woman with such an affliction was entitled forthwith to divorce her.

On the other hand, complete lack of pubic hair in women is a ground for divorce in Japan, according to Baelz.

Henri de Heer is credited with stating that pubic hairs were used for medicinal and pharmaceutical purposes in Europe in the sixteenth century. They were burnt, together with other substances, in order to revive wounded persons and staunch wounds by fumigation. But they could only afford relief to men if they came from the bodies of women and *vice versâ*.

Another form of sympathetic magic is associated with pubic hair on the Moluccan Archipelago. Riedel reports that on Serang, Eetar and the Kei Islands, the girls gave their sweethearts a few of their hairs from head and pubes as love tokens : this gift is reported as an infallible means to keep a lover faithful and devoted. This is a form of primitive logic and we find similar ideas and practices still in certain parts of Europe, as will be mentioned in a later chapter of this book.

Genital and pubic hairs are also remedies against evil spirits. Ribbe says of the Aru Islanders :

" Men, women and children wear charms and amulets hung round their necks to banish sickness and evil spirits. These amulets are little bags or pouches hung on thongs and containing such *pomali* (tabooed) objects as curiously shaped and coloured pebbles, pearls, animal's gallstones, pubic hair from women, and so forth."

In Serbia, if a peasant child falls very ill and witchcraft is suspected, a threefold fumigation is performed with hairs shorn from armpits and genitals of both parents. And the following exorcism is uttered : " Flee thou away, oh weird one and born of a weird one, thy place is not here ! Father and Mother created this life and defend it now with this burnt offering of hair and banish all harm from it, for it has no place here ! Flee thou away, thy place is not here ! " (F. S. Krauss).

Finally, we may remember that many races believe that the exposure of the genital organs is an infallible means of thwarting and exorcising evil spirits. This is a very profound archaic custom. It was even practised by Martin Luther, who was tormented by the nightly suggestions and visions of the devil and knew no means of self-defence, except the exposure of his own hind quarters.

[The question of the exposure of the body or of its parts leads to a discussion of the problem of *ritual nudity* into which we cannot enter here. Ghosts are said to be frightened of nudity, and in some parts of the world when a death occurs a man will expose his penis and a woman her buttocks (see Trebitsch). In a consideration of all these matters the *life-giving* nature of the genital organs should always be borne in mind. For a list of references to ritual nudity, see Goodland p. 718.]

In China, so some allege, there is an ancient custom of depicting the two sexual and procreative symbols, *Yang* and *Yin*, on the lintels of doors in order to banish evil spirits. This whole circle of concepts and associations shows how intricately and how deeply primitive elements and sexual elements are mingled with the life and thought of people in the most varied grades of civilisation, even at the present day and as any exact observation easily proves.

THE MONS VENERIS IN COMPARATIVE ETHNOGRAPHY AND SOCIOLOGY

We must now briefly consider sociological customs and ethnographical differences in the treatment of the mons veneris and body hair among various races. In many cases there are special ritual customs, hygienic or magical in origin and purpose.

We have mentioned certain analogous practices in discussing excision and infibulation. According to some authorities those severe mutilations include a portion of the mons veneris as well as clitoris and labia.

Probably the favourite and the most frequent method of treating, adorning or " improving " the mons veneris is by the removal of the hair (depilation). Among Mohammedan peoples depilation is enjoined on all women as a ritual. But it is also found in non-Moslem races all over the earth in the most various and the unlikely quarters and sections of the community.

The favourite Turkish preparation for removing pubic hair is *pigmentum aureum* (Arsenicum sulphuratum flavum) and burnt chalk in equal parts and moistened to a paste with rose-water. This paste is applied to the hairy areas and then removed after a short time, and the hairs are removed with it. This is the universal Oriental depilatory, known in Turkey as " *Rusma* " and in Persia as " *Nureh*," according to Polak. In Persia, as well as in Turkey, the married woman is expected to remove the hairs from her armpits and genitalia regularly in a warm bath, but the Moslem maidens and the Christian Armenians are exempt from this custom, according to Häntszche.

[Among the Turkish population in Bulgaria, Ivanhoff states that before marriage the pubic hair of both sexes is removed by means of calcium sulphate. It is considered sinful to indulge in sexual intercourse unless the hair has been removed.]

Polak declares that the term used for this procedure is *hadschebi keschidew*— to obey the law—but women of elegance and fashion pluck the hairs away with pincers till the growth ceases.

At one time the sale of *pigmentum aureum* in the Near East was so great that, according to Belon, the farmers of the tax on it were expected to pay their Sultans a yearly tribute of 18,000 ducats.

On the Guinea Coast of Africa, Monrad records the following custom among the young negresses. The unmarried pluck out their genital hair ; the wives let it grow freely.

Jacobus X. states that the Wolof women shave their genital hair with pieces of glass from broken bottles.

Hutter records occasional shaving in this region after childbirth and after each monthly period among the negresses of Cameroon.

Zache says of the Swaheli women in Tanganyika territory :

" They remove the hair from their genitalia regularly by means of resin from the Mtondôo tree (*Calopgyllum inophyllum*, according to Stuhlmann), which is rubbed into the skin, and then the hairs are pulled out. A more recent and fashionable depilatory is arsenic borrowed from the Arab cosmetic lore. It is applied together with chalk in a paste made with water, and then warm fomentations are applied. This is said to be less painful than tondôo-resin." The phrase used for epilation in the secret speech of the Swahili women is " to sweep the yard clear."

Epp declares that Malay women in the Dutch East Indies depilate themselves so thoroughly that the mons veneris appears quite hairless. But this is not a universal habit among all Malay women, nor have the Chinese women resident in the Malay Peninsula adopted the habit. There are apparently great differences of custom here ; for instance, Maass says that among the inhabitants of the Kuantan District in Central Sumatra, depilation was practised in the armpits " so that they should not look untidy," but not on the genitals, and in both sexes. But in another province of the old kingdom of the Menangkabau, namely, in Kampur-Kiri, there is no depilation in either region. While the Battak (also of Sumatra) pluck out or shave the pubic hair in girls as soon as it appears, according to Hagen.

Jacobs mentions the same customs as occasional among the Achinese women, and Roth among the Dyak women of Borneo, who use little pincers for the purpose.

Stratz says that Javanese women generally depilate themselves, though this is sometimes only partial. He adds that he has observed the same custom among Chinese and Japanese women.

Maurel gives these particulars of the Cambodian women : that the mons veneris was "generally shaved ; but the women who sought the company of Europeans easily gave up the custom."

The Annamese women depilate themselves carefully, so do most of the Cambodian women, according to Jacobus X.,

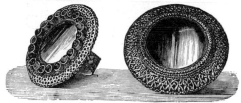

169 .—Indian thumb-rings with mirror (ârsi). (Museum of Ethnology, Berlin.)

who adds that in Southern China (Canton, etc.) it is practised only among prostitutes.

In various parts and provinces of India the custom prevails. Jagor told M. Bartels that rings of a special shape are used for the purpose, and gave two such rings to the Berlin Museum of Ethnology (Fig. 169). These rings are used solely for depilation and for this purpose they are worn on the thumb. They resemble unusually large signet rings with flat sharp-edged discs set with tiny mirrors, which both show the areas in question and reflect the light. The shaving is done with the sharp edges. The name for these rings is *ârsi*.

Rudolph A. Philippi of Santiago collected data from Chile on this subject for M. Bartels. Apparently depilation is not a universal habit, but is confined to special sections of the population.

There is further corroboration in a letter from Mr. A. Hörll, Professor at the State School of Talca in Chile. He was good enough to supply Bartels with the following information (dated November 18th, 1907) :

" During my frequent excursions and wanderings through the territory and settlements of the Chilean Arucanians, I have, so far as I was able to observe, found depilation of the mons to be very frequent, if not general. I have not been able to learn the reason. Apparently, the younger women simply copy their elders in this matter. I was able to see that several girls of about 18 were completely hairless in that region. They simply pluck out the hairs after lying uncovered in the sun for some time."

K. von den Steinen found complete epilation of the mons customary among South American Indian women at the source of the Shingu, among the Trumai, and other tribes.

Hyades and Deniker mention that one of their Fuegian cases had removed the hair from the mons.

Krämer says depilation of the female pubes and armpits is customary in Samoa.

Although practised by the Moslems of the Near East, depilation was not first invented by them. In the ancient civilisations of Asia and Egypt depilation was common; it spread thence to Greece and Italy. Aristophanes tells us that in Hellas depilation was mainly practised by the hetairæ and the brothel prostitutes; but the custom spread to the women of the ordinary upper class in Athenian homes.

170.—Genital tatooing, Ponape.
(After Finsch.)

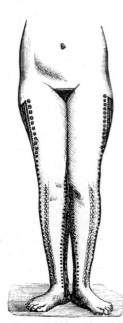

171.—Genital tattooing, Pelew Islands.
(After Kubary.)

In Rome Martial taunted his countrymen with resorting to depilation in order to make themselves appear younger than they were.

Many later writers record the persistence of the habit in Italy, probably for purposes of cleanliness and protection, according to Rosenbaum [who devotes a section to depilation in antiquity].

We may say that, on the whole, the available information tends to show that depilation is generally practised by such peoples and races as are not extremely hairy by nature. Exceptions to this rule are probably ritual in origin, i.e., interwoven with religious or magical concepts.

There are other methods of altering or adorning the genital area. Thus it has been already mentioned that the women of the Bismarck Archipelago dyed both pubic and head hair red.

Finally, we must consider the custom of tattooing the visible portions of the external genitalia. So far as we are aware, this is only done on certain South Sea

Islands.   Both the well-known authorities on Pacific anthropology, Finsch and Kubary, have given accounts of the practice.

Finsch writes that he believes genital tattooing to synchronise with, and confirm adolescence in the district round Hood Bay in New Guinea, but is not certain of this association.

On Ponapé (Caroline Islands), the girls are elaborately tattooed, as described by both Finsch and Kubary (Fig. 170). Kubary described the tattooing process as very prolonged : it starts when the girl is between seven and eight years old. At about 12 the hips and lower abdomen are dealt with.   " The adornment of the genitalia is so intricate and careful that both the labia majora and the vaginal orifice are tattooed."

Kubary continues in these terms about the Pelew Islanders :

" So soon as the girl has intimate relations with men, she is decorated with the indispensable *telengékel*—tattooing (Fig. 171) ; otherwise, no man would ever look at her.   The *telengékel* consists of a triangle which covers the mons veneris, and is bounded by a straight line (*gréel*). The area within the triangle is then filled out with black paint (*ogúttum*) and the base of the triangle which lies uppermost is finished off with a zigzag line. This line is known as *blasak*."

N. von Miklucho-Maclay also mentions the tattooing of the Pelew women.   He says that the mons veneris is filled in with a solid patch of tattooed work ; " that is, there are no special designs, geometrical or animal, on it.   The mons is not tattooed till the menstrual function has been established : parts of the labia majora appear to be tattooed ; at the same time, the genital hair is depilated.   Although the process of tattooing the mons veneris is very painful, I am told it is completed in one afternoon."

172 .—Genital tattooing, Núkuóro.   A sign of sexual maturity.   (After Kubary.)

He adds that the kariut, or short kirtle of pandanus fibres is generally put on so as to show the stars tattooed in rows along the thighs.

Kubary [3] states that the women of Núkuóro (Carolines) are less lavishly tattooed than on the Pelew group and Ponape.   Their tattooing is limited to the mons veneris, and is merely the traced outline of a triangle, whose internal area is left blank.   The two sides are fringed with diagonal lines and the base lies uppermost. Just above the base is a parallel horizontal line with short upturned hooks at either extremity.

" In spite of its sparseness, the tattoo patterns of *Núkuóro* are highly important, for all children born to women who have not been tattooed are put to death.   Tattooing is the sign of maturity and membership of the community of women.   It is, therefore, performed in company and forms one of the chief items of the Takotona festivities " (*cf.* Fig. 172).

N. von Miklucho Maclay's observation confirms Kubary's in a striking manner. He said in a letter to Rudolph Virchow :

That in order to inspect their tattoo patterns, he induced several girls to remove their *kariut* simultaneously, and was reminded of what Virchow said of tattooed nudity elsewhere : " Modesty is not in any way offended by the sight."   At the first glance, the girls seemed to be wearing triangles of some blue textile over the mons veneris.

THE FEMALE BREAST

THE RACIAL DIFFERENCE IN THE BREAST

IN this section of our treatise we have to inquire what are the precise differences, if any, in the structure and appearance of the breasts in various races and ethnic stocks.

The female breasts,* or mammary glands (*mammæ*) in adults, are situated on the thorax between the third and the seventh rib ; they are both sheathed and interwoven with adipose tissue, and it is this fat which largely determines their shape. The single glandular folds or lobes are traversed by strands of dense connec-

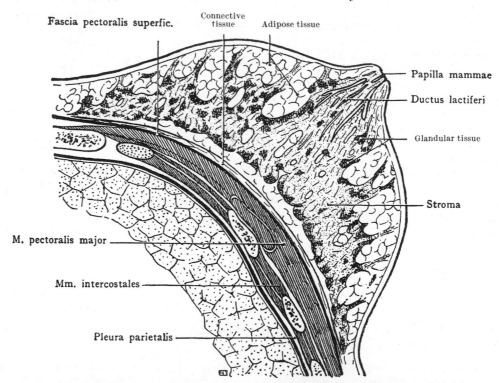

173 .—Sagittal section through the female mammary gland. (After Corning.)

tive tissue. The efferent ducts (*ductus lactiferi*) converge towards a protuberance which is more highly pigmented than the rest of the organs externally. This is the nipple or papilla (Fig. 173). In the prenatal stages of development the breasts

* [*Cf.* the recent study by Gläsmer and Amersbach, and for the lesser known material, see Witkowski and Snoop.]

are first perceptible in the shape of the so-called *linea lactea*, which run vertically backwards. Then the epithelium thickens and forms the milk glands. Milk glands appear among the mammalia (whose special characteristics they are) in two types of formation :

(1) As a row of small glands.
(2) As single large glands.

The linea lactea varies in position among the mammals. In primates and mankind it is in the thorax ; in the mare and cow nearer the hindquarters on the abdomen. In Fig. 174 a human embryo of 13·5 mm. length is depicted so as to show the *linea lactea* or *crista lactea*. The dots show where the gland will develop ; in

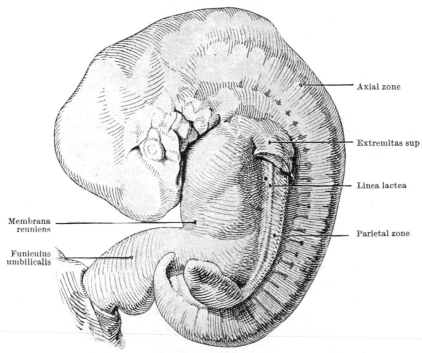

Axial zone

Extremitas sup

Linea lactea

Parietal zone

Membrana reuniens

Funiculus umbilicalis

174.—Crista lactea in a human embryo of 13·5 mm. (After Kollmann.)

most animal species there are multiple glands ; in mankind normally only two, one on either side of the thorax. But there may be accessory or supernumerary mammary glands in human beings. A. v. d. Heide finds three main structural types among these supernumerary glands.

(1) *Micromammæ*. These have all the characteristic qualities and parts of a mammary gland ; they have glandular tissue, ducts and papillæ, but all of small size.

(2) *Hyperthelia*. Supernumerary nipples, which have neither glandular tissue nor ducts.

(3) *Subcutaneous forms*. Consisting wholly of glandular tissue. The investigator (A. v. d. Heide) only found 35 cases of these and all were situated in the armpit. He takes these to be highly differentiated sudoriferous glands, which have been influenced by pregnancy.

The adjoined illustrations show the later development of the mammæ in the embryo. Fig. 175 A shows the thickened raised area of the ectoderm.

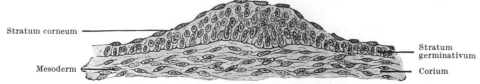

175 A.—Crista lactea in a human embryo of 13·5 mm. Stage 1. (After Kollmann.)

Fig. 175 B shows the second stage of growth, the local proliferation of the cells of the *stratum granulosum*; and

Fig. 175 C shows that the gland has spread from the ectoderm downwards to

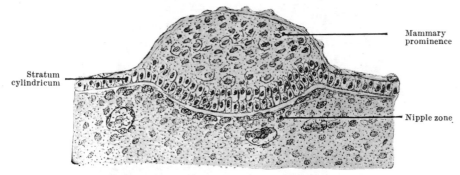

175 B.—Anlage of the mammary gland. Stage 2. Lenticular anlage.

the mesoderm and formed a pit. In the next stage (Fig. 175 D), we see two processes forming in the corium; and, as a final process we see an expanding glandular

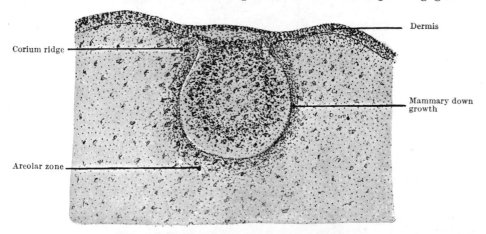

175 C.—Bulb-shaped anlage. Stage 3. Eight weeks.

structure and several secondary processes ramifying into the stroma. It may be added that Fig. 175 C is of the formation in an embryo of eight weeks, and Fig. 175 D of a later stage, when the embryo has reached 11 cm. in length.

The *area mammæ* is typical of the primates, but very slight in some anthropoids. According to H. Friedenthal, it is largest in the European races and in the Australian aborigines.

Friedenthal first observed a perceptible domed *nipple* among primates in a

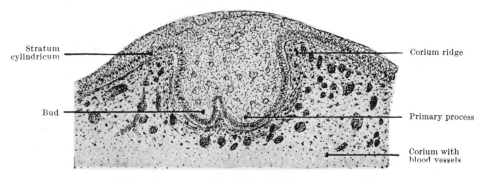

Stratum cylindricum

Corium ridge

Bud

Primary process

Corium with blood vessels

175D.—Process-producing period.   Stage 4.   11 cm.

young female chimpanzee in the Berlin Zoological Gardens at the age corresponding to puberty. It resembled somewhat the stage of development known as *mamma areolata* in human beings. Moreover, the supernumerary glands in the axilla are now known not to be a wholly human feature. In 1909 Brinkmann recorded cases in a gorilla and a chimpanzee. In one male chimpanzee and one female of about five years, this accessory gland lay in the deepest hollow of the armpit under a thick tuft of hair; and in a young gorilla there was an unmistakable rudimentary anomaly of this kind. M. Bartels, however, found no such symptoms in any orang or hylobates.

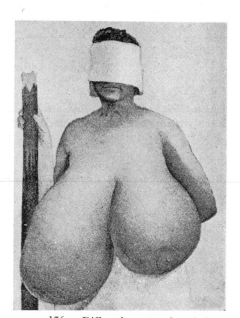

176.—Diffuse hypertrophy of the breast.   (After Warren.)

A well known and very frequent anomaly is *asymmetry* of the breasts, one side being much larger than the other. Variot and Lassablière made investigations and tabulations on 550 French wet nurses. They found that the left mammary gland was the larger in 51 per cent. of the cases, the right in 25 per cent., and that the two were equal in only 24 per cent. The milk capacity of the glands was proportionate to their variation in size. This discrepancy is doubtless partly due to the habit of the nurses of offering the left side first to the baby, but is also in some cases hereditary. Mme. Pellut Edwards found greater size of the left breast in more than half the cases of girls she investigated (55 per cent. of 51 total). Koeher has also found hereditary factors in mammary development. He records hypertrophy of both breasts in a 12-year-old girl, in whom menstruation had not yet appeared. Both breasts were as large as a man's head; and this extraordinary characteristic had appeared also in the girl's mother, maternal grandmother and great aunt. But, at later stages of growth, the breasts diminished and assumed normal proportions.

[Gould and Pyle record a number of instances of diffuse hypertrophy of the breast. In one case a girl of 14 had breasts weighing 259 oz. ; a woman of 30 had breasts weighing 52 lbs. In another case the breasts of a girl of 15 had circumferences of 94 cm. and 105 cm. respectively ; whilst in a woman of 26 the right breast hung down to the anterior superior iliac spine. In several tribes the native women fling the breasts over their shoulders when occasion demands (*cf.* also, Labbarque, Kohlgrüber, Lemuet, Pasquier.)]

As long ago as 1872 Dr. Heinrich Ploss indicated the importance of mammary structure in comparative anatomy and anthropology. The French anthropologists in the " Instructions " have also made an attempt to differentiate and classify the characteristic structural types in a clear and graphic manner. They say of the breasts in women :

" Elles sont tantôt hémisphériques, tantôt plus ou moins pendantes, tantôt piriformes, c'est-à-dire, en forme de poire."

But these categories are not comprehensive enough, or sufficiently graphic to replace any pictorial representations or more detailed descriptions. Nor do they exhaust all possible mammary shapes and types. Of recent years much more has been learnt in Europe of the coloured races, and photography has been developed and used by anthropologists to a wide extent. We are, therefore, in a position to affirm that there are actually ethnical differences in the shape of the breasts in women.

Hyrtl, was formerly of the opinion that " the breasts are hemispherical* only among the white and yellow races when in their compact virginal state ; in negresses, equally young and equally normal, they are more elongated, tapering, drooping (with a slight outward angle) and, in short, udder-like."

We must not forget, however, that even in one and the same individual the breasts pass through various phases of development of very different kind. Thus, in making any pronouncements on racial characteristics of the breasts, we should take into careful consideration the stage of life or physical condition of the individuals in question.

In every race the breasts of nulliparæ are distinctly different from those who have borne children and especially from those who have suckled more than one child. Lactation elongates the breasts to a greater or lesser degree, and is only too apt to render them wrinkled, slack, mis-shapen and of irregular contour. Advancing years, moreover, often turn them into mere flaps or folds of skin or even obliterate them, leaving only the nipple in token of their former site. It is one of the unaccomplished tasks of anthropology to decide and define the approximate average date and duration of these changes and the degree they attain in the various ethnical and sociological groups.

We are also ignorant of many of the details of the transition from the puerile or neutral phase of childhood to the typical feminine structure. Here, too, there are many differences.

As a rule, in dealing with racial differences in this region, we shall refer to their youthful or virginal condition in girls and young women in full sexual maturity

---

* [In the English-speaking countries it may be said broadly that the hemispherical type of breast is the general standard of beauty. When the nipple is erect there is slight tendency to the conical when viewed laterally. The breasts do not simply rest upon the front of the body. They rest horizontally both in front and at the sides, so that in the ideal form the nipples appear as if they were straining away from one another.]

and undeformed by the effects of parturition and nursing. Even so there are many differences in the different races and individuals.

One of the first distinctive features in the mounds of the breasts is their setting : do they rise suddenly from a comparatively flat surface, or do they gently swell upward in a gradual outward curve from the collar bone ? We must also consider their position : whether high or low on the thorax and whether nearer the median line of the body or more lateral and closer to the armpits. And their most significant characteristics are their size, their consistency or texture, and their shape.

Special attention should be paid to the nipples and to the areas immediately surrounding these, the so-called areolæ, which, as M. Bartels has pointed out, are also full of fine shades of individual difference. Indeed, neither the " Instructions anthropologiques générales," mentioned above, nor the " Eléments d'Anthropologie générale," by Topinard, have adequate suggestions for classification in these respects. It is indisputably one of Max Bartels' great services to the sciences of anatomy and ethnology that he both grasped the main differences and illustrated them in these studies.

His classification has not been superseded, nor can it be improved.

He distinguished four mammary types according to size :

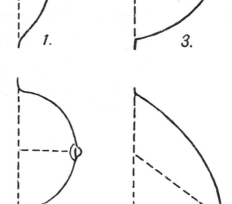

177.—Schematic representation of mammary shapes.

1. Bowl-shaped.   2. Hemispherical.
3. Conical.   4. Elongated.

(1) Highly developed or exuberant.
(2) Full.
(3) Moderate.
(4) Small, slight or flat.

Three according to consistency :

(1) Firm (erect).
(2) Soft (relaxed, drooping).
(3) Flabby (pendulous).

Four according to shape :
(1) Bowl-shaped, in which the height is less than the radius of their circumference.

(2) Hemispherical, in which the height is equal to the radius of their circumference.

(3) Conical, in which the height is greater than the radius.

(4) Elongated, as in the udder of the goat, and with nipples pointing downwards.

The fact must not be overlooked that drooping or even pendulous breasts may owe this quality as much to their conical shape as to their slack texture. Piriform breasts may be as firm as bowl-shaped or hemispherical. Moreover, the firmest breasts are inclined to droop somewhat in certain bodily postures, e.g., when stooping or lying on one side.

[Jayle has distinguished nine varieties of breast, the globular or hemispherical (*sein en globe ou globuliforme*) ; the conical (*sein conique*) ; the apple-shaped (*sein en pomme*), which corresponds perhaps to the bowl-shaped of Bartels ; the piriform (*sein en poire ou piriforme*) ; the *sein à tête de brioche*, by which is understood the breast which is surmounted by a prominent hemispherical areola ; the flattened

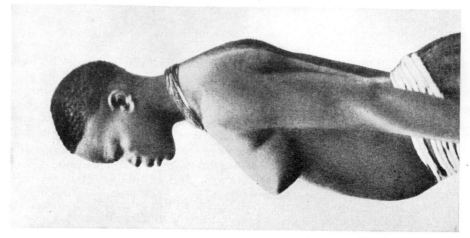

178 c.—Magungo with conical breasts.
(Photo, R. Buchta.)

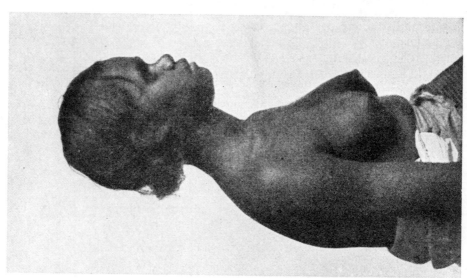

178 b.—Australian with hemispherical breasts.
(Photo, C. Günther, Berlin.)

178 a.—Hindu with bowl-shaped breasts.
(Photo, C. Günther, Berlin.)

(*sein en galette*) ; the flat (*sein plat*), where there is little perceptible elevation ; the flat-nippled (*sein platythèle*), and the endothelic (*sein endothèle*) in which the nipple is retracted.

It will be observed that Jayle's classification does not confine itself to the *breasts*, but includes variations in the areola and nipple.   Thus it is not so convenient as those which strictly confine themselves to the individual parts.   On the other hand Jayle is right in insisting on the *normal* condition of the breasts at various

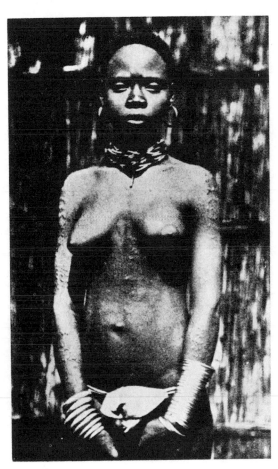

179 A.—Niam-Niam with elongated breasts.   (Photo, R. Buchta.)

ages, a point which we have also discussed in examining the vulva.   His account also is valuable in its discussion of the aspect of the various parts of the body in different positions.]

Asymmetry of the breasts has already been mentioned, and is apparently frequent among coloured races, as was observed by R. Burton in the Yoruba Territory on the Niger ; by P. and F. Sarasin among the Vedda of Ceylon ; and by Ling Roth, who records the case of a young Tasmanian whose right breast was fully and normally developed while the left was quite flat.   Max Bartels has stated that mammary asymmetry must have been frequently found in ancient India, for

" unequal breasts " were, according to Schmidt, among the physical qualities which suitors were warned against in young girls. This asymmetry also is marked in two of Falkenstein's photographs of Loango negresses, and also in one of a Herero woman (South-West Africa). P. Bartels found the same, to an unusual degree, in a photograph taken by Seiner (Fig. 146) of a Bushwoman and of an Australian black by Kerry (Fig. 181).

Mammary asymmetry, both in size and shape, occurs also in women of white

179 B.—Lepcha (N. India) with elongated breasts.

race. Rothe found 23 such cases of difference in shape among 1000 North German women, but there was never any great variation in this respect. Asymmetries of size were much more frequent, namely, in 38·3 per cent. of the cases ; and in 31·3 of these the left breast was the larger ; only seven had larger right breasts. The same kind of results were found by Variot and Lassablière in their examination of French countrywomen who were wet nurses. In 550 cases 24 per cent. showed equality in size, whilst in 50 per cent. the left breast was larger than the right, and in 25 per cent. the reverse. Variot, Lassablière and Rothe believe this is due to the right-handedness of the majority of women and the method of holding babies.

Brehm recorded the observation that in the Sudan, the babies and young children, riding on their mothers' hips, drew down one breast and thus elongated it.

Buschan and Mme. Pellut Edwards believe asymmetry hereditary, and confirmed the greater size of the left breast in most cases.

In 21 out of his 1000 cases Rothe found excessive asymmetry. In 57·14 per cent. of these 21 the left breast was of moderate size, the right small ; in 19·05 per cent. the left full and the right moderate ; in 9·53 per cent. the right full and the

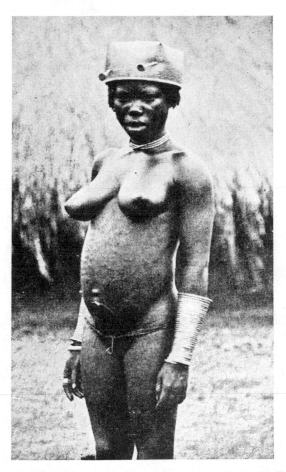

179 c.—Niam-Niam with elongated breasts.   (Photo, R. Buchta.)

left moderate ; 4·76 per cent. had exuberant right breast and full left, and the same number had the right moderate in size and the left small, or the left very full and the right full.   In 80·95 per cent. the left breast was the larger, and in only 19·5 per cent. the right (*cf.* Figs. 177 ff.).

Exact and numerous measurements of individuals, as distinct from descriptions of the general impression produced by whole races, photographic material, and especially casts would contribute helpfully to our knowledge of comparative anthropology in this direction.

As a rule, it is probable that early sexual maturity—as is frequent in the tropics

180.—Sicilian with large areolæ.   (Photo, v. Gloeden, Taormina.)

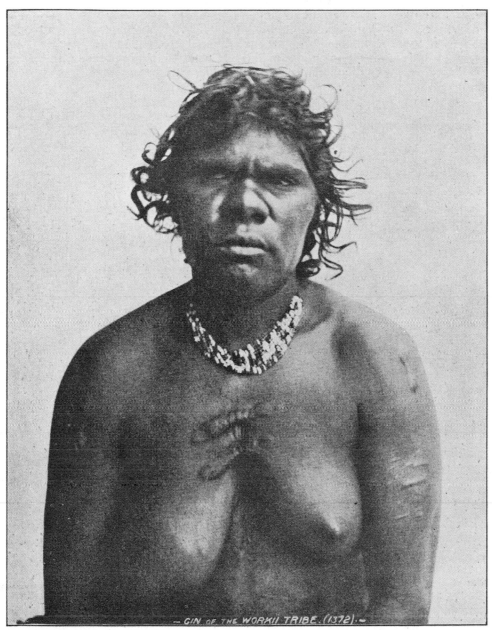

181.—Woman from North Australia with asymmetry of breasts. (Photo, Kerry, Sydney.)

—coincides with the early expansion and the early involution of the mammary glands.

THE AREOLA OF THE NIPPLES

The differences in the areola seem rather more individual variations than ethnical characteristics; nevertheless, there are undoubtedly also racial tendencies.

The areolæ vary in size, in colour and in shape. The skin which covers them is, in all cases, thinner and more delicate than that of the main mass of the glands.

Among European women the areolæ are pale or deep pink in blondes ; and in women of dark complexion they may have a brownish tint or even a line so dusky as to approach black. Little is known of these variations in colour among the yellow and black races.

The areolæ vary greatly in size, but in the same individual they are generally bilaterally symmetrical. Their outer circumference is generally circular, more rarely oval or ellipsoid. The average diameter of the areola is from 2 to 4 cm., but a larger size does not necessarily imply previous pregnancy. A case known to

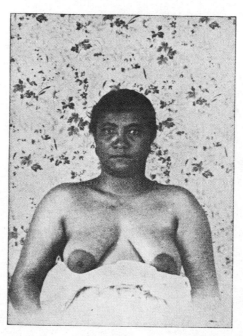

182 .—Hawaiian with very large areolæ. (Photo, R. Neuhauss.)

M. Bartels in Berlin was that of a young girl, a virgin between 18 and 20 years old, with full breasts and areolæ of unusual size, their diameter being between 6–7 cm.

[In the accompanying photographs various forms of areolæ are depicted. Fig. 180 shows a large type of areola in a Sicilian, whilst Fig. 194 shows a girl from the same locality in which the areolæ are somewhat small. Fig. 182 shows a woman from Hawaii in whom the areolæ are unusually large.]

The areola is not always sharply outlined in its circumference ; there are occasionally narrow-pointed edges which have almost a jagged appearance like a star. But, as a rule, the circumference is clearly defined by the difference of colour between the elevation of the breast and the more highly pigmented areola and nipple. Sometimes the areola is surrounded by a ridge of minute rounded projections set in a circle. These are collections of cutaneous glands and are termed *tubercula areolæ* (*cf.* Fig. 183 , and also Pl. XLVI. in Ellwood and Yerbury).

Natanson and Goldschmidt found two distinct kinds of *tubercula areolæ* : " Careful inspection with the aid of magnifying glasses showed that some of these

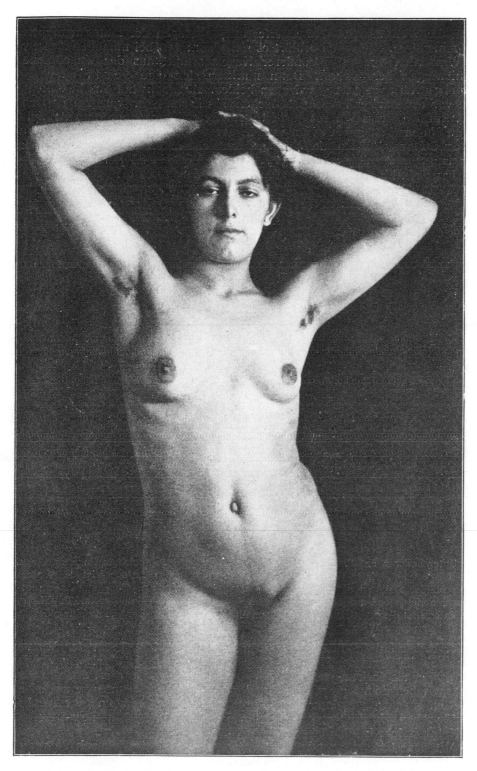

183 .—Sicilian showing rings of tubercula areolæ.   (Photo, v. Gloeden, Taormina.)

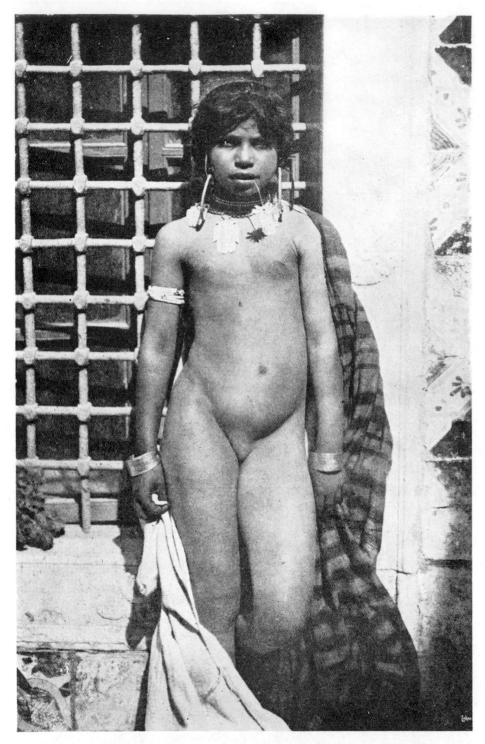

183 A.—Commencement of the development of the breasts in a Tunisian girl. (After Lehnert and Landrock.)

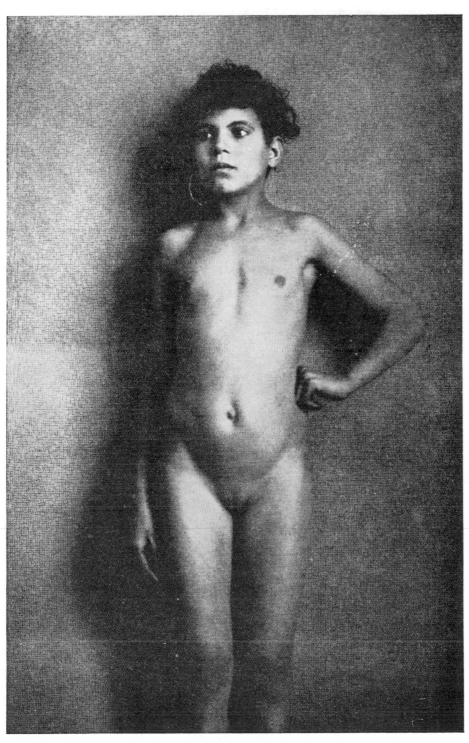

183 B.—Early stage of bowl-shaped breasts in a Tunisian girl.   (After Lehnert and Landrock.)

18 3 c.—Firm resilient breasts in a Tunisian. (After Lehnert and Landrock.)

183 D.—Early stage of pendent breasts in a Tunisian. (After Lehnert and Landrock.)

little nodules were of the kind found in both sexes and in all ages ; these are termed
' *tubercula Morgagni* ' ; they are rounded in form and always contain sebaceous

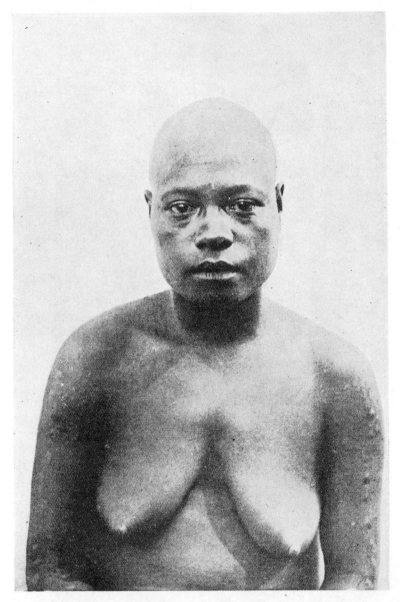

183 E.—Pendent breasts in a woman of 20 years from the Admiralty Islands. (Photo,
Mus. f. Völkerk., Dresden.)

glands which may have hairs growing from them and sudoriferous glands as well.
The other type of nodule is peculiar to the female breast and develops chiefly under
the influence of pregnancy ; they are larger and more sharply ridged, and are known
as ' *tubercula Montgomery*.'   Their structure is more complicated and diverse than

the former; they may contain accessory milk lobules or combinations of milk globules, sudoriferous glands, sebaceous glands with hairs, or only lacteal ducts

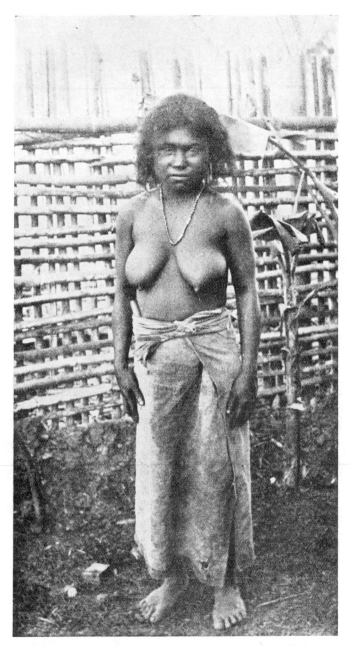

183 F.—A Negritto-girl with pendent breasts.   (After Schadenberg.)

rising from the base of the mammæ and sometimes combined with the accessory lacteal ducts."

184 .—Sicilian with raised and sharply defined areolæ.   Frequent form in Southern Europe
due possibly to racial admixture.

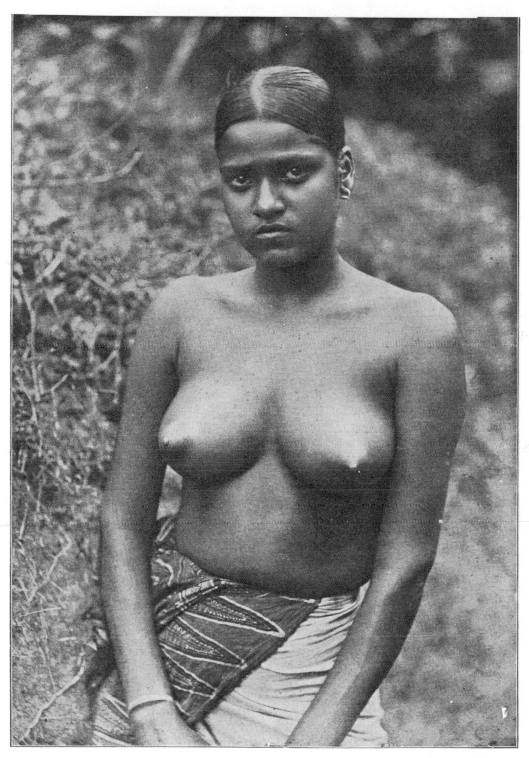

185.—Rodiya girl (Ceylon).   (Photo, F. Heger, Vienna.)

The shape of the areola is generally circular, but the manner in which it forms a part of the breast is varied and full of individual differences.   M. Bartels distinguished :

(1) *Disc-shaped Areolæ.* These are the prevalent form among European women.   They may be slightly raised as though the nipple rested on a tiny plate or boss, circular in shape, and raised a couple of millimetres, from the elevation

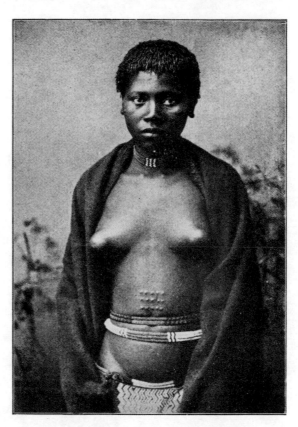

186 .—Case of unusually prominent rounded nipples, Natal.   (After Joest.)

of the breast.   Such raised aerolæ are found with a certain frequency among Spaniards and Sicilians (*cf.* Fig. 184).

(2) *Cup-shaped Areolæ.*   In certain coloured races the areolæ are segments of a sphere which is added to the larger hemisphere of the breast itself.   The young girl of the white race passes through this phase of formation in her development from the puerile to the mature stages of growth.   This form of areola may be large or small according to the individual.

(3) *Hemispherical Areolæ.*   It may be that the curve of the areola does not correspond with that of the breast beneath it and may form an independent protuberance with a sharply defined ring-shaped border.   A. Bloch, in a lecture to the Anthropological Society of Paris, described this type very aptly as " *l'auréole en relief.*"   It is found in Africa and Oceania, and among various Arab peoples (*cf.* Figs. 280 and 185).

G. Fritsch   drew attention to the prominence of the areola as an ethnic characteristic. He says of the women of the Ama-Xosa : " The nipple is not so developed and prominent as in Europeans, but the whole areola projects beyond the mammary elevation, having the papilla in its centre.   The child, when suckling, takes the whole areola between its lips like a sponge rather than a nipple."

(4) *Almost Spherical Areolæ.*   These are an exaggeration of the last-mentioned formation ; the basis of the areola, where it meets the main portion of the breast being smaller than its greatest circumference.   Krämer calls this the bottle-gourd

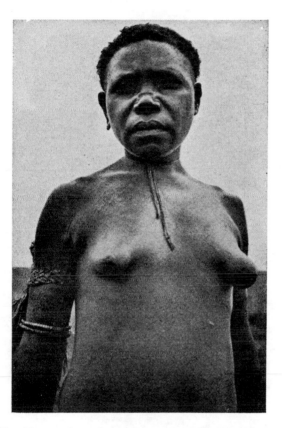

187 .—Breast of gourd type (New Guinea).   (After Neuhauss.)

form (Fig. 186 ; *cf.* Pl. II in " Negro Types ").   Among the most marked examples of this formation are the Papuan girl from New Guinea, photographed by Neuhauss (Fig. 187), and the Vedda woman from Ceylon (Fig. 188), in whom there almost appear two sets of mammæ, the upper being the areolæ.

[The evidence is not satisfactory enough, I think, to justify the inclusion of this areola among the recognised types.   It is very rare, and I have doubts as to its normal character.   Fig. 187 shows a girl of 20 from Quampu at the foot of Cromwell Mountain in New Guinea.   The breast may be said to be of the bottle-gourd type, but the areola is not over-developed, as can be seen from the right breast. Moreover, the example from Ceylon (Fig. 188) cited in the text does not illustrate Krämer's type.   It is certainly unusual and anomalous.]

THE FEMALE NIPPLE

In normal cases the nipple should rise up from the centre of the mammary gland. This natural formation, however, is injured or impaired in many young girls by tight and unhygienic clothing or (in the past more than to-day) by tight

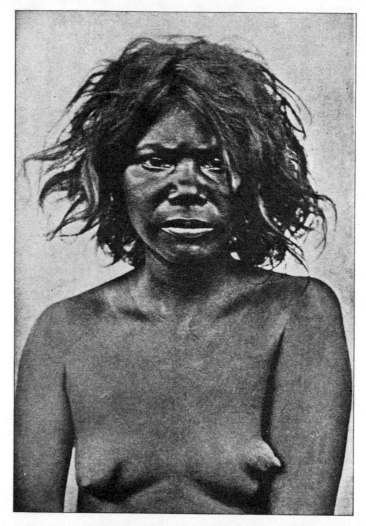

188 .—Unusual form of nipple in a Vedda (Ceylon).   (Photo, Saraisin.)

corsets, which constrict the breasts and flatten the nipples into their surface so that there may be not only a flat surface but an actual depression.

The total obliteration of both nipples has been recorded in one case by Kleinwächter :

The individual in question was a well-developed girl 23 years of age, of completely normal femininity in her general physique, but she had never menstruated and internal examination showed incomplete development of the genital tract and the labia, though the pubic hair was normal in amount and arrangement. Her breasts were of normal size for her years, but there was no nipple on either breast. On both sides was a rosy pink areola about as large as a florin, quite level with the surrounding skin, and there were no orifices of lacteal ducts or any such indications. This case is of some significance, for in other cases of pronounced infantilism of the genital tract, both breasts and pubic hair are very slightly developed as a rule. But in this girl the breasts probably consisted wholly of adipose tissue without glands and ducts. Thus, we have another proof that well-proportioned breasts do not necessarily imply the presence of normal glandular arrangement.

In the majority of women, however, the nipple rises from the areola, though even before pregnancy and lactation have left their traces there are very great

189 .—Phalangeal form of nipple, Guiana.

differences in its shape. We shall deal in a later chapter with these effects of pregnancy and lactation, and refer here mainly to the differences between nulliparæ.

M. Bartels has suggested the classification of mammillary forms into the conical (or cylindrical) or the circular (boss-shaped) ; the latter may be either flat or hemispherical.

If the last-named type is an extreme example, its base may appear constricted and thus an almost spherical mammilla may crown a globular or projecting areola, as described in the previous section (cf. Figs. 190 and 191). Another form is cylindrical or conical, and if the length is much greater than the basic diameter, we have a nipple which resembles a finger joint (cf. Figs. 192 and 193).

The size of the nipple, according to Max Bartels, has the following distinct gradations :

(1) Depressed.
(2) Flat or obliterated.
(3) Small.
(4) Moderate.
(5) Large.

Regarding shape, the same authority distinguished :

(1) Imperceptible, merging into areola.
(2) Boss-shaped or knob-shaped.
(3) Low cylindrical.
(4) Hemispherical.
(5) Conical.
(6) Phalangeal.*

Hörschelmann has made a careful anthropological study of the Esthonian woman and his classification is more detailed :

(1) Prominent and knob-shaped.
(2) Flat and knob-shaped.
(3) Small button-shaped.
(4) Conical.
(5) Phalangeal or cylindrical.
(6) Bifurcated with a longitudinal depression or a central " dimple."
(7) Retracted or depressed.†

He deals in some detail with mammillary furrows and depressions.   He says :

" I was at first inclined to attribute these irregularities to the pressure of clothing, especially of the upper rims of corsets, but I became convinced that there must be other reasons when I found the dimples and furrows in young Russian girls from the fishing villages on Lake Peipus where corsets are wholly unknown.   The real cause is a form of arrested development, for mammillary furrows and depressions are generally found in very young persons together with the very flat shapes and small sizes.   These develop later and merge into other forms in the older girls and in multiparæ.   The case of the deeply wrinkled nipples (called, in German popular speech, *Dornenbrüste*) is quite different.   I saw very few such irregularities on the nipple among the Esthonian peasant girls, but many more among the German women in Livonia.   It is possible, but not certain, that the pressure of tight clothing has some influence here.   The exact opposite of this furrowed nipple is the dainty, conical tip which seems to belong to very highly organised individuals (and races ?).   In itself, it is rare ; among the Esthonian nulliparæ, I found it in not more than 10 per cent.   But this percentage increased greatly when observations were limited to the physical *élite* among them.   In one year, I found this conical type among 15 out of 20 of the most comely and attractive girls.   Among the prostitute class it did not appear once.

The primitive looking phalangeal form increases in percentage in the older women ; but is always rare in nulliparæ and only frequent among multiparæ and the middle aged.   In early youth, the only girls with nipples of phalangeal type were of heavy, plain, and rather coarse appearance.

* [It would appear that in discussing these various types of nipple it is understood that the nipple in its ordinary condition is being considered and not the same in erection.   An almost flat nipple may become conical or even phalangeal when erect.   This condition increases the difficulty of classification and should not be overlooked in future inquiries.   For an account of the mechanism of erection in the female breasts, see Schumacher.]

† [It is not generally realised that the medical man distinguishes between a *retracted* and a *depressed* nipple.   In the former case contraction takes place from within, *retracting* the nipple : in the second the nipple has not even projected in the normal manner.]

The retracted nipples are those which lie beneath the level of the surrounding areola as though in a cavity. According to M. Duncan, in the pregnant, they are the result of lactiferous engorgement in the case of some women. Fitzwilliams, who speaks of 'inverted' or 'umbilical' nipples regards this as due to some abnormal condition in the muscular tissue in and around the areola."

It is regrettable that exact and reliable data are so rare as to be almost unavailable as regards the shape and size of the breasts in women of coloured races. There

190 .—Hemispherical nipples, Igorrot. (Mus. f. Völkerk., Dresden.)

are indications, however, that more attention is being paid to these matters, whilst in the case of Europeans some useful results have already been obtained.

For example, Dr. Fritz Rothe carried out investigations and recorded measurements on the material which his professional work in Luckenwalde (Mark Brandenburg) offered him. The number of individuals studied was 1000, and the work was done fairly thoroughly and we shall refer to his comprehensive results in the following section. There is also the dissertation by Hörschelmann, who worked at the Institute of Anatomy, Dorpat. Some of Martin's pupils have also done anthropological work on the breasts : thus, Sara Teumin measured Russian, Polish and Jewish women, and Dina Jochelson-Brodsky did the same for members of various North-Eastern Siberian indigenous tribes. Among the points noted by them, we may mention the absolute and relative distances between the nipples and their distance from other bodily regions and points. When the preliminary data are completed, we may perhaps find racial

191.—Hemispherical nipples, Tinguiane, Philippine Islands.   (Mus. f. Völkerk., Dresden.)

characteristics in certain of these measurements. Finally, and working on lines devised by
himself, M. Lipiez, with 340 cases, has represented and depicted the evolution of mammary
structure both absolutely and in relation to the whole development of the feminine organism at
puberty ; and came to the conclusion that the breasts take a longer time to develop their full
maturity than the other sexual characteristics, beginning earlier and terminating later.

Menstruation set in in every case between 12 and 16, whilst the development of the breasts continued till 18.

The population of the European Continent has been sifted to and fro, and in the course of time has been so thoroughly intermingled that no nation can now justly claim purity of racial descent. History has sought in vain to distinguish the genetic components of these various national blends, for crossing began centuries before recorded history. It is the task of anthropological science to come to the help of history. The investigation and comparison of shape of skulls, colour of skins,

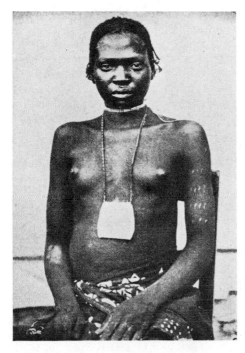

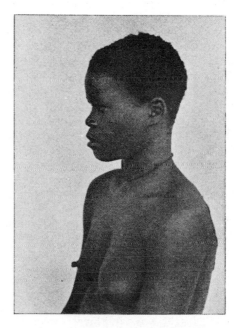

192.—Bari woman. (After Friedenthal.)

193. Loango negress with nipples of phalangeal type. (Photo, Falkenstein.)

hair, eyes, and especially and most recently, of blood groups, have already extended our knowledge and stimulated our enquiries.

Thus we are, perhaps, already in a position to maintain that there are genuine and definite racial characteristics in the breasts of women.

THE BREASTS OF EUROPEAN WOMEN

We must now again refer to the investigations and results of F. Rothe, who studied the breasts of 1000 women of North German nationality. His results may be said to form a basis for comparison with other anthropological and anthropometrical material. Rothe's investigations were begun at Max Bartels' suggestion and based on the divisions and definitions first suggested in an earlier edition of the present work.

The women studied by Rothe belonged to a somewhat limited group. Slightly over three-quarters of the total number were Brandenburg Prussians by descent;

the remainder came from other provinces of North Germany. Rothe carefully noted stature and complexion in all cases, as these may give indications of other ethnical mixtures. Moreover, he also recorded whether the women had had children and if so how many, also the number of lactations, social status and profession, age and nourishment. Thus the investigator carefully avoided the risk of attributing sociological results or the effects of age to racial factors only, as well as obtaining facts relative to sociological and functional influences.

We will first summarise Rothe's results as to the structure and shape of the breasts.

8·3 per cent. of these women had bowl-shaped breasts ; 16·2 per cent. cup-shaped, 51·2 per cent. hemispherical, 21·4 per cent. conical, and in only 2·9 per cent. were there examples of the " goat's udder " type. The determinant factors, according to Rothe, are primarily age and nutrition, whether sufficiently or under-nourished ; and then the influences of pregnancy and lactation. The hemispherical breasts are those of well-fed youth, unaffected as yet by the changes of pregnancy and lactation ; the disc-shaped, flat breasts are those of underfed women ; and the conical form is attributed to repeated maternity or to excessive malnutrition or its reverse.

There is a curious correlation between shape and colouring in one respect : the goat's udder shape (2·9 per cent.) was found mainly in women with light hair and eyes (that is in 82·76 per cent.), while 13·9 per cent. were light haired and dark eyed, and only 3·45 per cent. dark in both eyes and hair).

The size depended mainly on the condition of nourishment, which even masked the effect of pregnancy. As a rule, the breasts of parous women were smaller than those of women who had not borne children. This was an unexpected result, which Rothe believes due to the better nutritive state of the women who had not been mothers. On the other hand, the material shows the influence of lactation in enlarging the breasts in an unmistakable manner.

The correlations with stature and colouring are significant, though less frequent.

Three hundred and twenty-seven women out of the total 1000 are described as tall in stature ; of these 15·6 per cent. had very highly developed breasts. Among the 549 women of middle height, these full breasts were found in 10·93 per cent. and in 8·87 per cent. of the 124 small women. The " full " and " moderate " types of development did not vary much with general bodily·height, but small or flat breasts were much the most frequent among small women (28·23 per cent.), although some of these women may have been immature.

The correlations between sizes and complexions are as follows :

The women with fair hair and dark eyes had the largest percentage of the most highly developed breasts : i.e., 13·48 per cent. Then in order came the fair haired and light eyed—12·63 per cent. ; the dark haired and light eyed, 10·72 per cent., and the dark haired and dark eyed, 8·25 per cent.

Of the breasts of " full " type—the second grade of size—the fair haired and light eyed women had the largest percentage—57·75 per cent. ; the light haired and dark eyed, 35·96 per cent. ; the dark haired and light eyed, 35·71 per cent. ; and, finally, the dark haired and dark eyed, 29·90 per cent. The moderate size was most common among the dark haired and dark eyed women—43·3 per cent. ; next among fair haired and light eyed—34 per cent. ; next among the light haired and dark eyed—32·58 per cent. ; and, finally, among the dark haired and light eyed—17·86 per cent.

The overwhelmingly greatest frequency of small flat breasts was among the women with dark hair and light eyes—35·17 per cent. ; then follow the dark haired and dark eyed with 18·35 per cent. ; then the fair haired and dark eyed with 17·98 per cent. ; and, finally, the fair haired and light eyed had this formation in 15·64 per cent. cases.

We may conclude that functional and sociological influences are complicated by congenital factors affecting the whole individual organism.   Tall women had, as a rule, the largest development, and those with fair hair accompanied by light coloured or dark eyes had larger breasts than those with dark hair and light eyes, and above all those with dark hair and dark eyes.   These results are not due to chance, but are probably largely ethnical and racial.

The texture and firmness of the breasts depend primarily on functional experience ; that is, on gestation and suckling.   The breasts of a mother gradually tend to lose the erect elasticity of youth.

Rothe's statistics show no special correlation between colouring and consistency ; and he makes no special sub-division between mothers and nulliparæ in the figures as quoted.   In order to obtain results correlating the general pigmentation and consistency of the mammary glands, nulliparæ only should be considered.

The nipples showed considerable variations in size, which are mainly, no doubt, due to pregnancy and suckling, but appear also not unconnected with general colouring.   As a rule, women with light eyes had more developed nipples than dark eyed women, but both the largest individual nipples and the smallest number of little nipples were found among women with fair hair and dark eyes.

Their structure was, of course, mainly affected by lactation, which not only enlarges the mammillæ but alters their shape, making the conical form more boss-like or even phalangeal.

In the following sets of figures, the first (a) refers to women who have not borne children, the second (b) to women who have borne but not suckled them ; and the third (c) to women who have both borne and suckled.

	Percentage.		
	a	b	c
Knob-shaped . .	31·0	52·0	62·0
Cone-shaped . .	57·0	38·0	27·0
Low cylindrical . .	30·0	7·9	2·7
Phalangeal . .	0·89	1·5	7·36

The colour of the nipples varied as follows : red in 30 per cent., dusky brown in 27 per cent., reddish brown in 20 per cent., rose pink in 15 per cent., and pale brown in 6·7 per cent.   The paler shades predominate up till 18 years of age ; pregnancy darkens the nipple but, apparently, lactation turns the colour paler again.   There seems to be some connection with general pigmentation, for the red and pale shades are more frequent in blonde women and the brown in dark women.

The areola is greatly increased in dimensions during pregnancy, but not, according to Rothe, by the subsequent lactation.   On the contrary, he formed the opinion that parous women who had not nursed their children had much oftener exceptionally large or normally large areolæ than mothers who had nursed.   Moreover, the areola expands with middle life.   In the fair haired women, the large and exceptionally large areolæ were much more frequent than in the dark haired, whose areolæ were generally of moderate or small dimensions.

In shape the areolæ were classified as follows :

Disc-shaped, 61·8 per cent. ; bowl-shaped, 33·3 per cent. ; hemispherical, 4·9 per cent. ; spherical, 27·4 per cent. The bowl-shaped and the hemispherical nipples are those of youth, whilst the disc-shaped is that found in maturity and in advancing years. The spherical type of areola is almost exclusively found in quite young persons ; 50 per cent. of those with this formation were in their 15th year ; and from 45 to 47 per cent. between 16 and 19 ; about 30 per cent. of the cases between 20 and 25 ; very few over 30, and none over 45. Moreover, the spherical areola occurred more often in blondes than in brunettes.

Age influences the pigmentation of the areola and gestation and lactation deepen its hue. Dark complexioned women have, naturally, more often dusky areolæ, but on the whole general colouring does not seem to influence the areolæ to any great extent.

[A more recent series of observations of the breasts were made by Amalie Rhiel on Freiburg students between 17 and 33. One hundred and eighty-three were examined, and of these 45·86 per cent. exhibited firm erect breasts ; 8·3 per cent. possessed breasts which could almost be termed erect ; 23·68 per cent. had breasts inclined to sag ; and 22·65 per cent. had definitely pendulous breasts. In 8 cases the left breast was lower than the right. Measurements were attempted according to the method recommended by Martin (*Lehrbuch*, 198), and an approximation as to size is given. Eleven cases had very small breasts ; 29 small, 89 moderate, 42 large, and 4 very large. The nipples showed the usual variations. In 32 per cent. these were flat ; in 17·71 per cent. conical ; in 12 per cent. cylindrical ; in 20 per cent. low conical ; in 11·43 per cent. low cylindrical ; and in 6·86 per cent. a mixed form between conical and cylindrical. The goat's udder type is not mentioned.

In their studies of American college students Wilder and Pfeiffer made no attempt to classify the breasts, and it is probable that the majority of the measurements were made upon subjects clad in bathing suits . This method, we are told, " often renders feasible an extensive study of anthropometry involving both sexes."]

Up to the present we have very little material observed and recorded in a competent and reliable manner even as regards Europe alone, with the exception of these studies of Rothe and Hörschelmann's work in Esthonia.* Thus we have to fall back on the vague and general impressions of travellers and others.

Rothe's statistics prove what was already known in a general way, namely, that there are national and racial differences in Europe in this respect. Even in Germany and throughout Central Europe, for instance, shape and size of the breast vary from province to province, and stock to stock, quite apart from the influence of custom, diet and costume. Anecdotal material is abundant here. For example, in Silesia it is said that the bosom is generally flat and undeveloped, whereas in Mecklenburg on the Baltic shore and about Würzburg on the Rhine, and in Vienna, even quite young girls are said to possess finely shaped and fully developed breasts ; indeed, Austrian women have always been famed in this respect as the old rhymes testify. The Slavonic woman is said to develop earlier than the Teuton in this respect, but we have, so far, no means of proving this. The Croatian, the Dalmatian and other Yugo-Slav women and girls are celebrated for this particular charm, both in form and firmness. The women of the old Serbian kingdom were said to

---

* [Alette Schreiner made no comparative study of her Norwegian types, neither did Wilder and Pfeiffer in their study of American women.]

194.—Small nipples in a young Sicilian.

possess breasts of only moderate fullness. In Bulgaria, curiously enough, large breasts were considered ugly, and there were curious superstitions as to their cause. Girls are sometimes forbidden to sweep the threshold of the cottages lest their breasts become larger. Hörschellmann states that among the Esthonian women full contours are twice as frequent among them as moderate development or flat chests. This is caused, he thinks, partly by muscular hard work, partly by the fact that they are constantly nursing at the breast. " In Esthonian women we find 80 per cent. hemispherical, 8 per cent. bowl-shaped, and about 10 per cent. conical. The goat's udder formation is very rare." [According to Krauss some of the southern Slav women have such large and pendulous breasts that they can fling them over their shoulders (v. p. 399).]

Hyrtl was of opinion that climatic conditions influence mammary development

195 .—Women from Tanganyika Territory.

and that the breasts of women in dry and arid mountain regions never attain the dimensions common in fertile and marshy low lands. But this pronouncement may have been based upon, or influenced by the type of physique portrayed by Rubens and associated with his name. And these Rubens women were not by any means always or necessarily daughters of the Netherlands.* The study of contemporary documents and of the history of art has been able to identify the models who sat for various pictures by this artist. Their names and nationality are known ; they were Parisians, and we may conclude that their rounded contours express the taste of the age rather than the characteristics of any particular racial stock.

Admittedly, however, grace and symmetry are supposed to characterise the

* [The preference for the robust types, as are depicted not only by Rubens but by modern painters like William Etty and William Mulready, indicate a tendency to emphasise femininity as opposed to any approximation to the masculine. Zorn's superb Swedish peasant types illustrate this point and the scorn of D. H. Lawrence for the boyish women of his time is well known (see Park and Gregory).]

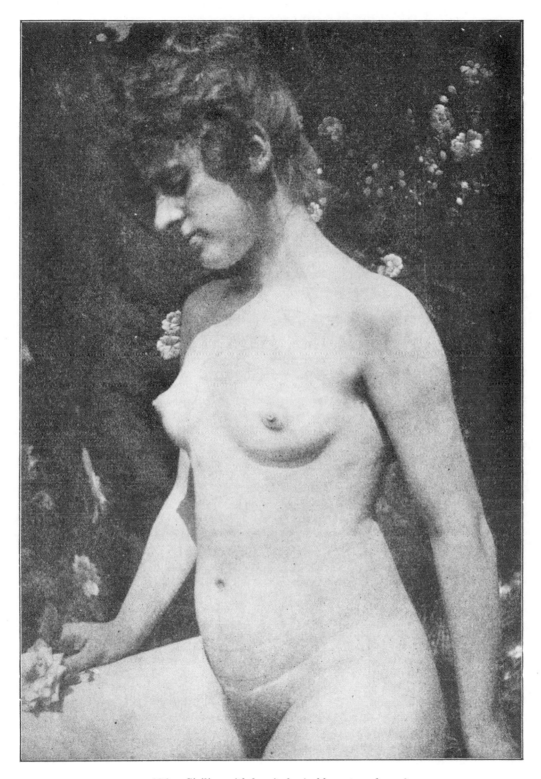

196.—Sicilian with hemispherical breasts and areolæ.

physique of the Parisienne and they are credited with well-formed breasts which are neither flat nor over-developed.

It has been assumed, perhaps too readily, that the Southern European women of Mediterranean race attain physical maturity earlier than the girls of Northern or Central Europe, and possess fuller and more highly developed breasts. It has, however, been maintained that the Castilian women have the least developed breasts in Europe and the Portuguese the fullest.

The photographic material available is largely from Barcelona and represents women in whom breasts, hips and buttocks are alike full and well-rounded. Several of these Spanish women show another peculiarity which is undoubtedly frequent in, even characteristic of, certain coloured races. The whole areola is raised above the surrounding and supporting breast and curved into a second miniature elevation separated by a sharply defined ring-shaped circumference.

M. Bartels observed the same appearance in several Sicilians (cf. Figs. 183 and 196). These characteristics have not been demonstrated in other European races and, as they are quite common and indeed typical among Africans, it may be that the admixture of African blood is responsible for their appearance on the north of the Mediterranean. Both Spain and Sicily were in constant communication with North Africa from very early times. It may be observed, however, that the breasts themselves are only moderately developed among Sicilian women. Similarly, only slight development is generally found in the aristocratic British types.

THE BREASTS OF AMERICAN WOMEN

The North American women of European descent have the characteristics of their original nationalities modified by American climate and habits of life.

In considering the aboriginal and mixed races we shall begin with the southern extremity of the Continent.

The Peshere women of Tierra del Fuego are said by Essendörfer to differ widely from the men of their tribe who are generally thin, for they have rounded figures and full breasts. This description was confirmed in the Tierra del Fuegians who came to Berlin, as Virchow observed that these women had very full breasts but not disproportionately or unpleasantly so, and they were of the slightly pendulous type with large but well proportioned nipples pointing downwards. .

Hyades and Deniker wrote :

" The breasts are set rather high. In young girls they are rounded, slightly conical in shape and erect. After some years, and especially after several births, they become pendulous, but remain somewhat conical rather than pear-shaped. As a rule, the breasts of the Yaghan women in both shape and setting resemble those of the Araucanian Indian women and differ much from those of Mongols."

Kupfer says of the Suya women (Matto Grosso, Brazil) : " The younger women have small firm breasts running rather to a point at the tips, the more mature have full breasts which are not unshapely." But on the whole the Indian women of South America are as much subject as other primitive coloured races to the gradual elongation and disfigurement of the breasts. For example, v. d. Steinen says that those women of the Bororo (Brazil) who have borne children have very pendulous breasts with large areolæ.

In Chile, and equally in California, the experience of child-birth affects the breasts in the same manner as among Europeans, according to Rollin, the surgeon in the expedition of La Pérouse.   Schomburgk gives a similar account of the Warrau (Guarauno) women in British Guiana.

M. Bartels was able to photograph some natives of Guiana ; a mother in her 'twenties had large, flaccid and pendulous breasts ; a girl of 13 showed the early swelling of the hemispherical type, whilst a girl of 19 exhibited conical breasts with hemispherical areolæ and prominent nipples of the same shape.

Rengger describes, as a peculiarity of the Guarani women, that the areola is raised and curved above the rest of the gland, and the same is seen in the photograph of an Indian woman from the State of Arizona (Fig. 197).

In Koch Grünberg's monographs he gives very full illustrations of South American Indian tribes.

Sartorius states that he saw native women in Mexico with almost conical breasts, and it is said that Eskimo women have well developed breasts also.

THE BREASTS OF AFRICAN WOMEN

Turning to Africa we find among the Egyptian women, according to Hartmann's account, breasts oval in shape and firm in consistency, but which soon become pendulous after repeated pregnancies.   In girls they are often well developed as early as in the 11th year and in women they often become pendulous between 25 and 30.   The women of Upper Egypt seem to have been celebrated in antiquity for the size of their breasts, for Juvenal writes, "quis [miratur] in Meroe crasso maiorem infante mamillam " (who marvels to see the breast of a mother in Meroe larger than her sturdy baby) ? *

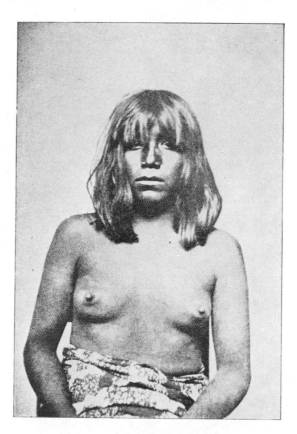

197.—Indian woman from Arizona with elevated areolæ.   (R. Neuhauss, photo.)

The girls of the Sudan, according to Hartmann, show a good deal of diversity.   "Many have a graceful, firm, delicately formed breast of soft texture, when young, hemispherical in shape, sloping more gradually above and more steeply below with curved areolæ and with short nipples.   More frequently the breasts in young women of the Sudan are more or less conical in shape and slope outwards.   The areolæ are globular while the nipples remain insignificant (Fig. 198).   This is not the most æsthetic form and becomes less so when the breasts wither and become pendulous.   As a result of much child-bearing, breasts may become shrivelled, and wrinkled flaps of skin are all that remain.   Other girls in their youth have broad chests and high-set, full breasts.   But these, too, become misshapen, flat and disfigured."   Hartmann

* Sat., XIII., 163.   Cf. T. Bell, p. 76.

found very pretty and attractive figures among the women of Northern Africa. In a few cases the breasts develop between 15 and 16 years of age. " The goat's udder shape, so praised and prized among the Arabs, is really only æsthetically displeasing to Europeans if it is too large and pendulous. To a moderate degree and in small dimensions, it harmonises with the slenderness and daintiness of the build common among those girls " (cf. Hartmann, who gives illustrative material in his book).

Hartmann, however, saw none of the flaccid, tubular and elongated breasts elsewhere so frequent in Africa: the young Dinka girls were sometimes of classic beauty in outline, but the mothers much less so.

Among the Nuba, a mountain people of Kordofan, the disfigurement began early; the breasts were elongated, with deeply wrinkled areola, and the nipples became hard and horny. Among women in Sennaar Hartmann observed and recorded hemispherical breasts and sensitive nipples of great beauty, among the younger women.

Brehm mentions another African tribe, the Mensa (Eritrea): in these women, the breasts begin to develop between 10 and 12 years old and are disfigured and deformed by 30. Juan Maria Schuver mentioned the curious colouring of the nipples among the Galla women: they were bluish, becoming a bright indigo with advancing age. Paulitschke considered full and finely shaped breasts characteristic of these Galla. According to Nachtigal the breasts of the Tibu women of eastern Libya soon become flaccid and the lack of adipose tissue causes mere empty folds of skin to take the place of finely formed breasts. Fortunately, in their latter stages they are never very voluminous and do not hang down far.

Similarly it is stated that the breasts of the Egba women in Yoruba are unusually large, but after the first pregnancy they wither and in old age become mere bags of skin. Cases are also known where one breast only shows full development while the other is scarcely apparent.

198.—Negress from the Egyptian Sudan with conical breasts and round nipples. (Photo, G. Schweinfurth.)

Lanessan states of the Pai-Pi-Brior Agni, who are neighbours of the Ashanti:

" That in youth the breasts are generally piriform, becoming very flaccid, long and pendulous in later years. The hemispherical form is very rare and is considered a sign of beauty " (Figs. 106 and 199).

Pechuel-Loesche gives a description of the characteristics of the Loango negresses:

" They are naturally lean and thin and seldom obese ; they have well-proportioned breasts, hard and coarse in young persons. They are rather conical with too narrow a base for their height (or length) and sometimes they are udder-like ; asymmetry is frequent. They soon become the sagging pouch-like disfigurements so often found in Africa and far from unknown in other continents and civilised races. The breasts of broader base and of hemispherical form are the more enduring and often a real adornment even in very mature women ; in the young, their only fault is the somewhat large nipple."

Falkenstein confirms this description, adding that the hemispherical form is very rare and the areolæ and nipples very marked.

De Rochebrune reports that the breasts are generally piriform among the Wolof ; and Bérenger-Feraud comments on the disfigurement that follows maternity in this people.

Hutter mentions the conical and elongated breast formation of the Bali negresses of Cameroon, and their early flaccidity. In young girls there is often great beauty of shape and firm texture. He records one marked case of asymmetry.

Paul Reichard says of the Wanyamwezi that the breasts begin to develop at seven years and to sink at 13.

" It has a smaller base than in women of our race and the nipple and areola are so formed that the appearance is as if a second breast was set on the first."

The Hottentots and Bushwomen —in addition to their other physical peculiarities—have been described by various travellers. Lichtenstein says these people have flaccid and pendulous breasts, while Fritsch found the shape of the breasts of the Hottentot women more like the European. They have relatively small and pointed breasts with prominent nipples and fairly flat areolæ, and not the large elongated type of breast which is elsewhere common. Barrow also men-

199 .—Ashanti girl of 16 years, whose breasts are already pendulous. *Cf.* Fig. 260 for view from behind. (Photo, C. Günther, Berlin.)

tions their large and prominent nipples and areolæ. With regard to the breasts of the Bushwoman, Afandi, who died in Tübingen, Görtz states that these were not pendulous. The areolæ also were not similar to those of the Hottentot Venus on whom Cuvier reported. In her case the areola measured 4 in. across and was provided with radiating wrinkles. In the Tübingen case the woman's areola measured $4\frac{1}{4}$ in. across but the furrows were concentric. The nipple also was projecting and not retracted as in the case of the Hottentot.   It was separated from the areola by a surrounding furrow.

The very strong development and large size of the breast in native girls of

200 .—Young girl from Natal with pendulous breasts.

South Africa has often been recorded photographically.   Their breasts tend to sag even in very young persons (Figs. 200 and 201).

In the interior of the island of Madagascar there dwells a primitive tribe which Audebert has described.   The young girls had firm, round and shapely breasts with somewhat developed nipples of black colour.   The degeneration and sagging of the breasts in mature women resulted from prolonged suckling of more than one child at a time, not only the youngest but such children as were old enough to reach the mother's breast while standing.

THE BREASTS OF THE WOMEN OF ASIA

Apparently the northern latitudes of Asia—like those of Europe—favour the preservation of youthful conditions and appearance in the female breast. Steller says of the Kamchadale that they had :

" Small round breasts, quite firm, even in women of 40, and which do not become pendulous early in life."

Polak describes the Persian women as being only moderate, but early, in breast development, or less than moderate. The breasts of the Armenians are much larger and fuller. The Persian is supposed to be an excellent wet nurse, which is another proof that functional capacity of the mammary gland is quite independent of the size of the breast. In fact, very full breasts are not considered the most adapted for lactation. Persian women wear a suspensory bandage to support the breast with separate embroidered pouches (Polak and Häntzsche), and avoid tight and heavy clothing.

Hodson mentions the long nursing period and hard work of the women among the Naga of Manipur ; women in their thirties look like old women. P. and F. Sarasin have some notes on the Veddah women of Ceylon. They found the breast conical in the young women, with phalangeal nipples and large areolæ. In two cases the areola formed a second smaller elevation, conical in shape. The breasts become flaccid after very few births and are obliterated in age. They record two marked cases of asymmetry in which the left breast was under-developed.

Jacobs speaks of the protuberant areolæ found in " more than half of all the women of Bali." It " forms a little

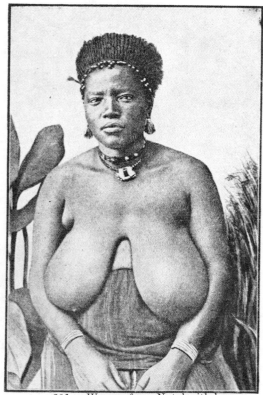

201 .—Woman from Natal with large pendulous breasts. (Joest Coll.)

mound of its own." Women who are nursing are especially noticeable in this respect. [For beauty in Bali cf. G. Krause and H. E. Yates.]

Among the Achinese (Sumatra), Jacobs found two different main forms : either round and spherical, or pointed. " The natives have special terms for each : tĕk broĕk (or half a cocoanut shell), and tĕk djantoeng (heart of a pisang flower). The first form is preferred by the young men.

According to Müller, the breasts of Malayan women are small, pointed and conical and the chest otherwise flat. But Finsch says there is as much variety here as anywhere, according to age and individuality.

202.—Negrito girl from Luzon with breasts and areolæ of hemispherical type.

"Sometimes the nipple is retracted and sometimes the dark areola is very prominent showing all the grades of size and shades of colour from light to almost dark brown."

Montano says of the Moro of Sulu :

"They have not the firm conical breasts of the native women. In the young Sulu women, the breasts are almost hemispherical but wrinkle soon and become pendulous in older women."

Modigliani says of the inhabitants of the island of Nias :

"During their youth, the women habitually display their breasts which are, as a rule, well shaped, erect and piriform with small dark nipples. But these natural attractions soon

203.—Hindu woman with large areolæ.   (Photo, L. Steiner.)

diminish and disappear ; and, after the first confinement, with its prolonged period of suckling and incessant household tasks, there is no trace left. The breasts sag down to the abdomen, their upper surface becomes seamed with deep furrows and no more is left of their former beauty."

So far as illustrative material, both in works of art and in photographs, is able to prove, Japanese women have shapely breasts of moderate size.

Koganei says of the Ainu women :

"Their breast is, as a rule, either of moderate size or large, pear-shaped or conical ; and sometimes pendulous, even in women who have not suckled their babies. Only rarely is the breast hemispherical and erect. The nipple is of moderate size, or large, and more often prominent than flat. The areola only slightly pigmented and generally light or dark brown in tint."

Mondière found the breasts in Chinese women

"Admirably proportioned and hemispherical, but with a strong tendency to become overloaded with fat and of excessive size between the ages of 25 and 28.

"The indigenous women of Formosa, in the southern portion of that island, are as unsightly to European eyes as their menfolk, being also as small and frail in physique. They have undeveloped breasts, small and conical."

The traveller, Ibis, who thus describes them, only saw a few more shapely forms among certain of the aborigines.

Mondière gives the following description of the Annamese women :

"Their breasts are generally symmetrical and hemispherical in shape ; the piriform type is rare, and, curiously enough, the women who have it are generally whiter in complexion than the rest. In the young nullipara, the distance between the nipples is generally 19 cm. These are small before adolescence, and then expand greatly during gestation, becoming very prominent in the later months before birth. The areola varies much, individually, but the paler the woman's skin, the larger and more highly coloured her areola. Its diameter, as I have been able to measure occasionally, may reach from 7 to 9 cm. The mammilla remains short till suckling begins, then it increases rapidly and remains prominent and deeply pigmented after the first long period of lactation. The breast seldom recovers its original shape as is the case in many women of white race, but it decreases in size and droops without becoming disfigured or unsightly."

Mondière found that a half-caste between Annamese and European resembled her Annamese mother in this region, but that her nipples were more prominent.

Maurel describes the women of Cambodia thus :

"The chest is well developed with firm, elastic and generally pear-shaped breasts. The nipple is usually short." The recorder only saw two nulliparæ with uncovered breasts, and says they were "slightly pear-shaped," adding "in spite of this formation, the nipples point straight forward and are less far apart than in other women by about 16 and 20 mm."

There are certain coloured races among whom the women preserve the shape and texture of their breasts after bearing and nursing children much better than among most primitive peoples. Thus, on the North-East Frontier of French Cochin China, where the borders of Annam, Cambodia (Siam) and Cochin China meet, there lives a tribe known as the Moi, of whom A. Gautier says : "Their women are generally plain featured but with good figures and full breasts, unwrinkled even after the first child."

Néis says of the Lao :

"The women never have excessively prominent breasts ; with advancing years, they become plump but not obese."

Montano reports of the Negrito of the Philippines :

"In young girls, the type of breasts is midway between the hemispherical and piriform. After the first pregnancy, they increase in size and droop downwards."

Riedel finally has given particulars about many of the Islanders of the Moluccan Archipelago :

The Buru girls have breasts of moderate size, flattish above and curved below ; after childbirth they sag and become seamed with unsightly furrows. On the Amboina Islands the breasts are badly developed as a result of deformation in youth and the areolæ are small. On Ceram women who have not borne children have very small breasts. On the Ceram Laut, Gorong and Watubela Isles the breasts of the women are small and piriform. But on the Kei group the young women have large full breasts with prominent piriform nipples. The women of the Temimber and Timor Laut (Yamdena) Islands have small but full breasts inclined to be pear-shaped, and the same is the case on Lèti, Moa, Lakor and Kiesar, and these are small in size, with dark or black areolæ. And on the Sawu group, Riedel states that the breasts are small and of the piriform type.

THE BREASTS OF THE WOMEN OF OCEANIA

From Indonesia and Malaya we pass to the inhabitants of the Pacific Islands, among whom the hemispherical areola seems particularly frequent ; and this rounded areola is separated from the breast itself by a circular depression (Fig. 204).

Kubary found highly developed, but somewhat conical, breasts among the women of Yap (Caroline Islands), and this corresponds with the comments of v. Miklucho-Maclay on the inhabitants of other South Sea Islands.   He says :

" In girls of from 12 to 15 who have borne no children, I found the peculiar formation already mentioned by me. The upper extremity was separated from the somewhat taut, firm, youthful base of the breast by a circular depression. I saw this formation in Papuan girls in New Guinea and in young Polynesians in Samoa. The mammary asymmetry which is far from rare, seems almost the rule as regards the areola. I have always found this depression to be more marked in one breast than in the other. The formation is not universal, but very frequent. I do not think it is directly connected with periods of genital activity such as menstruation and pregnancy, but I think it disappears after frequent suckling, for I never saw this depression of the areola among older women."

204 . Queensland girl, said by her mother to be 10 years of age, with hemispherical areola. (Photo, O. Finsch.)

The women of Ponape of the Eastern Carolines are described by Finsch :

" The girls' breasts have faultless contours, softly rounded, hemispherical, firm, without excessive fullness and only pendant in women who are actually suckling infants. The development of the nipple is very diverse, sometimes the dark areola is especially prominent, sometimes only the nipple itself is erect. In some young girls about puberty, the nipples are retracted or they are asymmetrical. In girls with full breasts where the areolæ are constricted but prominent the nipples are sometimes quite retracted."

The women of the Gilbert Island are very pretty and attractive in their youth :

Their shapely breasts are rather inclined to fullness. In girls with retracted nipples is to be seen a dark areola, the size and colouring of which vary very much with each individual. Often in young girls the dusky areola alone rises in hemispherical contour (Finsch).

On Maiana, Finsch described the girls as

" Having small, firm breasts with somewhat darker but not large areolæ and slightly prominent nipples. In older women, the breasts become pendulous by their own weight ; the nipples were still small, but highly pigmented, like the raised areolæ."

" Melanesian women have well-developed and shapely breasts in youth, but they sag after the first child is born and nursed " (Finsch).

The same observer noticed the girls on Motu Island :

" In one, between 13 and 14 years old, the breasts were small and dark in hue and the nipples, though also small, were lighter coloured than the surrounding surface. A 16-year-old girl, though still small, was more fully developed with fine hemispherical contours. The nipple was small though slightly projecting and set in a small dark areola."

205.—Young Samoan girl with developing breasts.   (Museum für Völkerkunde, Dresden.)

The breasts of the Fijian girls, if they have attained puberty, exhibit, according to Buchner, a projection of part of the nipple which appears as if constricted, and thus lends to the breast a pear-shaped appearance.

The Samoan girls, according to Graeffe, have " strongly developed, rather conical breasts."   Krämer gives further particulars :

" There is much diversity in the breasts.   Some are hemispherical or bowl-shaped with small nipples, and again one often sees cylindrical and pendulous forms (Fig. 205), and especially often the ' goat's udder ' type with conical nipples and wide dark areolæ. As the girls mature, their breasts expand and grow flaccid and drooping and there is a perceptible ribbon or fold of flesh and skin between the breasts. Or they become so much elongated that they can be thrown over the shoulder."

Ling Roth collected some particulars about the Tasmanian aborigines. He records a

"Well-shaped but somewhat wrinkled breast in a woman between 26 and 28 years old. A group of 20 women had very long and pendulous breasts. Two young girls between 15 and 16 had firm, shapely breasts but the nipples were too long and too thick in proportion."

Certain Australian aborigines, both men and women, were brought to Europe in 1884 and shown in Berlin at Castan's " Panoptikon," where many photographs were taken, and the facts are thus summarised by R. Virchow :

"The bosom of Tagarah (perhaps between 16 and 18 years of age) is quite beautiful, virginally firm and smooth, with full hemispherical breasts, large, somewhat prominent areolæ and flat, rounded mammillæ. Yemberi is perhaps in her twenties ; her breasts are full but flaccid with elongated nipples and fine wrinkles over their surface."

THE CARE, TREATMENT AND ADORNMENT OF THE FEMALE BREASTS

In certain races we find special treatments of the breasts which are probably not without share in causing malformations or anomalies. The ancient Hebrew compilers of the Talmud believed that in girls of the wealthier families, the right breast developed earlier than the left, since they wore their shawls on the right side and thus kept the right half of the thorax warmer, thus favouring the growth of the right mammary gland. But among maidens of the poorer people the left breast developed the sooner, for they lift water pitchers with their left hand and carry their little brothers and sisters on their left arms.

We have mentioned the vain fight of the anatomist Sömmering, and of many European doctors, against the evil of tight lacing, which deformed both breasts and internal organs. Not only civilised nations but also quite primitive races have practised a pressure or constriction which has affected

206 .—Greek girl with shoulder strap (αναμασχᾰλιστήρ). Terracotta from Smyrna. Louvre. *Cf.* the strophium or breast-band.

the breasts in their growing phase. Other primitive peoples, again, devote special care to developing these organs with a view to nursing and suckling children.

We all know the legend of the Amazons, and shall treat of them in more detail later on in this book. But there was also an attempt at shaping and moulding the young girls' breasts by means of a special garment among the historic Greeks (Fig. 206, and see Daremberg and Saglio, II., 980 ff., Vorberg, 616).

Among South African natives the breasts are carefully treated and developed ; even when the little girls are not more than seven or eight years old, their mothers begin to rub and smear their breasts with an ointment composed of grease and certain roots, pounded to a powder. They then grasp the areola and sensitive portions around the nipples and rub and knead them as though they wanted to tear off the whole gland.   At a later stage the nipple is intentionally elongated and tied round with strips of fibre.

Holländer reports of the Basuto women that they

" Pull and knead their breasts long before their confinements so that they may be able to suckle the children who ride on their hips."

In parts of New Guinea the breasts of growing girls were subjected to extraordinary treatment and superstitions, as Missionary Keysser reports of the Kai

206 A.—East African woman with breast-band.

in the hinterland of Finsch Harbour (see Neuhauss's monograph on New Guinea) :

" A number of ants of two special kinds are collected ; their heads are pulled off and they are rubbed on the breasts. The sharp liquid stings the skin, causing slight swelling which is increased by dabbing with nettles. The method is naturally not efficacious at first but must be repeated. The Papuans, however, are of the opinion that it makes the breasts grow more quickly ; and if the girl endures and perseveres, the good result will not fail to follow. But this cure must not be applied while the girl is facing the sea, for the waves that wash the shore would otherwise drown all her hopes and wash away her slowly expanding breasts. There is another necessary precaution to be observed : her cousins of the opposite sex are a constant danger. The girl must never walk in front of them, or they would certainly ' tread down ' her breasts as they tread the ground. If they are about and no evasion possible, the girl must always walk behind them."

Several African tribes have the custom of constricting the breast by means of a band fixed just across the thorax where the outward curve begins, and tied tightly so that the breasts are held down, and thus their formation and development are affected. Fritsch confirms this among the South African Bantu; the tying down of the breast is the insignia of the married woman among certain of the Bantu. [Coudenhove also speaks of breast flattening in Nyasaland.]

Fritsch   also says of the Ama-Xosa:

" In the prime of life, the breasts are not uncomely, and they are very plump and lacking grace and delicacy of form. As soon as they become wives, the signs of a rapid deterioration appear and their breasts sag and become like empty bags of skin. They consider this normal to

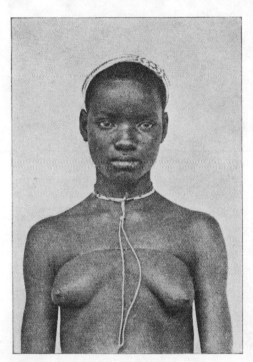

207.—Loango negress with tight breast-band.   (Photo, Falkenstein.)

woman in her prime, a beauty in itself and cultivate it by tying down their breasts. The result is that they are soon able to fling the breast over their shoulder to feed the child carried on their backs; or they suckle the child that crouches on the ground between them by lifting their arms. These facts are so often observed that the formation in question must not be regarded as a monstrosity but as normal among these people and is taken for granted in South Africa."

Bowdich praises the statuesque beauty of form in Ashanti girls of 13 and 14, but adds that

" The young women sedulously destroy this beauty for what is considered a greater, wearing a broad band tight across their breasts, until ceasing to be globular they project conically."

Falkenstein noticed the same custom on the Loango coast, a string or long strip of cloth (Fig. 207) being used, but he does not think that the breasts sag and wither early as a result of this custom since it does not interfere with their physiological development ; and he believes the women are simply following an ancient

208.—Bugakwe (river people). The third from the left shows tight chest-band ; the fifth exhibits a prominent areola. (Photo, F. Seiner.)

custom whose origin was perhaps some idea of primitive hygiene, but is no longer known to those who follow it. Pechuel-Loesche is of opinion that the Loango negresses try to raise the breasts again by means of the band or string which draws the skin tight.

Roscoe reports the custom in Uganda, where pendulous breasts are considered beautiful, of tying them down in order to produce early results.   The same custom prevails in the Congo, and Pogge reports it among the Angola, as well as all the other West African tribes visited by him.   In those regions a band is tied round the breasts of the immature girls in order—so Pogge thinks—to accustom them to the need of

209 .—Women and children from Pagai.   (Photo, F. Schulze.)

tying down their pendulous breasts in adult years as, otherwise, their incessant manual work would be hindered.

No doubt these customs have some effect on the development of the breasts. A definite furrow is made and there is considerable atrophy of the constricted tissues (see Fig. 207).   The Galla women of East Africa press down their breasts by pulling the upper edges of their clothing very tight, and Weiss says the same is true of the Wapororo (Bahutu) women (Tanganyika) : " so that in a short time and even in young women, their fine, full, erect breasts become flaccid and pendulous " (Fig. 206 A).   The same result is shown in a photograph of some Garikwe (Bugakwe) Bushwomen taken by Seiner (Fig. 208).   Moreover, Overbergh and Gaud both speak of the custom of lengthening breasts in the Congo.

In the South Seas there is a similar custom among the native women of the island of Uvea, one of the Loyalty group, A woman depicted by Bernard wore a narrow strip of material tied round her thorax so tightly on the upper edge of the breasts that there was a deep visible furrow.

Some considerable time before this, Hille observed and recorded that the negresses of Surinam slung a triangular piece of cloth with folded ends, tied at the back, across their chest and thus dragged down and pressed in the breasts.

This recalls certain South American aboriginal practices recorded by F. de Azara :

He found that among the Payagua on the River Paraguay, the older women tie leather belts across the breasts of the young girls as soon as they have reached full natural development, draw the belts tight and fasten them at the back. Thus, before the girls reach the age of 24, their breasts sag to their waists. Rengger corroborates this information. He is of opinion that the Payaguan breast is congenitally no more elongated than the European but that the deformity is artificial and acquired.

According to some authorities, the Annamese women in French Cochin China press down their breasts by means of a double bandage round neck and shoulders over a triangular " binder." M. Bartels found a constriction of the thorax just where the breasts begin to rise, corresponding to the African custom described above in a photograph from Pagai Island, one of the Mentawei group, west of Sumatra (Fig. 209). The material used here seems to be vegetable fibre, perhaps from rotang. But the custom is apparently not general, for some women of the same village have not tied their breasts.

Riedel states that the women of the Luang and Sermata groups in the Eastern Malay Archipelago wear a sort of bodice called kutang. This garment constricts the bosom and causes a certain amount of malformation.

Hindu women also sometimes wear a short, close-fitting bodice with pockets for the breasts so that they are not constricted.

In Europe, during the sixteenth and seventeenth centuries the Spanish women often practised a strangely archaic custom of which we are, however, unable to trace the origin or discover possible occasional survival in remote country districts. The breasts of young girls in the early stages of puberty were covered with leaden plates (cf. Finck), and the result was, in many Spanish ladies, positive concavity instead of prominence. Extreme thinness was considered beautiful at that time, and Countess d'Aulnoy describes the display of long chest and back, which was carried out to the greatest extent possible by the Spanish ladies of the seventeenth century. Indeed, she declares that their breasts are as flat and even as a sheet of paper.

As is well known, the latter half of the eighteenth century brought the exposure of the breasts into fashion throughout Europe. This meant the use of artificial supports in many cases.

The undue and unhealthy constriction of the breast is found not only in towns-people but among the peasants of certain districts in Central Europe. Buck made a report of the conditions in Upper Swabia where the tight clothing and bodices caused complete functional atrophy of the breasts, so that only the remnants of the nipples were left, and the women could not suckle their babies—so there was great infant mortality.

The same is the case in Dachau in Bavaria. They compress their breasts by means of a board-like apparatus from earliest youth, with the result, according to

Custer, that they cannot suckle their children, of whom from 40 to 50 per cent. die as babies. The same is the case with the countrywomen of Württemberg, whose costume is made to compress the breasts. Oppermann, Scherr and Ecker give the following account of the women of Bregenzer Wald :

"They have muscular, well-knit frames, straight shapely legs, wide hips, but no bosom. This strange deficiency is not unknown in mountain districts, but is all the more striking as the women are otherwise of quite exuberant build. This may be because of the wooden platters strapped on to the girls, even on those more favoured by nature than the others, thus preventing the development of woman's chief charm." Byr records of the same district : "The tight jacket constricts the body so tightly that it almost obstructs proper physical development and gives a deformed appearance to mature women."

According to Kleinwächter, the German population of Tyrol force the young girls into tight garments, which he compares to wooden armour, for the beauty of the breasts is not prized in Tyrol. The result is atrophy and inability to suckle for longer than about three weeks. In the parts of Tyrol inhabited by Italians this deformation is not practised and health and appearance benefit accordingly.

Among the Circassians the girls between 10 and 12 years old are braced into a broad leather girdle reaching from just over the bust down to their hips. This is then sewn tightly together or fastened with silver tags in maidens of wealthy and noble families (*cf.* Dingwall). The Ossete girls also wear a similar garment ; this is first donned between seven and eight years of age (but, according to Pokrowsky, not till three years later)—and not removed till the girl's wedding night, when the bridegroom cuts open the leather tags with his sword or dagger and removes the corselet. After this operation the breasts develop very rapidly. It is said that the

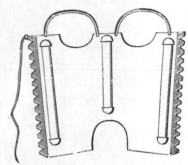

210 . — Constricting corselet used among the Ossetes. (After Pokrowsky.)

Ossetes took this custom from their Northern neighbours, the Kabardians (v. Seydlitz). The writer, Schora-Bekmursin-Nogmov, himself a Kabardian, says of the Circassians :

"They fastened their girls into saffian leather garments for seven years to give their figures greater symmetry. As soon as the girl was married, her bridegroom cut open the stitches in the leather with his knife without grazing either the leather or her skin, for it is counted dire disgrace to do either. Then the young wife began to grow and thrive so well that her breast became visibly larger in a few days. All these customs continue till the present time [1866]. The custom was harmful to health and many women died of consumption or anæmia."

Fig. 210 shows how tight and high the rampart of these corsets was. The young Kabardian (Fig. 211) is obviously encased in a similar instrument, and it is therefore impossible to detect the slightest forward and outward curve on her thorax. Oberländer quotes from Hamar-Dabanov a song referring to this custom ; the Circassian girl laments and entreats the releasing knife of her lover :

"Nine years are past since this girl was sewn up ; since her breasts were compressed. Sorrow is in her heart because her breasts are not free ! It is time for the knife of the youth to free her from her bondage ; but where is that youth, where is he ? "

The handsome Abadzeh tribe in the Kuban district of the Caucasus flatten their girls' breasts by means of wooden slabs (Djatchkow-Terassow).

The Kalmuck women also wear constricting corsets, and disfigurement of the breasts is mentioned also among the women of Queen Charlotte Islands by F.

211.—Young Kabardian with constricting bodice.   (Naturhistor. Mus., Vienna.)

Poole, whilst Currier says that the Cherokee women occasionally compress their breasts by means of flat round stones in order to hinder their natural growth. These senseless methods form a transitional stage towards actual mutilations.

[Modern brassières and corselets, which are made with strong elastic insets and with boned under-belts are used for compressing the breasts and buttocks and providing, in the words of the trade, " a perfect foundation which moulds the figure to smart slenderness." The subject of these supports in various parts of the

212.—Tattooing of the breasts in Tenimber. (After Riedel, I.)

world is discussed, with illustrative material, in the *Bilder-Lexikon der Erotik*, I., 200 ff. *Cf.* also *Die Erotik in der Photographie*, pp. 229 ff.

In 1921 a company was operating in New York City called the Boyishform Brassière Co., which dealt in breast-constricting devices which " gives you that boy-like flat appearace " according to the advertisement.]

Local tattooing is much less injurious than hard compression and constriction, and is performed for decorative purposes in various parts of the world. Among various tribes of Equatorial Africa, tiny longitudinal incisions into the skin of the breasts are not uncommon ; these incisions are arranged in either vertical or diagonal rows. Joest says that the Basuto girls

also disfigure their breasts, which are often very beautiful, by numbers of horizontal or vertical scars from incisions.

In the Moluccan Archipelago are found even more complicated tattoo designs. On the island of Ceram dots are arranged in curved lines, repeating the natural convexity of the mammary outline ; while on Tenimber, a star-shaped pattern is preferred with straight or regularly curved rays, and the centre of the star is the nipple (Fig. 212). Zulu women wear special amulets which hang between the

213.—Zulu woman wearing breast amulet.

breasts (Fig. 213). These manifestations of the desire to adorn and decorate are quite harmless biologically, for the functional use of the breasts in suckling is in no way hindered or obstructed.

MUTILATIONS OF THE BREASTS

We must now turn to certain intentional injuries inflicted on the breasts by women themselves or by their near relatives. The compressions and constrictions mentioned in the preceding section might be described as unintentional or unconscious mutilations. These specially affected the nipples, which were often made unsuitable for suckling. Unspeakable mental and physical suffering has been thus inflicted on young mothers; and we have collected evidence that such customs exist in primitive country districts of Europe to-day as well as in towns, and as far afield as in the Moluccan Archipelago.

The intentional and fully-conscious mutilation of the breasts (as it is practised in certain religious orders by the wearing of very tight under-bodices) aims at atrophying or obliterating these organs through constant compression and at making

214.—Skoptsi, 20 years of age, with mutilated breasts. (After E. v. Pelikan.)

the dedicated novice or nun as like as possible to the angels among whom there is neither male nor female. We need only refer to the cases of local custom in Dachau, the Bregenzer Wald and Spain to suggest that these were archaic customs which revived and have been preserved by the "heavenly-minded" atmosphere of Christianity.

There are also certain possible major operations on the breasts which remind us of the legend of the Amazons. We shall consider them in a later section, merely recalling for the moment that Strabo recorded that their right breast was seared off in childhood so that they could better throw the spear and draw the bow; whereas Diodorus Siculus (II., 45, etc.) maintained that both breasts were destroyed. Hence their Greek name, ἀ-μαζός, "Without breast."

According to Hippocrates, they belonged to the Sauromatian stock and lived by the Palus Maeotis (Sea of Azoff). A brass disc was made red hot and pressed on the right breast and the muscles and flesh so seared that it could not naturally develop, so that all their force flowed into their right arms and shoulders.

In paragraph 194, Code of King Hammurabi, *i.e.*, in Babylon, 2250 B.C., the breast was to be cut off if a wet nurse tried to replace a child committed to her care by a changeling.

Cameron noticed a peculiar circumstance among the natives of Akalunga on the shores of Lake Tanganyika, as well as in Kasangalowa. The women of those regions did not appear to display their nipples, but they appeared to have a hollow instead of a normal nipple. Cameron suspected some form of punitive mutilation here.

According to Roth, the Australian aborigines on Herbert River practised this mutilation on certain girls of their tribe so that they should not rear children.

215.—Scene from a fourteenth-century MS. of the chronicle of Rudolf von Ems. (MS. c. germ. 5, Bayr. Landesbib., München.)

As late as the nineteenth century mutilations and self-torments were practised by the Skoptsi, an obscure Christian sect of fanatics who were chiefly Russian in origin. We have had occasion to refer to these people already as regards genital mutilations. The detailed accounts by E. v. Pelikan and W. Koch mention cases known to the authors in which little girls of ten, nine or even seven years of age had had their nipples cut off, and yet these children persisted in the courts of law that they had thus mutilated themselves. E. v. Pelikan distinguished three degrees of mammary mutilation among the women of the Skoptsi, namely :

(1) The excision, the application of corrosives, or burning the nipples either on one side only or on both, the last being the most frequent.

(2) The excision of part of the breasts or the total amputation of both, which was much the more frequent form. There were long diagonal scars, resembling those following surgical operations involving amputation.

(3) Various incisions in both breasts, generally arranged symmetrically.

Koch reports that these people never performed genuine female castration, *i.e.*, oöphorectomy, but attempted to limit and frustrate sexual emotions and possibilities of intercourse by means of wholesale mutilations and ablations. On the whole, however, these mutilations appeared to be much less general among the women Skoptsi than among the men.

Their form of divine service seems to have included a ritual supper at which a small portion of a girl's mutilated bleeding breast was devoured instead of the Host, but the judicial enquiries and evidence is not very precise or satisfactory on this point (Fig. 214).

These Skoptsi trials recall the ancient legends of the early Christian martyrs with their wealth of torments and extravagant cruelties attributed to the persecuting zeal of pagans and the piety of the Christians. Whether mainly based on barbarous fact or on sadistic imagination, these legends are psychologically significant for students of human nature.

216.—Martyrdom of Saint Faith. (J. de Voragine, *Legenda*, 1488.)

[The attraction that the breasts have always exercised and their intimate association with the female sexual organs have undoubtedly been responsible for the hatred and dislike of those who were dominated by the morbid phantasies associated with Christianity.

As we have already seen, the beauty of the breasts has been sung for many centuries

217.—Martyrdom of Saint Agatha. (J. de Voragine, *Legenda*, 1488.)

218.—Martyrdom of Saint Christina. (J. de Voragine, *Legenda*, 1488.)

among all peoples.* As I have pointed out in "The Girdle of Chastity" (pp. 21 *ff.*), they received much praise throughout the Middle Ages, and Marot's famous poem could well be

* *Cf.* "L'éloge des Tétons," Mercier de Compiègne.

supplemented by the words of the anonymous author of "Les Amours de Charlot," when he writes :—

> "Téton, téton charmant, qui jamais ne repose,
> Vous semblez inviter la main à vous presser,
> L'oeil à vous contempler, la bouche à vous baiser."

Thus we find special attention being paid to the mutilation and destruction of these glands, and as we have seen, there have been attempts in all parts of the Christian world to obliterate these conspicuous signs of womanly beauty in order to divert men's minds from the things of earth and direct their thoughts to those of Heaven.]

The most famous of these legends was that of the Sicilian virgin, Agatha, who lived in Catania in the first half of the third century A.D. The Consular, Quintianus, wooed her to be his wife, but she refused him as he worshipped the heathen gods and, persevering in her refusal, despite prayers and threats, she was imprisoned in a brothel—a frequent fate in those legends. But as she refused and remained steadfast, she was tortured by mutilations of her breasts. This has frequently been depicted in art, but with a considerable amount of variation in detail. Thus, in a *Legenda Sanctorum* of the fourteenth century (Fig. 217) formerly in Mannheim, now in Munich (Staatsbibliothek Cod. Cat. 101, 771), and in the *Legenda* of J. de Voragine (1488, printed at Nürnberg by Anton Koberger), she, St. Faith and and St. Christina are represented as being mutilated. The famous painting by Sebastiano del Piombo in the Palazzo Pitti represents her as having her nipples torn away with red-hot pincers, and the Ribera, in Berlin, prefers sheer amputation of both breasts by the executioner's sword ; another version is by Lorenzo Lippi at the Galleria degli Uffizi in Florence : here she carries her amputated breasts on a golden charger and seems to offer them to God. Her feast is celebrated on February 5th, and wax images of her breasts are carried in her honour in Sicily to this day.

219.—Jewish martyrs suspended by their breasts. From a Hebrew MS. of the fifteenth century. (After Kohut.)

The last circumstance is illuminating. Wessely points out that at the annual festival of the *Bona Dea* two enormous images of breasts were borne in procession as symbols of maternity and the fertile powers of life : he adds, " Her name, Agatha, recalls the ' *Bona Dea.*' "

Other early Christian martyrs who are supposed to have met with the same form of torture before death are St. Faith (Fig. 216) and St. Christina (Fig. 218).

The same form of torture has doubtless been inflicted in warfare. Thus the town of Wimpfen, formerly the Roman *Colonia Cornelia* on the River Neckar (*cf.* Heid), gets its name from an ancient tradition that the women of *Cornelia* were thus mutilated by the invading hordes of Attila's Huns (Wimpfen is said to be a corruption of Weibs-Pein). There are also traditions to the effect that an analogous torture was used in the persecution of the Jews in mediæval times and later. In a fifteenth-century Hebrew manuscript (copy by Kohut), women are represented as suspended from low branches of trees by cords or ropes looped round their breasts. But further details are lacking as to whether this agony was meant to be final or temporary (Fig. 219).

THE FEMALE BREAST IN FOLKLORE

European superstition among the common people takes much account of the breasts, generally with reference to the function of nutrition, and thus as a branch of popular or traditional medicine. We shall deal with this subject later. It may be mentioned here that in Upper Austria and Salzburg it is believed that the smaller the jug in which the water is fetched to the midwife to wash the new-born

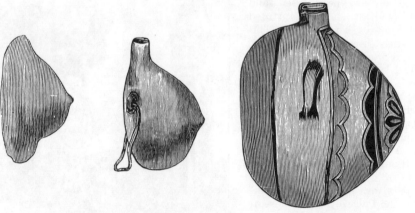

220 A.—Vessels for carrying water in the form of the female breast, Zuni, Arizona. (After Cushing.)

girl, the smaller will be her breasts when grown to womanhood (Pachinger). We may cite the riddle heard by Dufays in Mulera-Ruanda : " What are sharp as spears, yet slay not ?—The breasts of a maiden."

In classical antiquity it was firmly believed that genuine and fully functional hermaphrodites could and did exist : creatures with male genitals and, at the same time, the female breasts and rounded form. They were often depicted in paintings, frescoes and statues. Baumeister attributes the origin of this belief to Asiatic nature myths : " of a bisexual bearded Venus, as the perfect nature deity."

Imagination went further along these lines, and Pliny, following Calliphanes, wrote of a race of hermaphrodites : " living beyond the Nasamones and their neighbours, the Machlyes," these were the " Androgynes of both sexes who copulate now as men, now as women. It was said that their right breasts were flat and male, their left round and female."

The African Kabyles of Djurjura have a singular superstition, recorded by Viré. A wanderer across a place of tombs hears a sweet song at night which lures him to follow the sound. Suddenly he perceives a little woman, or rather young girl, quite black all over but very pretty ; she flees before him, slowly at first, then quicker, and he is compelled to pursue. Her pace gets quicker and quicker, and suddenly her breasts grow longer and longer and she throws them backwards over her shoulders, leaps into a ditch and her pursuer falls after her and breaks his neck.

The same idea of spectral breasts of unnatural form and length was current in ancient Peru. J. J. v. Tschudi records the local Indians' belief in spectres called Hapiñuñu (Hapi = seize and ñuñu = breasts). These creatures have women's form but with long hanging breasts ; they fly by night and seize grown men, carrying them off between their breasts.

Ehrenreich records a somewhat similar legend among the Brazilian Caraya :

" The cannibal wood demon, Mapinkuare, is often accompanied by his consort Patiniru, the one-breasted, who squirts poisoned milk at the wanderer lost in the forests."

The constricting garments (Fig. 209) worn by the Ossetes are to prevent growth of the breasts, as they have a belief that very generous development is a sign of illicit love affairs.

The Zuni Indians of the Pueblo group in Arizona have peculiar pottery which closely imitates the contours of he breast and nipple (Fig. 220 A). These are water pitchers carried on the back and supported by a band fitting over the forehead to leave arms, hands and legs quite free for the climb up steep cliffs from the water's edge. These pitchers are known as " mé he ton ne " ; the root word is " mé ha na "—woman's breast. The water is as necessary to life as the mother's milk to her babe. Probably, in former times, these pitchers had their aperture where the nipple protrudes, but this was changed and the spout is now like a neck on the summit of the circumference (see illus-

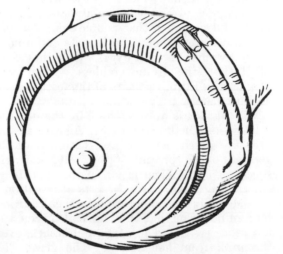

220 B.—Breast bead, Cornelian, Ægina, 1100 B.C.

tration). Even now, while a Zuni woman is using one of these, the mammillary lip is left open and only closed with a clay stopper when the work is quite done. This she does with averted eyes. Cushing, to whom we owe this interesting information, asked the reason, and was told that it was dangerous to look at the pitcher while closing the aperture ; a woman who did so might become barren or, if she had children, they would die young, and those who drank from the desecrated vessels would fall sick and pine away.

Cushing makes a significant comment on the mental processes involved : the aperture of the vessel represents the " fount of life," and she who closes it must not let herself be aware of what she is doing, but turn her eyes away.

Rosen has recently drawn attention to the breast-shaped money boxes used for children in Italy, and also found in Greece,* Silesia, Mecklenburg and East Prussia. Thilenius has traced them in Saxony (Dresden), Thuringia (Gotha), Alsace (Strasbourg), Moravia (Brünn) and Slovakia. In Florence these little boxes are given to women who are confined, and whoever visits the mother and admires

* [For milk in Greek and Roman worship see Wyss.]

the child puts a little gift into the box for the benefit of the baby. In the ruins of Pompeii and in the Middle Ages, very similar boxes are found to have been in use. Rosen thinks they were related to the cult of St. Agatha, the patroness of suckling mothers, and before that to the Great Mother herself. But Thilenius ascribes the resemblance to chance. The evidence is not as yet conclusive in either sense.

[Beads are also found shaped like the female breast. Beck has recorded their existence in Ægina as early as 1100 B.C. They are often made of cornelian, and Fig. 220 B shows one of them. A hand clasps the breast, which is almost globular in shape, the hole for stringing being just above the fingers.]

George Ebers records the survival of the ideas of pre-Christian times and cultures among the Christian Copts of mediæval Egypt : " The images of their Divinity—and also of their female saints—were never designed to gratify the eyes ; although their heathen predecessors had sought to represent the goddesses they worshipped as gracious ' ladies bountiful,' with regular lineaments, sometimes with a smile on their lips and always with the finely rounded bosoms characteristic of the maidens of Egypt, then as now. This charm has always been praised by the poets and singers of that people even oftener and more fervently than the symmetry of the features ; beautiful breasts and abundant hair symbolise the supreme loveliness of woman in their eyes. Thus they celebrated not only the face but the breast of Hathor, the divine goddess ; when her image was borne in procession from Dendera to Edfu, two acts of the festive ritual were the unveiling ('ap) of her bosom and its display to her worshippers."

" Hathor is always the fair, the good and the kind, and when we behold the celebrations in honour of St. Agatha at Catanea in Sicily and the waxen votive breasts offered her, we are reminded of the divine bosom of Hathor, the great goddess of Egypt and of the well-known theory that the Christian martyr is the successor and reincarnation of that nature goddess, whom pagan Egypt revered as the mother from whose breasts all creation received life and nourishment."

Max Bartels has made a further addition to the discussion of these associations by reminding us that they have also been attached to the Mother of Jesus. Among the relics treasured in certain churches, even in North Germany, are specimens of the milk from her breast. The great Cistercian Abbot, Bernard of Clairvaux (died 1153), received the singular favour of nourishment with the milk of Our Lady. (He was henceforth termed mellifluous, honey-tongued, for his eloquence was irresistible.) Two ancient pictures, both anonymous and dating from the fifteenth century, represent this miracle. They are in the Wallraf-Richartz Museum in Cologne. Both represent the Abbot in devout homage : in the first picture he kneels with his pastoral staff in his hand. An angel floats behind the Madonna, holding a crown over her brow ; she carries her son on her arm. The second picture shows the Madonna and the Saint in a landscape setting, both behind a wall which shows only the upper part of their bodies. Haloes surround both heads and the infant Jesus sits naked and enthroned on a cushion set on the coping of the wall. In both pictures the Madonna has bared her left breast but both artists have avoided any direct contact of the giver and the receiver ; the Saint bends his head and the Madonna presses her left breast with her right hand, holding the nipple between index and middle finger : thus she presses the milk from her breast in a fine stream towards the adoring Saint.

WOMAN IN HER PSYCHOLOGICAL ASPECT

THE SEXUAL IMPULSE

" Between two beings so complex and so diverse as man and woman, the whole of life is not too long for them to know one another well, and to learn to love one another worthily."— *Auguste Comte.*

WE have now discussed the various sexual differences. There remains the sexual impulse to be considered.

Here is clearly apparent the interplay between endocrine secretions and nervous system. The human nervous system can be divided into three categories :

(1) The *Sensory* (the stimuli), within and by which the direction of desire is settled.

(2) The *Associative* (whereby the stimuli spread). These include hormonic factors, which are, of course, ultimately based on chemical changes ; and psychic factors (Mnemonic images (or memories), Mnemonic Complexes and Emotions).

There are two tendencies or great emotional currents here :

    (*a*) The *Synergistic* or *Affirmative.*

    (*b*) The *Antagonistic* or *Inhibitive.*

(3) The *Motor* (which, unlike the other two main *categories*, is influenced by the conscious mind and will). This includes the actual reflexes and actions of the sexual impulse (*Contrectation* and *Detumescence*).

A brief outline of the human nervous system is essential to the proper grasp of these distinctions. Detailed descriptions of the nervous system are included in every standard work on physiology.

General Outline

The majority of investigators are agreed that the nervous system is composed of cells of a special type possessing processes of varying length by which they are interconnected. The cells are termed neurones and the interlacing processes fibres. Both in the cells and the processes very minute and delicate strands are distinguishable, and these are known as *fibrils*, and the special protoplasmic substance composing the neurones, as *neuroplasm*. In the individual *neurones* there is a substance resembling the chromatin of the gametic nuclei, known as tigroid and which has been supposed to be used up or consumed if the nervous system is subjected to great strain.

Two nervous systems can be distinguished : the *peripheral* and the *central.*

The neurones are not evenly distributed throughout their course, but in certain areas they are grouped together in numerous clusters known as *ganglia.*

The peripheral nervous system has minute terminal twigs or *rami.* They are divided into centripetal or afferent fibres, also known as sensory ; and centrifugal or efferent, also known as motor fibres.

The centripetal or afferent nerves may be divided into two groups : one receives and transmits sensations of pressure, warmth, cold, pain and what can only be

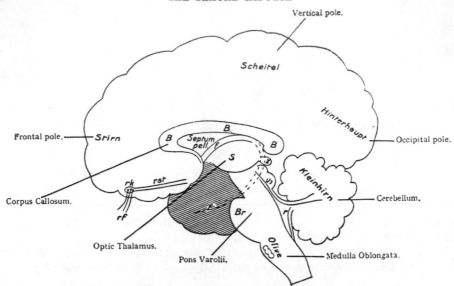

221.—Medial aspect of right half of the brain. (After Pfeifer.)

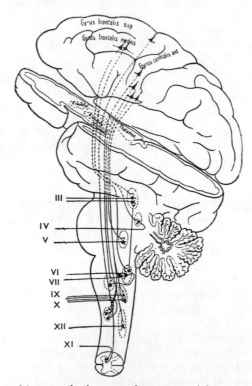

222.—Origin and intracerebral course of motor cranial nerve. (After Bechterev.)

described as "muscular sense." The other group is specifically sensory, *i.e.*, it is more highly differentiated and includes the nerves of eyes, ears and palate. The centrifugal or efferent nerves send the impressions received from the various stimuli

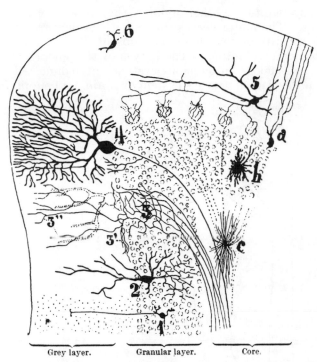

Grey layer.   Granular layer.   Core.

223.—Transverse section through a cerebellar folium. (After Stöhr.) (1) Small granule cells ; (2) Large granule cells ; (3) Nerve fibres ; (3′) Horizontal fasciculus ; (3″) Fasciculi of grey layer ; (4) Cells of Purkinje ; (5) Basket-cells ; (6) Small cortical cells (their nerve process is not shown). (a) Neuroglial cell of grey layer ; (b) Short branches of neuroglial cells ; (c) Long branches.

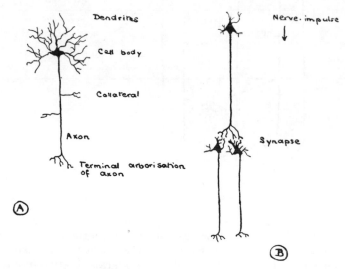

224. (A). Section illustrating the human cerebral cortex. (B). Diagram of the arrangements of the layers of cells in the cerebral cortex. (1) Cajal cells. (2, 2′) Small pyramidal cells. (3) Large pyramidal cell. (4) Polymorphic cell. (5, 5′) Cells of Golgi type. (6) Surface ending nerve fibres. (a, b) Neuroglia cells.

from the central nervous system to the other organs : they consist of motor, secretory and inhibitive nerves.   The motor nerves transmit the stimuli received to the muscular system, which consists of two different kinds of fibres : the striped or voluntary and the smooth or involuntary.   The nerves of the smooth or involuntary muscles belong to a special or autonomous system, interconnected with but not directly dependent on the central nervous system or brain, and supplying blood

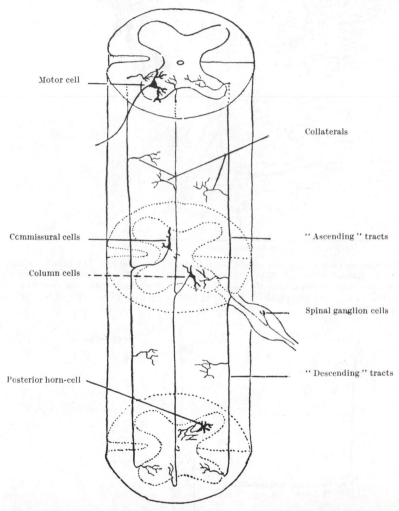

225.—Diagram showing position and course of nerve cells in the spinal cord.   (After Stöhr.)

vessels, intestines and glandular structures.   Two systems or sets of nerves may be distinguished in this group.   They are known as the sympathetic and para-sympathetic.   Both are rich in ganglia ; the secretory nerves are included in the autonomous group.   The inhibitive nerves check or moderate bodily movements.

The central nervous system culminates in the brain and extends along the spinal cord.   Genetically it is most accurate to divide it into the *Palœncephalon* (old Brain), which is common to all vertebrates, and the *Neencephalon* (new Brain), which evolves beside the Palæencephalon in all species from the amphibia upwards.

The palæencephalon consists of the spinal medulla, the medulla oblongata, the cerebellum, the mid-brain or mesencephalon, the thalamus, the corpus striatum and the olfactory lobe.

The spinal medulla (Figs. 225, 226) has a grey and white substance : the latter encloses the grey in a sheath, and transverse microscopic section of the marrow shows that the grey substance has a regular pattern, somewhat resembling the letter **H.** The vertical bars of the **H** are termed horns or roots, and are grouped as dorsal and ventral ; and each spinal nerve is attached to the spinal cord both dorsally and ventrally. The spinal nerves are arranged in pairs along the spinal cord, a pair to each segment of the spine. The centripetal or afferent nerves—those which

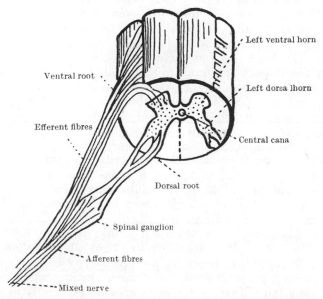

Left ventral horn

Ventral root

Left dorsa lhorn

Efferent fibres

Central cana

Dorsal root

Spinal ganglion

Afferent fibres

Mixed nerve

226.—Schematic section through the spinal cord. (After Edinger.)

convey the sensory stimuli to the spinal cord—pass into the two rear bars of the **H**, *i.e.*, into the dorsal roots, and send stimuli to the front bars or ventral roots, which convey them to the centrifugal and motor nerves and thence to muscles, glands, etc. Thus is formed a circuit or path of reflexes. But there is also a connection with the higher centres, through the white substance and the medulla oblongata ; by this route the various nervous stimulations are conveyed to the pyramidal cells of the cerebral cortex or neopallium. Within this most recently evolved portion of the brain the spinal reflexes are transmuted, rearranged, modified or inhibited, and then sent back to the spinal marrow and externalised thence by way of the centrifugal nerve channels—as movements and actions.

The Sensory Factors

(The direction of impulse)

All external stimuli are received by the senses, of which the number is commonly accepted as five : smell, taste, sight, hearing and touch. This is, however, quite an inadequate view : modern research distinguishes about 20 senses in the human race : we know, for instance, that taste and touch may be analysed into several distinct constituents, and smell, although the least studied and investigated of all, is also probably much more intricate than was formerly supposed.   Every external impression received through the senses is registered in the form of an excitement, excitation or stimulus.   And the central nervous system " interprets " these sensory stimuli as *emotions* or conscious *sensations*.

Moreover, if the living substance of the nervous system be subjected to excitation, electric currents may be observed.   The region at rest is here positive to the region in activity (Action current).   We may assume that energy leaks into the adjacent areas ; thus, if a sensory nerve is excited there is an effect on its corresponding motor nerve, providing either a muscular twitching or a complete circuit. But if the motor nerve is electrically excited there is no similar response on the sensory side.   Therefore, we conclude that every functional sensory nerve must have the property or faculty of transforming latent or kinetic (active) energy received from without the body into the particular synthesis of forces which we term *nervous excitation* (Fröhlich).   But there are also conscious sensations which are not provoked by the impact of stimuli from outside the body, but arise within the body itself as a result of organic processes, such as hunger, thirst, fatigue and the functions of evacuation from bladder and bowels.   And these primitive organic processes are connected with definite feelings of some degree of either pain or pleasure.

The sense organs—or rather their nerves—have a further peculiarity ; their degree of receptiveness to special stimuli varies very widely ; this is termed a specific disposition, and this receptiveness is not necessarily associated with either pleasurable or disagreeable sensations, though both types of sensation often accompany any heightening of stimulus ; or, again, a stimulus may be painful in a slight measure and pleasurable when its acuteness increases—a fact of much significance in sexual matters—or the reverse.   Stimuli are described as either adequate or inadequate.

And for every kind of stimulus there is a certain degree of intensity at which it becomes perceptible.   Thus there are degrees of light which do not affect our eyes. The limit of stimulus capable of becoming perceptible to our consciousness is termed its threshold.   There is great diversity here, both among various species of living creatures and among individuals of the same species, especially as between human beings.

Thus, in olfactory sensations the threshold of consciousness is reached much sooner in dogs than in human beings.

We will now examine the most important sense organs from our special point of view.

Taste is probably the least prominent.   Even in cunnilingus and similar practices, the sensations are probably tactile and olfactory.

Neither is hearing so important, though there are great individual differences in this respect.   The particular tone, pitch and modulation of a voice may have intense erotic attraction.   Musical compositions, particularly on stringed instruments, have this power to an even higher and more widely compelling degree ; some works—particularly orchestral—are definitely erotic.*   Of course the sense of hearing is the receptive agent in erotic anecdotes and descriptions and jokes, but the substance of these is assimilated and associated by the cerebral cortex, and thus

---

* *Cf.* Chapter III., pp. 24–26, in " Ideal Marriage : Its Physiology and Technique," by Dr. Th. H. Van de Velde.   (William Heinemann (Medical Books) Ltd.)

the type of stimulation here is complex, depending on memory and fancy, and not directly sensory.

Sight is extraordinarily important in relation to sexual impulse in civilised mankind to-day. But here, too, it is not so much the crude material as the finished product of mental association, imagery, memory and suggestion. And according to the standard or concept of beauty, racially or individually accepted, sight may be the chief agent of sexual selection. But here, too, association is inextricably interwoven with perception and stimulation. Thus the heterosexual person finds the opposite sex physically attractive, emotionally interesting ; the homosexual, their own sex ; the fetichist, some object—feet, hair, articles of clothing ; and the anti-fetichist and moralists find satisfaction in destroying or polluting whatever is attractive and enjoyable to their fellow creatures.

Touch is as important as sight. There is a definite feeling of pleasure in contact with certain substances and textures, and the contact of the sex organs is the culminating phase of sexual satisfaction. Hirschfeld has pointed out that the sensations of tactile pleasure in certain areas of the body (erogenous zones) make these areas the most frequent " *breaking points* " of inhibitions and intentions contrary to the uprush of instinctive desires.

Perhaps the sensations associated with smell are the most important,* although, unfortunately, the functions of the olfactory lobe have been much less studied than those of the visual or auditory centres. It is to be assumed that the perceptive organs of smell receive infinitesimal chemical particles of the odorous objects : thus smell is a specialised tactile sense. The sense of smell exists in all vertebrates from the fishes upwards.

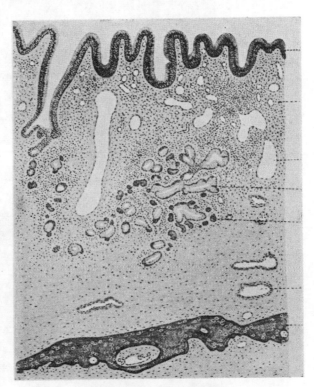

227.—Vertical section through the mucous membrane of the inferior nasal concha.

* *Cf. Van de Velde.* " Personal qualities or idiosyncrasies are of great significance in the association of sexual emotion with the *sense of smell*. This is the case both in perception of and reaction to olfactory stimuli and as regards the special personal odours. Here there are important *social* variations and both olfactory susceptibility and the range and intensity of personal odours are probably greater in women than in men. Olfactory susceptibility is a very diverse and uncertain factor. There are persons in whom it hardly exists. There are certainly many who have no conception of the sexual significance of odours and who are not conscious of any specific reaction to odours. Inasmuch as they are here anæsthetic and unappreciative, they lose a delectable relish to love. I would advise such persons to give their attention to the subject of odours, to become acutely conscious of the enjoyment they derive from the subtle and various scents exhaled by the body they love." " Ideal Marriage," p. 26. See also *op. cit.*, pp. 27–39, and Dan McKenzie : " Aromatics and the Soul." London, 1923.

There is a process of chemo-tropism which has been observed even among flies by Loeb : but probably the process here is independent of any sensations on the part of the insect and is a matter of chemical affinity. Many creatures show an unmistakable association of smell and sexual excitement during their rutting or breeding seasons. Birds spread their tails, ruffle their plumage, and secrete odoriferous substances. There is reason to believe that the particular distribution

228 .—" Nougi," or nose greeting of the Maori, New Zealand.

of hair on the human body has an olfactory use ; the skin, sudoriferous and sebaceous glands of head, armpits and genitalia are olfactory zones.

Among devotees of the. peculiar sexual manifestation we term *fetichism*, it has been remarked that their favourite objects are those apt to be saturated with human exudations : feet, shoes, stockings, chemises, handkerchiefs and hair.*

* *Cf.* The story of Henri III. of France, who was consumed by a fit of passion after having wiped his face with the sweaty shift of Maria of Cleves.

There is a further curious genito-olfactory interaction which has been discovered and recorded by Fliess. There are certain regions in the lower region of the conchæ in the nose, near the tuberculum septi, which strongly resemble the erectile tissues of the genitals. The resemblance is twofold : first, it is structural ; in both areas there is a network of minute blood vessels which does not empty itself directly into the venous system but interlaces over a relatively considerable sphere and thus easily becomes congested. These " genital " areas of the nose are innervated from the spheno-palatine ganglion, which is connected with the carotid, through the petrosus profundus—the sympathetic branch of the caroticus internus. And there is not only a structural likeness to the genital tissues but also a certain functional interaction, as has been proved by the frequent and severe attacks of nose-bleeding in the years just before and during puberty and the menopause ; and by the dilation and congestion of the nasal passages during menstruation. (Further details on this subject have been given by Hagemann, Schiff, Falta and Seifert, who refer to nearly 300 authorities on this subject.)

Red-haired or auburn women and girls are known to have pronounced personal odours. And prostitutes know that masculine potency may often be stimulated if they bring the nose of their lover into contact with hairy parts or shoulders.

Kissing is a complex contact in which tactile and olfactory sensations are mingled with cerebral associations and also probably with definite flavours, in some cases at least.* Its pre-human and primitive human evolution are curiously uncertain, but possibly the lover's mouth to mouth kiss of the modern West evolved through the "nose-kiss" of primitive peoples and Eastern Asiatic civilisations (Fig. 228).

Titillation also and the activity of the dance tend to excite odoriferous secretions and thus are erotic means of stimulation.

Jäger has pointed out that olfactory impressions are closely interwoven with instinctive antipathies and repulsions as well as attractions. Such effects are not only individual but racial, for there is reason to believe that every race has its peculiar odour, which is imperceptible or pleasing—or at least inoffensive—to its own members, but much the reverse to persons of widely different ethnic type. Teleologically we might consider this as Nature's antidote to possible miscegenation, but, whatever its hypothetical " causes," the facts are indubitable. The black and yellow races are generally repugnant to our European sense of smell ; but the yellow races find the white man quite as objectionable. (For further details we refer the student to Gustav Jäger, Zwaardemaker, Scheuer, Havelock Ellis, Adachi, Richard Andrée, G. Klein, E. Schultze, Monin.) Friedländer compares human racial antipathies on this basis to the enmities of different species of ants. And the individual sense of smell may be equally acute and pronounced in its effect on emotional relationships. It is probable that every human being has a peculiar individual odour : most of us are unable to perceive this, but dogs are in no doubt : they identify human beings obviously by their smell. And these particular exudations or effluvia must be perceived very definitely by the nose and brain of the dog, for they adhere to and emanate from the master's person, anything he has often touched or worn, and even the imprint of his shoes on the ground or floor. Even if a man washes his feet in salicylic acid solution a good sporting dog will pick up and follow his scent : the dog will even perceive and follow the scent of a bicyclist. And we can only conclude that there must be an analogous process between human

* For a full treatment of this subject, see Th. H. Van de Velde, " Ideal Marriage : Its Physiology and Technique " (William Heinemann (Medical Books) Ltd., London, 1928), pp. 151–164.

beings, although, in most cases—at least in modern urban environments—well below the threshold of consciousness. We shall have occasion to revert to this topic again.

However, in mankind, the sexual impulse is highly composite and intricate. Diverse elements contribute to its complex and the direction of desire is not dependent on the senses alone (*cf.* Schiefferdecker). We must now consider the

Associative Factors

(The Impetus and Inhibitions of Desire)

We have seen that the stimuli received by the medulla spinalis may operate further, either through simple reflexes or through cerebral conduction via the white medullary substance to the medulla oblongata. If the stimuli received in any given space of time are mainly and definitely sexual, the whole central nervous system is flooded with hormones from the endocrine glands : that is to say, it is chemically eroticised.

The tracts of the medulla spinalis terminate in the cortex of the cerebellum and are partly crossing and partly non-crossing. Their terminal fibres envelop the cortical cells (Purkinje), so that the cerebellum can be regarded as a kind of receiving station (Fig. 223).

It is thought that the medial region of the cerebellum apparently controls the normal static functions of the body and its two hemispheres co-ordinate bodily movements.

The palæencephalon includes, further, the mesencephalon or mid-brain ; the optic tract sweeps round to the mesencephalon. If this portion of the brain is removed through accident or operation there is an extreme slowness of all reflex movements. We must, therefore, assume that every muscular contraction of the bodily periphery, though set in motion by the cerebellum, is inhibited in the—operated or defective—mesencephalon. Under the mesencephalic vault is the so-called *aqueductus Sylvii* (aqueductus cerebri), named after the anatomist, Sylvius (1614–1672). The aqueduct (or transformation of the mid-brain cavity) connects the fourth ventricle with the third, and has a layer of grey matter, very rich in fibres and cells, and, apparently, in some way associated with the autonomic system (*e.g.*, heart beat, vasomotor or circulatory stimulation, uterine contractions and erection, etc.).

In the thalamus opticus there is probably the main cell centre of the sensory paths. The interaction and connection of thalamus and cortex (and cortical action alone) enable us to perceive and differentiate size, shape, densities and positions of objects.

In the olfactory lobe the chemical sensations received through the nose are registered. And all these important centres are connected with the cerebrum through fibres of the corona radiata. And they also supply the paths for voluntary or volitional movement (from cerebrum to periphery) through the pyramidal cells.

The *cerebrum* is divided into two hemispheres which are ovoid in shape and separated along their upper surface, which is vaulted or convex, by the longitudinal fissure, a deep narrow groove. Each hemisphere contains in its interior the mass of grey substance, the basal ganglia : the cells of the cortex being known as the *neopallium*. The surface area of the neopallium is crinkled into folds and furrows (sulci and fissuræ) and intersected by convolutions or gyri. In and around these folds are the sensory areas and their circumferent associative areas, according to

Flechsig. The same authority claims that the associative areas only have very slight neural connection with the palæencephalon but are closely interlaced among themselves. There is no doubt that the cerebral cortex is the centre of all the highest and most elaborate psychic processes. Thus the neopallium is the seat of perceptual activity and learning processes.

The palæencephalon or older brain gives us muscular movement of an involuntary type and sensory impressions, and it is even able to construct fresh relations or sequences between sense and movement : but it cannot register or elaborate associations, those complex memory pictures the constituents of which may be combined and recombined afresh.

All reflex actions and many so-called instincts are localised in the palæencephalon and the forms of animal life in which the palæencephalon alone exists are creatures of reflexes and instincts. But as the cerebral cortex begins to evolve, and as it grows larger in area and more complex in structure, the faculties and potentialities of action, sensation and perception increase also : cognition and apperception, habitual and purposive action and, finally, the intellectual processes which are developed in man. These are supposed to be located mainly in the cortical areas of the frontal cerebral lobes.

The Motor Factors

(The Release of Impulse)

The nerve channels conducting the stimuli—received and registered by the central nervous system—to its peripheries are both motor and secretory, or muscular and glandular. The nerves of the glands stimulate their special secretions, and release a flow of hormones, by which the whole organism reaches a certain degree of tension, without any assistance or participation of the will. This reflex mechanism cannot be brought about or stopped at will : it can only in the course of time be rendered inoperative so that sexual release becomes inhibited. The reflexes are carried to the terminal organs by the nerve tracts. These cortical reflexes have been produced artificially in the course of experiments by Bechterev and Mislavski— among others. Artificial stimulation of part of the anterior frontal lobe in rabbits, or of the gyrus sigmordens in bitches, caused repeated contractions of the vagina— an effect increased by stimulation of the thalamus opticus, or the central end of the vagus nerve ; whereas if the peripheral end of the vagus be stimulated, the vagina is relaxed.

Psychic stimulation may also produce changes of colour ; alternate flushes and pallor ; here the cerebrum acts on the nerves of the capillaries. In itself, blushing is due to vaso-motor action and has nothing to do with any inborn sense of right and wrong. It is an expression of excitement.

The decrease or ebb of any intense stimulation is termed its decrement and corresponds in degree to the intensity of the preceding excitement.

In ordinary life we prefer to speak of a reproductive impulse. Such does not exist in the sense of being *conscious*, for reproduction is solely the result of copulation, so that with Hartmann or Wundt one could speak of reproductive instinct. But it would be better to speak of an impulse of copulation or sexual impulse, for this alone is released through sexual excitement. Should pregnancy intervene, reproduction is solely the result of copulation, which itself was derived from the excitement of desire. Moll has analysed the human mating impulse into two components. One is local, *i.e.*, genital, and culminates in orgasm. This he terms the urge to detumescence.   The other component leads to the approach, the contact and the caresses, which are part of normal sexual relationships : Moll terms this process contrectation.   Contrectation develops long before functional maturity of the genital organs and is active in children. It is certainly stronger in many women than the urge to detumescence, and both Theile and Pelikan believe that this impulse for contrectation is hardly diminished in men who have been castrated—if the castration took place after puberty.   Mother love is a sublimated and specialised contrectation (Figs. 229 and 230).

Hirschfeld has dealt well with the sexual instinct and the emotion of love in his inaugural address to the First Congress of the World League for Sexual Reform on a scientific basis, in Berlin, 1921.   He said :

"(1) Love is a complicated series of reflexes.   Its centripetal phase is the erotic image or impressions, conveyed through all the senses, in an intense exhilaration and expansion of consciousness, to the brain.   Its central phase is the erotic urge, physically based on nervous tension and vascular congestion, and its centrifugal phase, the erotic expression, which transforms latent into dynamic energy.

"(2) The specific capacity for sexual reactions and the aim towards which the reactions are directed, *i.e.*, the sexual tropism or impulse, have a wide range of variation, in both amount and quality ; and they are most intimately interwoven with the whole individuality.   As Friedrich Nietzsche remarked : 'The degree and essential nature of any human being's sexuality extends into the highest pinnacle of his spirit.'

"(3) This endogenous quality or individual sexual constitution is in the parental germ cells from whose division a living being develops preformed as to inborn qualities.   Its special character is mainly dependent on the very variable 'blends' of the intrinsically male and the intrinsically female.   In all living creatures produced by the conjugation of the two sexes, there are characteristics of both sexes, though to very different degrees.   Here the famous axiom of Leibnitz is constantly verified : 'Tout va par

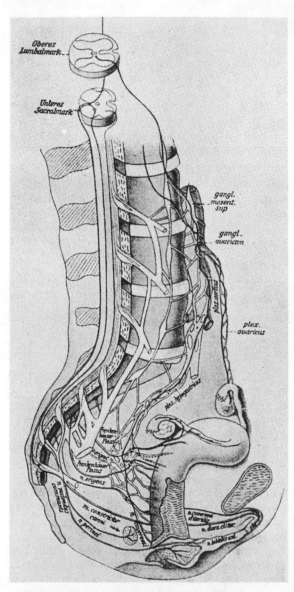

229 .—Schematic representation of the innervation of the female genitals.   (After Dahl.)

degrés dans la nature et rien par sauts' (Nature always moves step by step and not in leaps and bounds).

" (4) The need of sexual relaxation or functional activity postulates the saturation of the active centres with the products of the ductless glands, the endocrine secretions influence the brain and the brain stimulates the external secretions. The law of psycho-hormonic parallelism is one of the most important in sexual science. If the gonads are male in character, the masculine characteristics develop; if the gonads are female, feminine characteristics emerge. If there is a blend of male and female glandular structure, the characteristics partake of both

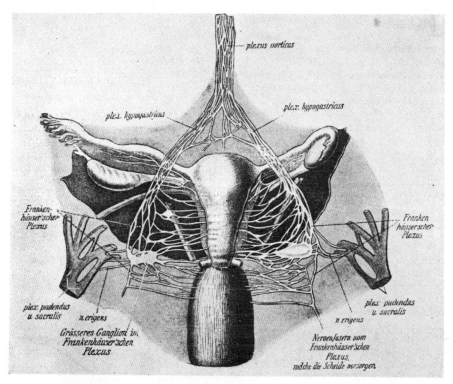

230.—Macroscopic view of the hypogastric nerve plexus of the nervus erigens and the cervical ganglion. (After Dahl.)

sexes. If the gonads are mutilated or injured, the sexual characteristics are defective, and if the gonads are wholly lacking, the result is an asexual anomaly.

" (5) The sexual needs of the majority of human beings have just as imperative a demand for occasional fulfilment as the needs for food or sleep. The mind and will may inhibit, excite or consciously repress sexual needs as they do other needs. But such repression is not possible for any length of time without serious bodily and mental results. As in all bodily and mental functions, so here, the best way of living is to avoid either starvation or surfeit and to keep the via media between a necessary minimum (of activity and experience) and a maximum which shall not prove intolerable to the powers and the balance of the personality.

" (6) The significance of sexual love is not limited to its biological result of reproduction. Rather is an adequate sexual fulfilment one of the chief conditions of a good life, both in external efficiency and mental health and poise.

" Love serves and increases life in three ways. Love makes life worth living for the individual for the intense exhilaration and peculiar sensations it is able to bestow. Love unites diverse beings to one another and forges links between them from which man develops into a higher being. Love causes the individuals to expand beyond themselves.

" Love is potential life. Life without love is mere existence.

" In the history of human love, three stages may be differentiated.

" In the earliest of these, sexuality was mainly a reflex mechanism, as amongst lower creatures.

" There followed a second stage, in which we now are. In this phase, inhibitive mechanisms became paramount. Humanity has constructed codes of different kinds which find expression in contemporary customs and morals.

" Thus, in this second phase, we find the most fantastic ethical and practical extremes : compulsory virginity and compulsory prostitution, for instance, and even more extravagant opposites.

" But for the last few decades, there has been a new light on humanity's horizon, which slowly grows.

" The third stage in the history of human love must establish harmony between inhibitions and reflexes. It must avoid indiscriminate licence and indiscriminate abstinence ; the abstinence which Edward Carpenter so well called ' the renunciation of this world for its shadow.' "

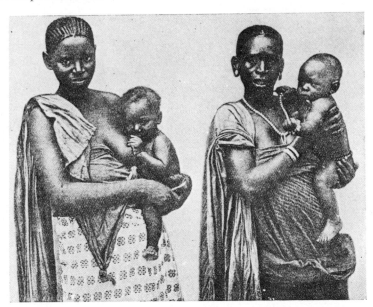

231.—Swahili women and children. (After Vincenti.)

NORMAL AND MORBID BASES OF PSYCHOLOGICAL DEVELOPMENT

If we are to arrive at a just estimate of the normal as well as the morbid sexual impulse, we must begin with the child. It is not generally easy in the case of the child—at least in its early life—to recognise the manifestations of the sexual impulse, and yet there can be no doubt that it is there. Many see in the corresponding actions the result of imitative impulse. Many admit pleasurable sensations without defining with which impulse they are to be connected, although they observe that the child seeks out the causes of the pleasurable sensations more or less ardently. Here Freud and his school undoubtedly deserve credit for having done the preliminary work.

Infantile Sexuality

In this two stages may be observed. The polymorphous, lasting till between four and five years of age in most cases, and the first educative or period of repression.

We know that sexual sensations exist and even emotion may be active long before sexual maturity or aptitude to reproduce. Endocrine secretions begin in the body of the unborn infant or fœtus. And, in early childhood, many cases are recorded of children who touched and rubbed their genital organs until they gave unmistakable signs of acute excitement and relief in a manner resembling adult or adolescent masturbation. Sadger, Hirschsprung, Fleischmann, Kassowitz, Neter, Heubner and Friedjung have documented and described such cases as early as nine days after birth. Apparently, the erogenous zones of later life are already sources of voluptuous pleasure at a year old, or less, *i.e.*, from birth, potentially at least. And there are not the sensations of disgust and shame which develop later. Therefore Freud terms this phase " polymorphous-perverse," and Sadger maintains that the child's innocence and purity, *i.e.*, its lack of interest and feeling in sexual matters is a myth, to which the facts have never corresponded.

The people who are shocked at this may well bear in mind that a child with no sexual vitality has probably very little vitality at all. Mental development runs parallel with sexual development. If we want to have thriving intelligent children we must not expect them to be deaf and blind in this respect alone.

K. Th. Preuss has spoken of the magic of bodily orifices, and has emphasised the attention these parts receive from many primitive peoples as, for example, in the records and monuments of ancient Mexico.

These specimens of archaic art and ritual may be at least partly attributed to a special infantile " orificial eroticism," which has survived puberty and adolescence. As a general rule, all bodily apertures are erogenous. The mouth is specially so. The act of suction is an innate instinctive reflex, and this reflex is not confined to the act of lactation but extends to other portions of the body, whether that of the sucker or of other persons. And there may result not only a pleasant sensation but a distinct sexual relief. Lindner points out that children often rub their erogenous zones, as well as attempting suction. Galant has given an account of a young woman who retained these habits in later life and expressed herself as follows : " The pleasure of sucking during childhood is the same as the sexual voluptas of the adult." The anus has also a certain power of voluptuous sensation. Bleuler and others have given instances of this in children. And there is not only an anal but also a urethral pleasure-complex in children ; it has been maintained that there is no such sensation as disgust in the human young before their fourth or fifth year. Sadger has collected much relevant material on this, and also we must remember that ears and nose may be, and in children often are, areas of pleasurable exploration.

Coprophilia. Freud pointed out that in children interest in sex could not, in its first manifestations, be distinguished from interest in excrement. The structure of the human pelvis has placed the rectal passage and the genital passage (or, in man, the genito-urinary passage) in close proximity to one another and the association of the two functions has been established even where consciousness does not link them together.

There is also a skin or dermal eroticism. Sadger has dealt with it in detail. Tickling and contact, however light, with the inner surfaces of the thighs will often produce erections and uncontrollable fits of laughter in children.

Muscular eroticism is connected with the development of muscular power and co-ordination, and the exercise of power over others, especially by provoking movement either of flight or defence, is very marked in children. It may manifest itself as definite cruelty to animals or bullying of smaller and younger children. Some physiologists believe in a specialised muscular sense, a faculty which enables us to apprehend the absolute and relative positions of our bodily parts, and the weight and density of external objects. Basler considers that the muscular sense is based on the stimulation of those centripetal nerves which are situated in the muscles, and equally on the sensibility of bones, fasciæ and sinews, and that it surpasses the sense of pressure in delicacy of perception.

There is also a pleasurably-toned compulsion to sniff and inhale the smell of hair, skin, and even sex organs, in children. This is not necessarily " corrupt," but often naïf and spontaneous.

There is a highly significant impulse to expose and display the body, especially to specially beloved or favoured persons, and not only to display but to behold. It is probably correct to speak of infantile exhibitionism as general in early childhood. Children, before five years, are inclined to watch one another in the performance of excretion and micturition and the games of " father and mother " and " doctor " are certainly spontaneous rather than imitative.

Freiherr von Reitzenstein made a curious observation on a boy of five years old, whose whole education was normal and practical, and whose impulses were certainly not degenerate. This child was in the habit of drawing rough outlines of " people " ; and he always made a straight dividing line between the thighs. He was asked " what sort of people ? " and replied invariably " a girl." He was asked to draw a boy, but made no attempt to indicate any sex organ. It was considered unwise to ask him why he drew a genital organ for the girl but none for the boy ; but it may be confidently assumed that he was only interested in depicting the sex organ of the girl, no pleasure being obtained by drawing his own.

In the earliest stages of infantile sexuality children do not conceal their instinctive interests and habits even from adults. There follows a period or phase of repression, through deliberate education by adults, and, in this phase, the child is only " natural " and not on its guard among other children, especially about its own age.

Freud has pointed out the traditional and usual sequence of repressions in the second phase of infantile sexuality. First of all the interest in urine and excrement (coprophilia) is rebuked, and the concept of disgust and " nastiness " is developed or imposed. Unfortunately, this repression and reprobation of the excretory functions extend, both with structure and association, and more or less definitely to the sphere of sex. Sex and dirt, sex and disgust become identified. The same repressive process extends to all the other polymorphous sexual interests and they are penalised ; thus dread and fear of punishment and painful consequences are attached to them. Disgust and anxiety combine to form the sensation of shame and the emotion of modesty, and these powerful complexes, though not innate, are re-enforced by the atavistic urge of self-defence or self-protection, especially in woman. This urge is pronounced in animals and helps to accumulate and increase voluptuous sensation, and is thus a powerful engine of natural and sexual selection, as Havelock Ellis has remarked. Only prolonged, intensive and, to some extent, skilful wooing by the male can overcome this mixture of fear, repugnance and self-preservation. Thus the strongest and most ardent males have the greatest opportunities of begetting future generations—in primitive communities. The most pronounced form of sexual self-defence in civilised communities is coquetry. Coquetry does not necessarily aim at denying, but wishes to prolong the pleasant sensation of being wooed, thus sharpening the desires of the lover. But as sensations of guilt, disgust and dread are also strongly associated with sex, hypocrisy arises. Modesty develops a wide register of tones and semitones and expresses vasomotor processes through blushing and pallor. But blushing is the sign and product of a certain degree of congestion and excitement, and has nothing intrinsically to do with any objective external canon of right or wrong. It depends on the response which the excited or amorous person expects from his or her environment; in the dark or in security and seclusion, they hardly play any part (*cf.* Havelock Ellis and Giessler). But all these repressions of natural urges and their associated complexes are of the first importance in determining character and outlook of the growing child.

[Psycho-analytic investigation into the sexual life of civilised children has been much intensified of late years through the development of the so-called " play technique " devised by certain continental workers and adopted by English and American analysts (*cf.* M. Klein, " Symposium on Child Analysis "). A survey of the literature of the early years of the twentieth century was given by Pastor Pfister in his book on love in children, and since that date development has been rapid.

Without appraising the evidence put forward by psycho-analysts for their somewhat startling theories and methods it may be said that the present tendency seems to be towards more importance being attached to the factors of disappointment and frustration than was formerly the case. The works of Sigmund and Anna Freud, Hug-Hellmuth, M. Klein, etc., will be found useful in studying modern methods in child analysis, and the results which are claimed to be achieved thereby.

In girls a potent source of future troubles is said to lie in a so-called " penis envy " which they cherish and which is connected with an alleged castration complex. It is urged that the Œdipus tendencies of the growing girl are ushered in by oral desires for the father's phallus. She desires to deprive her mother of the possession of her father's penis, and thus gain it for herself. Freud himself was of the opinion that what makes the girl turn from her mother is the fact that she considers her responsible for her own lack of a penis. Small girls are said by psycho-analysts to cherish phantasies about " the enormous powers and huge size and strength " of their father's organs, which ideas rise from their own " oral-, urethral- and anal-sadistic impulses " (Klein).

Whatever may be the truth (or otherwise) of Mrs. Klein's original and stimulating observations, her views do not find acceptance in certain quarters, since Anna Freud has developed a technique differing from that favoured by Mrs. Klein in important particulars. Both methods are, however, said to yield the most excellent results.]

The Period of Puberty

(Phase of Fixation)

At puberty the inchoate polymorphous sexual impulse is definitely " orientated " or directed towards a preferential type of object or response; the previously acquired repressions still continuing to modify the direction and quality of desire in many ways. And the activities of the endocrine glands give the personality its distinctive sexual idiosyncrasy or blend of male and female. There are two groups; those functionally " normal," *i.e.*, tending to processes helping reproduction, or those functionally "abnormal," *i.e.*, tending to processes where reproduction is not possible. If the emotional trend in sex is quite definitely determined and limited in one direction, we speak of its fixation, and this may be either (biologically) normal or abnormal. This is based mainly on the structure and secretions of the endocrine glands, and can be either exclusively heterosexual, *i.e.*, on members of the opposite sex, or homosexual, *i.e.*, on members of the same sex. And it must be clearly understood that between the extremely virile man and the extremely feminine woman there are a whole series of less specialised types of physique and temperament, which Hirschfeld has termed Sexual Intermediate types. And there is no doubt that the differences of physique and faculty are accompanied by various definite differences in their specifically sexual tastes and inclinations. We shall presently enumerate the main categories. But there is one group which deserves special mention, for in their case environmental influences are often decisive. In these persons there is an endocrine basis which would and does indicate in the main a certain definite emotional trend (or mental attitude) which is, however, occasionally deflected somewhat towards other objects of desire or methods of satisfaction. The causal mechanism here is somewhat complicated, but during the polymorphous phase of early childhood all possible " perverse " inclinations were present and we may assume that any of them might have become the dominant fixation. A humane, enlightened, happy and wholesome early environment and education would have left the real endocrine idiosyncrasy sublimated but not stifled, to " play lead." But such education and early environment are all too rare. Sheer neglect or traditional moralism give no direction and cultivation of the emotions and/or simply repress any sort of sexual impulse. There follows, especially during the tumultuous mental growth and stress of puberty, a repression which leaves the emotions at the mercy of active extraneous stimuli. And these stimuli are wholly a matter of chance. In institutions and schools, during the years between 11 and 18, a whole sequence of abnormal influences may be brought to bear on the immature personality and may completely change the disposition. But there may be some degree of endocrine anomaly if the acquired habits of puberty take hold of adult life.

Actual bisexuality excludes definite fixation. Bisexual persons are those in whom homosexual and heterosexual inclinations are almost evenly poised ; who may be strongly attracted both to men and women. Thus we may distinguish three main groups of positive sexuality alone. A pronounced biologically normal trend which expresses itself in heterosexual desire ; a pronounced abnormal trend which must lead to homosexual desire ; and a pathologically unstable trend which may lead to both heterosexual and homosexual desires under the influence of early repressions and environmental conditions, which may influence the normal endocrine factors and activate the abnormal.

The repressive processes of puberty are specially important in persons of neuropathic constitution. And puberty is the period of sexual crises ; the period of being " misunderstood " ; of storms and stress ; of extravagant ideals and vague dreams ; of maladaptation to realities whether of environment or other individuals ; of extreme irritability, moroseness, exhaustibility, alternate excitement and depression, agonies of shyness and painful aggressiveness. And there may be a whole series of physical neuroses, St. Vitus Dance with painful grimaces ; stammering, nail-biting, epileptoid phenomena, obsessions—running away from home or school, arson (pyromania), and others of the same kind. There is also a highly pitched idealism, often without habits of practical consideration and kindness to others and without real experience of the world.   All these manifestations have become acute since the war of 1914–1918.   These years have unleashed the tendency to extremes which exists in puberty ; often there is criminality, violence, robbery, murder, assaults, " love pacts," drunkenness, blackmail ; and all these are not prevented by the acute conflict between traditional religion—with its emphasis on authority and salvation—and the stress of the accumulating sexual urge.   Puberty may be a time of religious " conversion," of exquisite romantic devotion, of enthusiasm and idealism.   It may also produce criminals, hooligans, prostitutes and procurers.

The repressive influences of education and environment are, in part, necessary for human order and achievement, but, in part, highly dangerous to efficiency, sanity and happiness ; especially when repression is enforced regardless of the special constitution and temperament of the young creature, and when it is based on the moral codes of traditional religions.

Early educative and environmental impressions, however undesirable, may be obliterated in the course of vigorous physical and mental growth, especially after normal and to some degree satisfactory sexual activity has begun.   But, in persons of neurotic or neuropathic constitution, the mistakes of their parents may persist throughout life in morbid deviations of various kinds.   Young persons at puberty try automatically and unconsciously to discover objects for their intense organic and psychic unrest : these we may term " sexual equivalents."   These are of the most diverse kinds : sentimental—but often highly emotional—attachments to teachers, fellow-pupils or casual strangers ; many games and sports, dancing— often the only conventionally conceded form of relief for young girls—" moonlight and April " verse, music ; or erotic books and illustrations, together with masturbation, but not the kind of self-relief of the adult.   If these safety valves—or those provided by certain individual hobbies and interests—are closed, the results may be serious neuroses and, if the threat and terror of religious superstitions be added to a situation already difficult enough, there may be life-long mental injury.

Girls have the automatic relief of recurrent menstruation ; but there is no doubt that the monthly period is a time of mental unrest, and neuroses may then develop very easily.   These considerations assist in explaining certain criminal traits in women, the development of their character on the one hand and marked development of the sexual impulse on the other.

Normal Bases of the Sexual Impulse

The normal functioning of the sexual impulse is on the lines which make reproduction possible.

Normal adult sexual desire is therefore heterosexual, *i.e.*, directed towards the opposite sex, and is neither below a certain degree of urgency nor uncontrollably strong.

Therefore, on the basis of biological and neurological facts, we suggest the following definition of love.

Love between the sexes (or in abnormal cases, between persons of the same sex) is a relationship founded on or aiming at sexual acts and processes.   It is activated by *special stimuli* which decide its direction ; and limited by the chemical function of the endocrine glands, expressed through the associative processes of the cerebral cortex : it is a state of intense excitement and, therefore, not static or permanent. Certain harmonies of sentiment and habit may transmit it ; and passionate love may merge into a lasting emotion of which there are many other component parts.

To-day the term love is often used in a false sense. Here the definition will be limited to that outlined above. A platonic love, which has no sexual interests or elements does not exist; such an emotion is friendship, sympathy, affinity, comradeship, but not love.

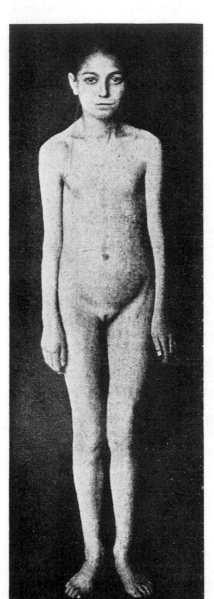

232.—Infantilism in a 13-year-old girl. (After Meige.)

As love depends upon external stimuli there must be some special feature, some conspicuous and appealing charm which focuses attention and commences the whole cerebral associative process; this special feature, attribute, or quality has peculiar power and often decides the duration of the erotic spell. In other words, almost every human love has a strong fetichist or symbolist basis, and, indeed, sexual love is largely fetichism. Nevertheless, certain degrees of fetichism are both biologically and emotionally abnormal; as when sexual excitement *and* sexual satisfaction are provoked by an inanimate object (shoes or gloves) or by a part of the human person (feet, hair) without any reference to the organic unit of the whole. Love has also strong exhibitionist elements. To display oneself to the beloved being is a deep human urge, but it becomes abnormal if exposure alone is sought and is sufficient to provoke the climax of sensation and relief.

Even the most emotionally normal and balanced human beings will have recourse to some kind of sexual equivalents or substitute gratifications, under prolonged and complete deprivation of normal satisfaction. Many become masturbators by necessity (*e.g.*, in prisons or cloisters); others may develop artificial homosexual habits (in barracks or in ships); or dances, theatrical performances and fugitive contacts may provide for girls a certain kind of relief. But such relief is delusory, and if the normal deprivation is prolonged it leads to the sexual neuroses. Freud has rightly said, "Neuroses are impossible in normal sexual life."

Pathological Traits

We cannot deal with this subject in detail, but as it is immensely important and still somewhat obscure, we must refer to its main factors here. Abnormal sexual desire, like normal sexual desire, has two main facets and forces: psychic and hormonic. Hormonic anomalies may be quantitative, *i.e.*, they may manifest as defect or as excess; and these may be shown either in the physical or emotional spheres. The specific genital glands or gonads may be lacking (Eunuchoidism, *cf.* Saenger) or of arrested development (Infantilism*). These manifestations are probably due to disturbances of the hypophysis or pituitary gland. Or the quantitative endocrine anomaly may show itself as uncommonly slight and weak (hypo-erotism) or as overwhelming and continuous sexual desire (hyper-erotism), as Messalina is supposed to have possessed (Fig. 233), and called nymphomania.

Hyper-erotism has various forms and blends, psychic and hormonic. The impulse may be extremely facile and indiscriminate (polyerotism), or it may be directed to one person to an inordinate and supreme degree (superfixation).

Both excess and defect of desire may lead to professional moralism and declaration of great austerity—combined with persecution of those less austere.

Quantitative anomalies in the endocrine glands may also reveal themselves in very late or very early menstruation. Normality is a varied and uncertain concept here, but we may perhaps claim that menstruation commencing after 18 years of age or before 10 is abnormal. The phenomenon of infantile menstruation is considered in a later chapter.

There are also qualitative endocrine anomalies : here belongs the wide territory of the intermediate type, the *homosexuals, androgynes, transvestites* and the "*metatropists*" of Hirschfeld, where the *rôles* of the sexes are reversed.

What has been called hormonically determined homosexuality is very different from the substitutional pseudo-homosexuality to which reference has recently been made. Of course, the orthodox Freudian school of psycho-analysts (Freud and Stekel especially, but *cf.* O. Schwarz) consider homosexuality an acquired neurosis.

233.—Messalina.   Bust by F. Alinari, in Florence.

Näcke's view is based on cerebral structure ; he believes that there are bilateral brain centres of libido and that one—generally the homosexual—atrophies in the course of development. Fliess observed that left-handed men tend to be of less pronounced physical and mental virility and left-handed women of less pronounced femininity than the right-handed. Saaler believed that homosexuality is based on the persistence of a " sexual centre " located on the right side of the brain (controlling the left side of the body) and associated with the characteristics of the opposite sex. But, though some of these observations and deductions may be quite accurate, they hardly offer an adequate explanation of sexual intergrades and inversion. Kräpelin, Ziehen and other psychologists believe that homosexual trends are determined by chance in the early experience of individuals ; occurrences which make ineffaceable impressions (*cf.* Kronfeld). The precise genesis of homosexuality is much less

* See Apert.

important than the need for knowledge of its nature : for public recognition of the fact that homosexuality is not a deed but a desire ; not an action but an emotion.

Homosexual emotion is more easily expressed in contrectation than in detumescence. For where there is detumescence there is a distinct reversion to one of the polymorphous phases of infantile sexuality. Thus the preferential bodily methods of gratification in male homosexuals are either anal or oral.

Hirschfeld has investigated and enumerated homosexual methods of physical gratification. He finds four methods between homosexual men : (*a*) *Manual* or *digital*, which, according to Hirschfeld, is preferred by 40 per cent. ; (*b*) *Oral*, preferred by another 40 per cent., and, like the first, often practised mutually ; (*c*) *Femoral*, preferred by about 12 per cent. ; and (*d*) *Anal*, the favourite method of only 8 per cent., although this particular action is generally considered typical of male homosexuality, or even identified therewith.

234.—Bust of Sappho. Berlin, Altes Museum.

Among homosexual women there are (*a*) *Digital* contact and gratification, and (*b*) *Oral*, which is often considered the typical Lesbian, or Sapphic, caress. The (*c*) *femoral* type of gratification also exists in the modified form of close pressure and friction of thighs and sexual organs : the term *tribadism* (τρίβειν, to rub) is often applied to this practice alone. Remarkable (*d*) development of the clitoris sometimes enables women to practise some degree of vaginal insertion, but this is not common among the white races.

Finally, there is the use of the artificial penis or dildo, an instrument of wax or rubber (*cf.* Figs. 235 and 236), which one woman puts on and inserts into the vagina or anus of her partner (see also **WOMAN IN THE SEX RELATIONSHIP., 50, 52)**.

Krafft-Ebing maintains that there are two main types or degrees of feminine homosexuality. He differentiates what he calls viraginity in which the mental and emotional attitude is masculine, and " gynandrism " in which the woman has structural (somatic) resemblances to the male type as well. But Hirschfeld is of opinion, and probably rightly, that we cannot draw any definite distinction here.

The exact shades and grades of abnormality designated androgyny, transvestitism, and Hirschfeld's " metatropism " may be briefly defined.

Androgyny may be somatic and psychic, or psychic only. The somatic idiosyncrasies include a prominent Adam's apple, deep and strong voice, flat breasts and hair on the face. Psychically, there is great energy, especially for public affairs and political life, or for violent sports : and many of the leading exponents of women's rights are undoubtedly androgynous to a greater or lesser degree. There is sometimes an attraction and affection for the corresponding intermediate male type, and this combination is not seldom to be found in marriage.

Transvestitism is an allied manifestation, which often approaches neurosis. Transvestites have a profound urge to clothe themselves and behave as members of the opposite sex. This impulse is so powerful that restraint upon it sometimes causes transvestites to attempt suicide (Talmey). There have been women who endeavoured to enlist as soldiers and even who served in the ranks without being detected till some accident or fatal injury occurred. There is probably a certain androgynous-transvestitism in the frequent use of male pseudonyms by women writers, *e.g.*, George Sand or George Eliot.

What has been called *metatropism* is the subtlest of these manifestations. Metatropism in women means a special attraction to and affection for men of very fragile and even effeminate type ; and a markedly protective and dominant attitude towards them. Metatropism,

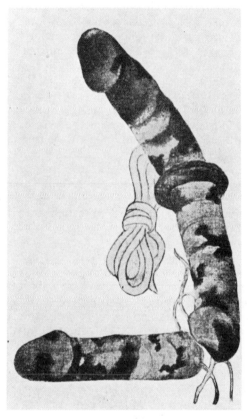

235 .—Japanese dildo. One is single for solitary gratification. The other is double for use with a partner. (After Krauss.)

236 .—Madigo of the Hausa women. It is made of wood covered with leather and perforated, and is provided with strings for attachment to the body. The bag is filled with the diluted sap of the *dalaku* tree.

androgyny and transvestitism are, in short, phenomena merging into one another and different types of sexual intergrades. Although there may be some such manifestations which are of psychic origin or the results of environmental repressions, the fundamental basis is endocrinic disturbances.

We now turn from intersexual types to the negative abnormalities, so called because some important element in the sexual emotion is wanting or repressed. Such a condition is found in contrectation. Here we may find the two forms of genuine auto-erotism : (*a*) habitual masturbation, by choice and not through the compulsion of necessity, but as a preferably adequate form of sexual satisfaction ;

(*b*) Narcissism (the auto-monosexuality of Hirschfeld), in which satisfaction is obtained not directly by means of physical excitation of the individual's own body, but indirectly, through the contemplation of that body.

The failure to achieve detumescence is an important factor in a woman's life. The wish to become a mother and to possess a child without sexual contact is somewhat frequent, and there are some authorities who assert that detumescence must be awakened in girls by the male, whilst the desire to be fondled and caressed is normally always present.

Of great importance are the associative disturbances. Here we have the great group of fetichist manifestations. Fetichism is to some degree strictly normal, but, when within normal limits, there is always an association between the sexual symbol in the forefront of consciousness and the whole body or whole personality of the human being to whom the symbol appertains. But, in morbid degrees of fetichism, the organic and psychic personality is not associated in the attraction to the special symbol, *e.g.*, the hair or gloves. Even quite apart from the whole body to which they appertained, the symbols may excite and release desire.

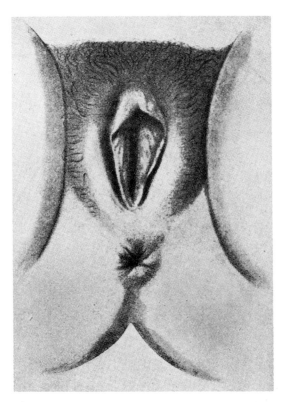

237.—Vulva in a case of habitual masturbation. (After Mayer-Ruegg.)

Another very frequent and significant associative perversion is algolagnia : a condition in which pain and cruelty provoke voluptuous sexual pleasure. Algolagnia may be either active or passive. Passive algolagnia makes experiences which inspire pain, disgust, discomfort or humiliation in normal people, arouse excitement and pleasure if connected closely with sexual factors and even produce orgasm. This type of response is termed masochism (Fig. 238) from the Austrian author, Leopold von Sacher Masoch* (1836–1895), who constantly dealt with it in his stories and essays. The opposite to masochism is sadism, which makes the infliction of discomfort, humiliation, fear and pain on other persons the occasion of sexual excitement, pleasure and satisfaction. It is named after the French author the Marquis de Sade (1740–1814). There is a certain basis for this in the polymorphous perversity of early childhood ; and we may possibly even find traces in the wooing and mating of various animal species. Like fetichism, sadism, or rather algolagnia, is interwoven with normal sexuality : biting, pinching and gripping caresses are, in a sense, a manifestation of algolagnia, but one of the most characteristic and pronounced forms is probably flagellation, or the whipping

* For an account of his life see Ellis, III.

craze. This phenomenon is connected with religious neuroses, ideas of sin and penitence, and has often become an epidemic in mediæval times and in cloisters and even educational institutions.*

238.—Torture chamber in the establishment of a masochist, Hamburg.   (After Wulffen.)

It is significant that masochists are often powerfully built, active and virile, and sadists equally often frail and physically feeble ; and there are extreme cases

* [This theme has been treated with a wealth of illustration from ancient and modern sources by Fuchs and Kind.]

of algolagnia, both passive and active among women. There is an element of pleasure in others' pain or of absolute identification with those who inflict or suffer it in the craze for watching motor-races, sporting events, prize fights, bull and cock fights, hunting and blood sports. This was also the main secret of the popularity of executions when they were allowed to be witnessed by the public.

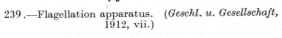

The nature of the early stimuli and their association has been demonstrated by Professor Pavlov's experimental tests on dogs. Dogs have an increased flow of saliva at the sight or smell of their food. Pavlov accompanied the offer of food with various sounds, and these were then alone sufficient to cause the signs of hunger and appetite (Conditioned reflexes). Claparède showed that coloured discs were just as impressive as sounds in association with food, and even a startling and unpleasant sensation, such as an electric current, became a source of positive, i.e., to some extent pleasurable excitement when associated with food. It is supposed that there must be some similar cerebral association in algolagnia. Flagellation is more easily understood than other pleasure-pain perversions, since the whipping is generally on the buttocks and thighs, which are so closely adjacent to and nervously interwoven with the genitalia that increased blood supply to these regions helps to create detumescence.

239.—Flagellation apparatus. (*Geschl. u. Gesellschaft*, 1912, vii.)

The most "normal" sexual life has its ebb and flow, and in woman's organism there are recurrent changes at every menstruation, as well as during the peculiar stress and strain of puberty, pregnancy and the menopause.

Phenomena connected with repression play an important part and are some of the most fruitful sources of neurosis. If the sexual impulse of any human being is prevented from attaining the relief and release of expression along the lines suitable to their personality there is repression, which manifests itself in various morbid symptoms. Freud considers four neuroses to be of sexual origin, viz. :

(1) Neurasthenia, (2) anxiety neuroses, (3) hysteria, and (4) compulsive neuroses.

Endocrine inadequacy or unbalance has much to do with neuroses, as well as the repressive mechanism. The biological framework sets the form as it were for the psychological pattern.

Sexual neurasthenia is very prevalent. Its manifestations begin with fatigue, weakness, failure of memory and judgment, and develop through a variety of

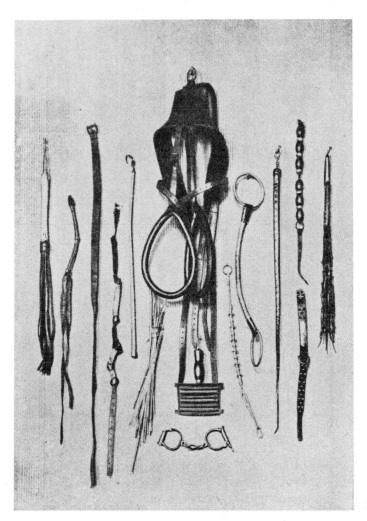

240.—Apparatus for masochistic performances seized in the establishment of a Hamburg masseuse. (After Wulffen.)

physical symptoms, such as headaches, pains in the heart and chest, extreme irritability and sensitiveness to noise, inclination to weep, pains in back and loins, palpitations, cold hands and feet and even skin eruptions : in some severe cases violent nausea, vomiting, colics and jaundice. As a rule all these bodily and mental distresses vanish very soon if, and when, there is individually adequate and satisfactory sexual expression. Hysteria derives its name from the Greek term for the womb or belly. But the name is so far misleading in that its manifestations are not confined wholly to women. The symptoms include trembling, stammering, violent blushing, cramps and faulty muscular co-ordination. There may also be abnormal insensibility to injuries and pain. One of the most curious hysterical forms is vaginismus, in which the vagina closes convulsively before or during inter-course, or under examination. (The male equivalent is *ejaculatio præcox*.) Anxiety

241.—Gräfin Auguste Strachwitz, who controlled a sadistic establishment in Berlin.
(After Wulffen.)

neuroses or phobias include the dread of enclosed spaces (claustrophobia), of empty spaces (agoraphobia), of thunderstorms, of small animals or insects (mice, frogs, worms, spiders), etc. There is also specifically sexual hypochondria, the various forms of which include the exaggerated or chronic dread of contracting venereal disease, the fear and dread of the sexual act, leading to insults and hatred of the partner, whether man or woman, the girl's or woman's fear of defloration and the man's of impotence. Still worse is the fear and suspicion in morbid jealousy, and religious fanaticism, especially when it is intensified and becomes religious " mania."

All these are, or can be, preliminary to the enormously important compulsive neuroses. For every human individuality must be changed, physically and psychically, if its particular inherent urge to sexual activity—whether normal or abnormal, average or morbid—is denied and inhibited. The emotions thus vehemently repressed, gather momentum and break through or seek to break through in other ways : these subconscious urges towards manifestations are termed neuroses by Freud, and we take this terminology here. The repressed libido tends to regress, or take a backward course along the paths of its individual development, i.e., it returns to infantile forms. For instance, it becomes exhibitionism when in a state of sexual excitement. It is far more frequent and pronounced in men than in women. Among children the impulse of general exposure and display is marked, as among adults in sporting circles and on the stage. But this general human tendency becomes morbid if concentrated or restricted to the genital organs. And, apart from their special morbid idiosyncrasy, exhibitionists are mostly very modest. They have often been habitual masturbators in their youth, and have a sense of guilt and a deep dread of women ; these symptoms show that their peculiar sexual trend is based on a sense of their inferiority or inadequacy for normal satisfaction ; often there are other concomitant symptoms of degeneration. The act of self-exposure in exhibitionists is always a response to certain fetichist stimuli, and as soon as these stimuli are perceived the exhibitionists tremble, suffer from palpitations and rushes of blood to the head, and lose all control and sense of safety which, otherwise, prevents the exposure of their genital organs. When the compulsive urge ceases the exhibitionist is overwhelmed with shame if the spectator of his act is disgusted or offended ; but delighted if the exposure is treated as a joke and received with laughter ; and this, too, shows an infantile trend. Among female exhibitionists the breasts or the buttocks are exposed rather than the actual sex organs.

There is also a psychic infantilism which may accompany normally developed genital organs : in these cases the sexual relation has become a sort of childish game and they feel themselves attracted to sexually immature persons or to young children. The personality and manners of these persons tend to be childish in some respects, and there is, sexually, total indifference to the normal adult.

Paidophilia is often combined with exhibitionism. Other sexual types act in a childish manner and wear baby clothes, etc. The reverse trend is specially found in girls of infantile development who are drawn towards elderly men (gerontophilia) ; or the same type of abnormality may appear in elderly or old men as an irresistible inclination towards children, and leads to distressing crimes and assaults.

An even more primitive abnormality is coprophilia, in which the sexual urge regresses and deflects into special interest in the organs and functions of excretion. The coprophilia of the infantile polymorphous phase is normally replaced by interest in the opposite sex and by certain æsthetic considerations. If the heterosexual inclination is repressed by morbid codes of morality, lack of opportunity or sense of inferiority—then the sense of disgust is obliterated and the sex impulse gratifies itself in its most primitive undifferentiated manner, extending from mere watching the excretory processes of others to actual manipulation and consumption of the excremental products.

Compulsive neuroses may also undermine male potency and cause premature ejaculation. Or they may manifest as a horror of sex and of all sexual " motifs " in art and letters : in fact, as sexphobia, which seeks out and pursues all sexual objects and activities in order to denounce and punish. Hence repeated reports, police drives, the manufacture of " crimes," the mutilation and destruction of works of art. Some sexphobiacs collect pictures and books of erotic type and then soil and mangle them ; or they throw dirt or ink on women's dresses or statues, pictures, etc., and thereby obtain sexual gratification. Religious ideas of expiation and penance are often associated with flagellation, and endocrine unbalance, as in puberty or after the climacteric in women, is often a factor in their production.

Moral Degeneracy

Unrestrained sexual gratification may sometimes lead to complete anæsthesia in normal relationships combined with the obliteration of all normal adult inhibitions. These cases are extremely rare, and probably even rarer in women than in men ; they have no anthropological significance, and may, therefore, be passed over in this study.

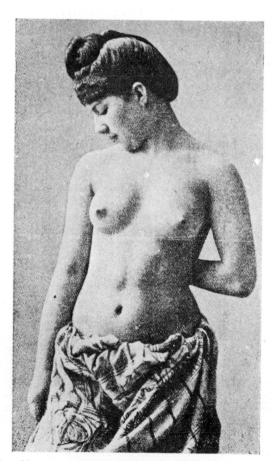

242 .—Fully developed breasts of the type called " *beauté du diable*." Bohemian. (After Stratz.)

243.—German girl of nineteen years.

WOMAN IN HER ÆSTHETIC ASPECT

FEMININE BEAUTY

According to Schopenhauer, the " beauty " of woman—" the squat, narrow-shouldered, wide-hipped and short-legged sex," is naught but a delusion of the " masculine brain clouded by the fumes of instinct." But the majority of men remain of a different opinion.

Anthropologists have endeavoured to analyse and define " beauty." Cordier, in 1860, maintained—in a thesis presented to the Anthropological Society of Paris—that there was no *absolute* beauty in human physique, but a variety of racial types and ideals, and, therefore, no race could claim a monopoly of beauty.

Delaunay disputed this on the basis of the so-called *organotrophic laws* formulated by Claude Bernard, who believed that every organ and portion of the human form possessed a special optimum of development and that harmonious proportion and relation of these organs constituted beauty in each human individual.

But we can hardly investigate and formulate the special model types for each and every race ; nor can anyone seriously maintain the existence of absolute and eternal æsthetic laws in these matters. The negress and the Kalmuck girls are as lovely in the eyes of the men of their races as the Madonnas of Raphäel were to their painter. But we may assume that a certain vital, wholesome normality is essential to loveliness in women. The body should be capable of fulfilling its special sexual and racial functions. Eckstein has pointed out that this is merely an extension of the demand that *all* organs of the body should be functionally fit in order to be æsthetically pleasing ; *e.g.*, eyes, teeth, shape of head and face. Further, Eckstein continues, these special racial types perpetuate themselves by sexual selection.

Moreover, we shall see that a greater or lesser degree of feminine attractiveness or comeliness is largely dependent on material conditions and grade of culture in each individual and racial example.

THE FAVOURABLE INFLUENCE OF RACIAL MIXTURE ON BEAUTY IN WOMEN

The most pronounced and extreme examples of racial and ethnical types are the result of marriages within the same race and class. These are specially noticeable among the *Hindus*, especially the high caste Hindus who only marry within their own caste, and have done so for centuries, following the Laws of Manu. Gobineau and Meiners praise the personal beauty and distinction of the Brahmin caste. But they, too, are not free from admixture of race, and there are great possibilities in some racial blends. According to Pruner, in the children of an Arab father and a Negress there is more resemblance to the maternal type. But if a Negro mates with an Egyptian woman the children have woolly hair, but are otherwise Egyptian type and the third generation has straight hair and merges completely into the Fellahin.   European and Turkish fathers and Abyssinian mothers produce children who might be taken for Spaniards or Portuguese in their appearance, but seem to lack a certain facial expression.

Van der Burg and Beyfuss, who " agrees with his observations on all points," say that " the children of Chinese fathers and Javanese mothers are of decidedly Mongolian type, and resemble their fathers in habits and ways of thought and action as well, particularly in their business aptitudes."

The Javanese-European blend produces a conspicuously pretty half-caste, for it modifies the partly *retroussé* nose, the width of the smiling mouth and the peculiar slit of the narrow eyes. Schmarda praises the attractiveness of the half-caste Euro-Malayan woman. And there are extremely pretty women among the half-castes of European and Japanese parentage (*cf*. Fig. 244).

Berghaus praises the mulatto women of South America in comparison with the indolent, apathetic Brazilian women.   He says they have a delicate and slender build, their arms are relatively short, their hands charmingly dainty, their breasts beautifully curved and firm, and their feet tiny and like their hands ; they are incomparably more attractive than the white women, being full of gaiety and animation as well as grace of form.

Richard Neuhauss has recorded the case of a Kanaka woman from Hawaii who had children by several fathers of different races.   One of these fathers was a full-blood Polynesian from Hawaii, one a Chinaman, and the third a Melanesian.   The Chinese half-caste child had narrow eyes and salient cheek bones ; the third, spirally twisted curls and a noticeably large white area in the eyeball.

In Honolulu, Neuhauss saw two half-castes by the same father, a German, who had only very slight traces of their Polynesian descent.   In fact, these male

244 .—Half-breed girl : Japanese mother and European father. (After A. Friedenthal.)

half-castes seem to have resembled their fathers, but the result was quite different in some half-caste girls whose mother was a Kanaka, while their father was a Norwegian with blue eyes and light hair.   The two daughters had dark skins and typical native features, thick noses, dark eyes and hair and stout heavy figures.   According to Riedel the children of Chinese fathers and Arú (Aroe) Islanders show differences in pigmentation, according to sex, the boys being darker-skinned than the girls.

Finsch found some beautiful girls among the Maori-European half-castes of New Zealand ; but none who could be termed beautiful among the full-blooded aborigines.

In Micronesia the half-castes of mixed European and Gilbert Islander parentage are easily distinguished from the Micronesians of full blood by their lighter colouring, soft, red lips and an expression which reminds the observer of the European.

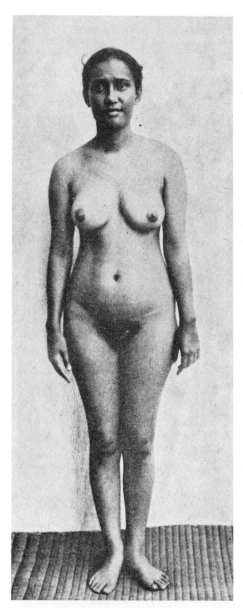

245.—Half-caste. Father, Scot; mother, Hawaian. (Anthrop. Ges., Berlin.)

The children of Europeans and Ponapé women from the Caroline Islands cannot be told apart from European girls, we are told, except by a slightly more swarthy complexion; and another crossing with the white race makes its offspring indistinguishable from full-blood Europeans in features or colouring. The same is said of the Samoan-European half-castes. Finsch speaks of a two-year-old girl, the daughter of a white father and a woman from New Guinea, who was like a deeply sun-bronzed European baby with delicate red lips, intensely dark eyes and curly fair hair.

Nordenskiold is another witness to the attraction of the half-caste in another region, namely, Greenland. He says:

"The women were neatly and carefully arrayed, and some half-caste girls with brown eyes and healthy, chubby, almost European features, were rather pretty."

The illustration 246 shows a family of Greenland Eskimos with a European father. In the top row are the father and the Eskimo mother, between them their young son, and seated, the two daughters. N. A. E. Nordenskiold's description applies perfectly to these girls.

In the North-West of America there are people of mixed blood often termed Bois-Brulés, the descendants of French trappers and explorers and the Indians of various stocks. The women of this half-breed race are, as a rule, whiter in colouring than the men and appear pale in comparison. Many of these *métis* have skins as delicate and white as European women, and regular, chiselled features, there being some truly classically lovely girls among them. A Mexican half-breed is depicted in Fig. 247.

The main racial mixture in Chile, between Spaniards and the natives, is also favourable to looks according to Treutler. These Spanish-Indian women and girls have, as a rule, a clear, pale complexion, black hair, abundant and rather coarse in texture, very brilliant and expressive eyes, aquiline noses, narrow, thinly pencilled, but distinct, black eyebrows, which form perfect arches, very long silky lashes, magnificent teeth, very small ears, hands and feet, finely formed breasts, and much grace of movement.   There are even some blue-eyed blondes among them.

In Peru the European-Indian half breeds are termed Cholos and are much comelier than the unmixed natives (Fig. 248).

246.—Eskimo half-breeds. In the front row are two girls ; behind them the European father and Eskimo mother with their son between them. (Photo, Herrnhuter Missionsges., Greenland.)

Steller writes as follows of the Kamchadale

" Among the broad-faced women, there are beauties equal to the most admired Chinese womankind. But the daughters ot Cossacks from Russia and native mothers are so comely that their beauty may well claim perfection. Their faces are commonly long and oval, and the blackness of their hair, eyes and brows, the whiteness, smoothness and delicacy of their skins, and the rosy pink of their cheeks give them a special charm. And they are notably ambitious, cunning and secret in their ways : know how to keep silent and much given to the pleasures of love.

Thus, they captivate even such men as have kept free from illicit dalliance all the way from Moscow till they reached their country."

A careful and detailed comparison of the results of various racial mixtures would be of considerable anthropological interest. Beauty is often increased or produced by ethnical blends, but is not always their result. What are the circumstances and conditions which decide this factor ? When and why is the paternal type dominant, and when and why the maternal ? Exact knowledge on these points might assist us to judge which stocks are the survivors and which are not.

There may be degeneracy due to unsuitable racial mixtures. For Schliephake gives this account of the Eskimo who dwell near Cumberland Sound, although an isolated case proves but little :

" The smallest individuals by far that ever I saw were half-breeds. They were brother and sister, offspring of the concubinage of the mate of a whaler and an Eskimo woman. The father had been in these parts 20 years before and was of Portuguese origin."

Nevertheless, we have a substantial amount of material in support of the view that racial admixtures increase comeliness and attraction in women at least. Of course, this physical improvement and attraction may be not absolute but relative and subjective ; it may be an illusion of the white man because half-caste woman naturally approximates more to his own racial type. But there are two arguments against this view. N. A. E. Nordenskiold states that the Eskimo are now learning to regard their own type as less attractive and desirable ; and Kropf says that the Ama-Xosa prefer the lighter skins and straighter features of the daughters of women of their own race by white fathers,

247.—Mexican mestiza. (Photo, C. B. Waite.)

and that such girls are much sought after. The same is reported in Southern India.

The most trivial details of physique and appearance in persons of mixed race may be of high anthropological significance ; and any accurate information on the subject must be recorded and taken into consideration. Bartels was quite right on this point, but there has been very little reliable and genuine testimony so far. This was shown in the course of the discussion at the Anthropological Congress at Nürnberg in 1913, where the speakers nearly all voiced the standard of German colonists. But, of course, comparative physiology and æsthetics cannot be settled from the point of view of any one nation or any one group of individuals.

PHYSIOLOGICAL DEGENERATION IN WOMEN

If a people, after having enjoyed a high degree of culture and prosperity, sinks to a lower level, both mentally and materially, this degeneration is plainly registered in the manners, habits and appearance of its women.   Let us cite only one example

248 .—Cholo girl : Peru, River Marañon. (Photo, G. Hübner.)

from the many which history records.   In antiquity Cyprus was a centre of civilisation.   The famous shrines of Aphrodite, the Goddess of Love, brought women from all Mediterranean lands to worship and to pray for what they most desired. Excavations have recently brought to light evidence of much prosperity and a comparatively high degree of culture ; and the women of Cyprus must have shared in these good things both material and mental. What is the case to-day ? The main portion of the island, the fertility of which was once so renowned, has been laid waste ; many of its inhabitants are steeped in ignorance and poverty. Samuel White Baker has depicted the apathy and misery of the women of Cyprus in 1879. He describes the crowd of women and children who surrounded him and his travelling companions on February 4th, when the temperature was too low to pitch a camp (43 degrees) :

"They indulged their curiosity, shivering in light clothes of home-made cotton-stuffs. The children were generally pretty, and some of the younger women were good looking; but there was a total neglect of physical appearance, which is a striking characteristic of the Cypriote females. In most countries, whether savage or civilised, the women yield to a natural instinct, and to a certain extent adorn their persons and endeavour to render themselves attractive ; but in Cyprus there is a distressing absence of the wholesome vanity that should induce attention to dress and cleanliness. The inelegance of their costume gives an unpleasant peculiarity to their figures—the whole crowd of girls and women looked as though they were about to become mothers."

Baker gives further details and confirms the impression that we have here (*cf.* also B. Stewart, writing about 1905) of the representatives of deterioration, sexual, racial and social. Degeneration in a people produces slatternly and over-worked women without enough natural vitality to care for their appearance, and the incessant hard work will tend to obliterate what is characteristically feminine in mind and physique.

There are striking examples in certain country districts of Germany, *e.g.*, in the Upper Palatinate, showing the influence of occupation on appearance, bony structure, and even vocal pitch, as Riehl has so trenchantly remarked in his "*Naturgeschichte des Volkes.*" Nevertheless, in this same Upper Palatinate, Brenner-Schäffer found the most exquisite faces with delicate features and expressive eyes among the little children, but he admits : "They were unspoiled raw material ; their development, the realisation of their possibilities is unfortunately very inadequate. The girls are pretty in their first bloom of youth, then they grow coarser and heavier, and, after a few confinements, they appear middle-aged matrons."

Goldschmidt found that in the North-west of Germany, freshness and comeliness rarely survived childhood among the poorer classes :

Heavy work with immature bodies makes them lank and skinny, draws wrinkles round eyes and mouth and makes the movements awkward and clumsy. He had often thought that a mother who showed him her child was the grandmother.

A practised observer, he continues, can tell the status of any man or woman among our country population, for ease and agility of movement and good carriage show that their early years were not burdened by excessive toil.

Even the structure of the skeleton is affected by certain environmental conditions, and characteristic sexual differences are almost obliterated. G. Fritsch, for example, considers that shoulders and pelvis, absolutely and relatively, are less typically masculine and feminine respectively among the South African tribes than with Europeans ; the pelvis especially is neither, but tends more to the male type.

Finally, we must not overlook the abnormally early physical decline of primitive women owing to underfeeding and poor living conditions. Reichard thus describes the pitiful effects on women among the Wanyamwezi (Lake Tanganyika) :

"The wife and mother ages at 25 or even 20, as a result of the burden of work, and is transformed ; her features are deformed and wrinkled, her breasts become slack like pendulous bags and hang almost to her waist ; the abdomen is either enormously fat or hollow, and the buttocks are very prominent. The arms are extremely thick and muscular as a result of constant grinding of corn."

Vortisch   gives similar descriptions of the negresses of the Gold Coast ; and Müller   of the Australian black women.

In fact, the more degraded and unfortunate her social and material position, the earlier the advent of old age in woman. This rule holds good throughout the world.

THE GEOGRAPHICAL AND ETHNICAL DISTRIBUTION OF BEAUTY IN WOMEN

There can be, clearly, no absolute and final judgment in the matter of personal beauty.* But Europeans may, nevertheless, be permitted to compare the appearance of members of other races with the æsthetic ideal which has been built up among their own people throughout centuries of civilisation.

Undoubtedly the Mongolian type does not attract the white race at first, either in the men or the women of Eastern Asia. We do not instinctively admire the flat, wide faces with their disproportionate breadth at temples and cheeks ; the small, obliquely set eyes, the thin straight eyebrows, the salient cheekbones, the broad flat root of the nose and its rounded tip, the short chin, projecting ears and unrelieved sallow colouring of the skin. And yet there are women of Mongolian race, especially among the Japanese, who though not strictly beautiful according to European standards, can certainly be called extremely pretty. The secluded, indoor life of the women of Eastern Asia in all but the poorest classes gives their skins a pale, unwholesome look. And, to the European eye, the sexes resemble one another closely among the peoples of the Far East ; an impression due to the slight growth of beard among the men and the peculiarly wide, loose clothing worn by both sexes.

What shall be said of the extreme type of Negro physiognomy from the point of view of European æsthetics ? We find very little comeliness in the black—or at least dark-skinned—faces with the big-boned faces and the prognathous jaws, the thick, everted lips, open nostrils, woolly hair, bull necks, thin calves and large flat feet. But this extreme type is not the only one throughout Africa. The missionary Kölle, who knew his flock well, has said : " The typical Negro physiognomy, as described and depicted in our books, would be dismissed by negroes themselves as a caricature, or at the most an inferior approximation to reality." Many observant travellers and anthropologists praise the slender bodies of the young girls in their brief bloom as undoubtedly charming. Even the Hottentot women, who appear to us grotesquely hideous in mature age, have very small and delicate extremities and slim, delicate bodies when they are young, according to Barrow. He says that some might serve as models of perfection, with their round firm breasts and large erect nipples.

Where is the native land of beauty as the modern European understands it ? Beauty, which is independent of artifice. It has been said that there is a zone of the earth's surface running roughly from East to West which does produce the loveliest women and that it is a matter of personal preference which region or race in that favoured zone is awarded the prize. The countries in question include Persia and the Caucasus, especially Georgia and Circassia, European Turkey, Italy, the northern

* [Cf. G. Lynch.]

part of Spain, France, England, Germany, Poland, Denmark, Sweden and some parts of Norway and Russia. But we all know that in some of these countries the average level of looks is very humble indeed and that close approximations to the æsthetic ideal are rare and incomplete if reckoned in percentages of the total female population.

There is so much difference in the judgment and taste of individuals that we will only cite a few acknowledged authorities on æsthetics. Winckelmann declared that radiant and perfect beauty was, so to speak, indigenous to Rome and its surroundings and attributed it to the soft Italian climate. He emphasised the comparative rarity of the unfinished-looking, flat, crude or insignificant features so often seen north of the Alps; the lineaments were finely proportioned and delicately chiselled, and the whole cast of countenance either statuesque or expressive. Winckelmann even declared that the poorest men of the people in these favoured regions had heads suitable as models for works of classic art; and that the country women in the most remote villages often reminded him of Juno herself. But we shall see that not all observers agree in this matter !

In the beauty competition organised in 1888 at Spa, there were 19 prizes distributed among a very numerous crowd of applicants. These 19 prizes went to women and girls from eight countries; one to the United States of America, three to Belgians, six to France, one to Italy, three to Vienna (Austria), three to Prussia (Berlin two, Posen one), one to Sweden and one to Hungary. The first three prizes were awarded to the American girl, a Belgian and a Viennese, respectively.

[Annual beauty competitions are now constantly held in various parts of the world. The Twelfth Annual International Beauty Contest was held at Galveston, Texas, in 1931. The Belgian, Mlle. Metta du Château, was awarded the title, having defeated the U.S. entrant in the final ballot. In 1932 the prize went to Turkey, "Miss America" receiving special commendation for the general form of her legs. These competitions, however, are of little service to the anthropologist, since the clothing worn by the participants effectually prevents the whole body from receiving attention. As giving a general idea of the rough prevailing standard among the white race they are useful. Thus in the 1931 competition nearly all the entrants were slim, "Miss Belgium" herself being a short brunette with a small head, slim body with well proportioned hips and rather long arms.]

BEAUTY IN EUROPE

In the following pages there is a brief sketch of the characteristic appearance and attractions of the women of various races throughout the world. All such opinions and judgments are clearly subjective and thus dependent on individual taste and prevailing fashion.

Almost all travellers in Italy praise the dark eyes of the Italian girls and women and the magnificently proportioned figures and majestic carriage of the Roman women par excellence. But a closer and longer observation tends to cool down the enthusiasm of first impressions. Indeed, Bogumil Goltz compares these first impressions to the illusions of the Fata Morgana ; he refers specially to the mental capacities and activities of the Italian women, but what he says applies equally to their physical attractions.

On the Island of Sicily Ploss found attractive faces and comely figures to be very rare among the women, while the men are often very good-looking. Hehn's remark about the scourge of hunger and the comparative freedom of the Sicilians from its menace and from the trials of the northern winter can only be taken as affecting the men of Sicily and Southern Italy, where they live in the open air and pile all their burdens on the heads of their wives or the backs of their hapless donkeys.

The Spanish women are famous for their looks. Bogumil Goltz says that their appearance

249 A.—Two English girls. (Dover Street Studios..)

expresses their temperament : he praises " their beautifully moulded figures, their grace and dignity of movement, their resonant voices, the dark brilliance of their eyes and the vivacity of their gestures. Their physical development is precocious and their maturity brief, the effect jointly of climate, dirt and sensual pleasure." * The Italian, E. de Amicis, declares that an

* *Cf.* Havelock Ellis's " The Soul of Spain " for a very subtle and appreciative study of the Spanish woman.

Andalusian is the most likely of all women in the world to suggest and tempt men to abduct her by her mere appearance and manner.

The Portuguese woman has a distinct physical personality which differs from the Spanish in many respects. She is quieter, more serene and reserved, less addicted to the dance and all

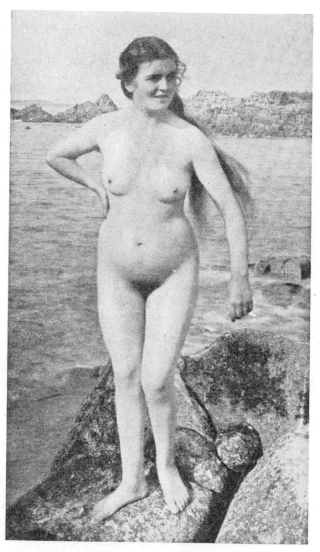

249 B.—Blonde European. (Photo, R. A. Giesecke.)

public festivities. Schweiger Lerchenfeld compares her to a precious but faded work of art, with an aura about her of centuries of memories. The sensual vitality of the Spaniard is lacking in her.

In modern Greece, feminine beauty is very rare; so rare, according to Adolph Bötticher, that the sight of it is amazing whenever it occurs in the interior of the country at least. "The Greek girl matures very rapidly and often bears her first child by the time she is 13 or 14.

She nurses her children till they are five or six years of age and generally more than one at a time. And so she ages rapidly and the hard work in the harvest field and at the loom combine to coarsen her features and break the elasticity and uprightness of her carriage : a contrast to the ease and royal dignity with which the Greek men, even the poorest peasants, hold themselves and move." Bartholdy confirms this description. " They have often finely formed breasts

250.—Blonde European : urban dweller.   (Photo, R. A. Giesecke.)

which are soon deformed and relaxed and the whole figure becomes corpulent. Their distinctive attractions are the graceful outline and carriage of head and neck. The women of Athens have been noted for centuries as inferior to all their countrywomen in looks, even to the Albanian women "—although the latter are much less handsome than their men. In the mountain districts, they are raw-boned and hard-featured ; in Southern Albania, the Grecian type appears occasionally, but without its beauty : the faces are almost all plain, according to Schweiger-Lerchenfeld.

The women of Malta are not Italians, nor do they resemble the Greeks. There is something Arabian about their oval faces, sharply cut aquiline noses, and glowing eyes under thick lashes. They are tall and slender and their complexions dark.

Franzos has praised the Roumanian women of all classes : he describes them as very pretty with graceful, rounded supple figures, brown skins, black eyes and hair. Kanitz has less

251.—European brunette ; urban dweller.   (Photo, R. A. Giesecke.)

appreciation of the Bulgarians, whom he describes as high-coloured, fresh-complexioned but ageing rapidly.

The Serbian women have the reputation of comeliness. Franz Scherer, for instance, says : " Nature has favoured Serbia both in its landscapes and, as no one will be inclined to doubt, in its womenfolk as well. Very fine looking women are often seen in the Serbian towns, with features of classic regularity and often of really surprising beauty. Their dark eyes and hair and pale but lustrous skins set off their beauty of line and ensemble, when framed in the supple and splendid national costume they make a perfect picture."

The Serbians (or Croatians) of the former military frontier (between Old Serbia and Austria) are described in detail by Baron Rajacsich, who found them very different from the feminine population of Syrmia and Banat. They had more powerful, thick-set muscular figures, with greater development of breast, hips and calves, and denser hair, particularly thicker eyebrows than the dwellers in the vast plains. There is something of the Greek type in Serbian women's faces : since Greeks mixed with southern Slavs in the Balkan peninsula.

In Montenegro, according to Bernhard Schwarz, the women are graceful in their girlhood, though much shorter in stature than the men, but they age very soon, becoming raw-boned and wrinkled, for they are the general beasts of burden, carrying incredible loads along mountain paths while their hands, horny with toil, knit incessantly.

The Turkish (Osmanli) women are, it is said, of less mixed blood than the harem ladies of Constantinople. They are, as a rule, plain rather than pretty and with very large mouths and straight, rather large noses. But they have luxuriant hair and fine eyes, more often dark than blue (Didaskalia, 1877). De Amicis has described the Turkish women of Constantinople, who are, of course, of very mixed blood, as follows : Generally fat and, as a rule, of short stature with

252.—Dark European : urban dweller. (Photo, R. A. Giesecke.)

very white skins, under a layer of cosmetics, black eyes, soft red lips, oval faces, small noses, round chins and rather full lips. Their necks are long and supple and their feet dainty and small.

Polish women are amongst the most admired racial types of Europe and the world. Schweiger-Lerchenfeld says : "They really have something almost dazzling about them, for their features are almost classical in their regularity. They are much more graceful than the Russians and show better taste in their dress and general appearance. Moreover, they are also, as a rule, of quite different and more delicate build and their skin colour seems more transparent and finer. Their dark eyes are full of vivacity without the melting, liquid, almost sensuous blue of the eyes of the Northern Russian. The Polish lady is full of beauty and distinction and has a grace which is only approached by the women of Mediterranean lands."

The same author finds a great diversity of opinion as regards feminine beauty in Russia. There is great variety of type. The Ukrainian is of much warmer and livelier temperament than her blue-eyed sister of the north and her physiognomy and colouring are much more southern. She tends to be taller and slighter than the North Russian, her eyes are dark and full of expression, her black hair is bound round with a becoming snood or fillet. There is a resemblance to the Polish type in her slenderness and grace of build. The Central Russian girl is shorter, but her bones are much bigger and more solid and her figure tends to be plump. The eyes are light coloured, the glance direct and friendly, full of gaiety, but without the intensity of the south. The hair, ashen or flaxen in its fairness, is typical of the north."

The loveliest Swedish women are those from Dalecarlia. Du Chaillu compares the finest Swedish complexions to " apple blossoms floating in milk " ; he praises the delicacy of colouring and skin texture as beyond compare. The Swedes alone, he declares, are able to pride them-

253 .—European brunette : urban dweller.   (Photo, R. A. Giesecke)

selves on possessing cheeks of the particular rosy tint which seems in a sense to be absorbed by the skin and gives them an indefinable charm.

Southern Germany has many samples of the brunette type. Ranke [1] describes the typical pretty girl of Upper Bavaria as slightly tanned and often black-haired, with a slender muscular figure and deep brown laughing eyes, full of spirit and vivacity. The same direct, decided, vivacious type is to be observed in blonde and blue-eyed girls from the Bavarian Highlands. Figs. 249–253 show a few examples of European beauty.

BEAUTY IN ASIATIC TYPES *

According to our standards, the racial group to which the Ostiak, the Samoyed, the Koryak and the Kamchadale belong is not beautiful, and travellers from Europe almost all mention the unattractiveness of their womenfolk ; " devoid of grace and so like the men that they can hardly be told apart when dressed and at first sight. Their skins are usually sallow and their

* [Cf. E. M. Bowden.]

stature low." N. A. E. Nordenskiold says that some of the younger girls among the Chukchees were rather pleasant looking—but surrounded with an atmosphere of dirt and fish-oil. The Votyak (Finno-Ugrian) women are short and plain with reddish hair, according to Gmelin and Pallas, and the latter authority found few pretty women among the Mordvins in Russia. The Kalmuck women were more attractive, and Kollmann mentions a Kalmuck beauty, the mother of three children, who was a member of a group exhibited in Basle. His description of her is as

254 .—Tatar woman from Baku. (From the Ordén Coll., Vienna.)

follows : " Taller than the others, slender yet strong. Small hands and delicate bony structure, a thin nose with a slightly curved bridge which relieves the width and flatness of the face, the eyes are widely open, the epicanthic fold very slight. She has long lashes and thin eyelids unlike those of her Kalmuck and Samoyed relations. The whole physiognomy reminds one of many men and women from Southern Hungary."

Ermann says of the Yakuts : " The women are often very well built with regular features, black sparkling eyes and much animation, but they lose their looks very soon."

Among the Siberian Tatars " the women's faces," according to Vambéry, " are notably regular and sometimes pleasant. Their skin is much whiter than the men's, their hair long and very dark ; their bodies are softly rounded with well-made hands and feet. They carry their shoulders well, but protrude the abdomen and are disfigured by the characteristic salience of their cheek bones and the inflamed eyes, reddened by smoke-filled rooms and tents."

Burnes says the Turkoman women are blonde and often pretty. Fraser says that Goklen

255.—Kurd.   (After Schweiger-Lerchenfeld.)

women " are sometimes sallow and ugly, and others younger and very pretty with warm, nut-brown and ruddy tones in their complexions, regular features, pleasant and intelligent expressions and piercing black eyes."

Among the Afghan people, the men are famed for their magnificent appearance and physique, but the. women are insignificant in comparison.

The women living on the Yarkand Daria are generally pretty with fresh, pleasant faces and small, shapely feet.

256.—Dusun (Borneo) woman and child.

Polak describes the Persian women as of medium height and neither thin nor stout. They have large, well-opened, almond-shaped eyes, languorous and sensuous, and finely arched eyebrows meeting over the root of the nose. The shape of a Persian woman's face is highly praised if it is round rather than oval; the poets of Persia celebrate her as the lady with face like the moon. She has exquisitely shaped feet and hands, broad lips and bosom; and a skin more olive than fair. Her hair grows very thickly and is generally of a dark chestnut tint. Artificial aids to beauty are much in use; the face is painted and eyebrows blackened. In carriage and movement the Persian is elegant, easy and agile.

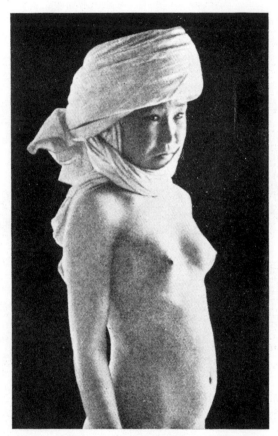

257.—A " Kirghiz " woman of 33.   (Photo, E. Ganz.)

Crousse attributes " a robust, full-blown vigorous beauty, as becomes a powerful race " to the Armenian women. E. de Amicis mentions their " full and fine proportions, corpulence, white skins, aquiline profiles and large long-lashed eyes; their faces," he adds, " have not the intellectual look of the Greek women." Another author again mentions the frequency of fine figures among them and their regular features, oval faces, bright black eyes and dense black hair.

Certain regions of the Caucasus have been for centuries reputed the Eldorado of women's beauty. They supplied the most highly-priced and highly-praised slaves to the harems of Turkey, Egypt and North Africa. The Mingrelian, Circassian and Georgian women had the reputation of the greatest delicacy of complexions and symmetry of feature and the most magnificently developed figures. The French traveller Chardin visited the Caucasus in the nineteenth century and praised the height, grace and perfect proportions of the Georgian women, their walk being particularly easy and agile. The Circassians he also considered very beautiful, with high foreheads, black pencilled eyebrows, lustrous eyes, finely shaped nose and rosy, laughing mouth showing beautiful teeth : the chin well rounding off the perfect oval of the face. And he concludes : " In Mingrelia there are wonderfully lovely and majestic women, with splendid figures and classical faces, and eyes that captivate all whom they behold."

258 .—Siamese women. (Photo, O. Häckel.

Pallas and other writers confirm this account ; but find that Circassian women, though attractive and handsome, are below their dazzling reputations. They have very white skins and good figures, but comparatively short lower limbs. They cultivate their slenderness—which is greatly admired, although, as a rule, the Near East prefers very plump women—by means of special diet of milk and constricting girdles, like corsets. Bodenstedt found " only four who were really beautiful, as we understand beauty in women. But all were very slender with small ears, hands and feet. Dark eyes and black hair are no more frequent among them than at home : the majority have fair or light brown hair and blue or hazel eyes."

Mantegazza has praised the beauty of the Hindu women and their tenderly emotional and passionate nature. They generally have some attractions, such as great dark, luminous eyes, thick brows and lashes, the shoulders, arms and bosom of a Greek statue, and little feet, free from the deformity of tight shoes and displayed to advantage by anklets.* But they have sallow, colourless skins, weak, slender legs, and teeth blackened by chewing betelnut.

259 .—Burmese woman.   (Anthrop. Ges., Berlin.)

Among the many diverse races of the Indian peninsula is one, the Nayar (of Southern India), who practise a form of group marriage, amounting to almost free sexual relations, and these customs, which have prevailed among the Nayar for centuries, have not injured either their fertility or their physique in general. Jagor claims that it has had a selective influence which is far from deleterious, and described the Nayar women as extremely dainty, strictly clean in their habits and persons, of very graceful and seductive appearance, and, in spite of the intense

* [The clothing of Hindu women, with its lack of restraining influences, enhances their beauty, as Rothfeld has pointed out and illustrated in his book on the women of India.]

heat of the climate in which they live, their skin is much whiter than that of most Indians. Jagor points out that in Sparta there was a eugenic selection in procreation which produced a stock superior in masculine vigour and courage and feminine beauty to all other Greek peoples.

Among the women of the Igorrote on the Philippine Islands there are features as delicately cut, and skins as white as any pretty European girls, according to Hans Meyer.

Finsch states that in Malaya he saw many pretty figures with well-shaped breasts. Stratz

260 .—Javanese water-carrier. (Anthrop. Ges., Berlin.)

gives greater detail in describing the Javanese : " The typical features of the women of Java are an abundance of straight, glossy, deep black hair ; dark eyes, dazzlingly white teeth and a dainty slender build with graceful, rhythmically swaying gait. Their complexions show a great variety of pigmentation, from the palest sallow olive tint to the deepest purplish bronze. Their black hair has sometimes a faint reddish tinge in certain lights ; but girls with dark red-brown hair are very rare and there are no blondes among them. Their lower limbs are proportionately short and slender, and the upper thigh much less rounded than in European women. Shapely legs and calves are rarities among the Javanese."

The pure-blooded Malayan types in Java are often beautifully shaped and, although their

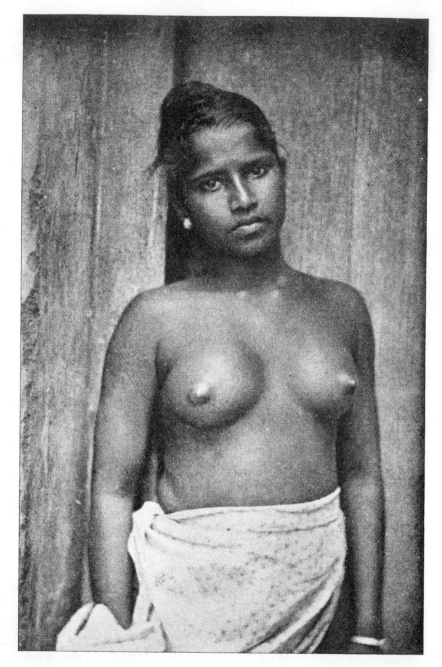

261.—Singhalese. The breasts show convex areolæ. (Photo, Prof. Ehrenreich.)

faces are not beautiful in our sense of the term, there is something very graceful and agreeable in their appearance. The same is true of the Dyak women in the forests of Borneo, who, according to photographs, exhibit figures that are often extremely graceful and their faces pleasant.

262.—Two Geisha girls celebrated for their beauty.   (Photo, E. Baelz.)

Women in the Malacca Peninsula and parts of the island of Sumatra seem to be more heavily and squarely built ; their skins, described both as olive and coppery brown, show no flush of colour in the cheeks ; and their tongues, gums and lips have an even deeper purple tint than those of their menfolk.

[The ideas of beauty among the Battak have been described by Leeuw (p. 246). The hair must be black and the smooth skin brownish-yellow. The eyebrows must be arched and the

263 .—Japanese woman with painted face and eyebrows and blackened teeth.

eyes must glitter like Chinese mirrors. Teeth should be even and the lips red as a mango fruit. The whole body should be symmetrically formed and as smooth as a kernel of rice.]

The Singhalese of Ceylon also have examples of face and form which—apart from the skin-colour (an additional attraction to some)—would be considered quite beautiful, or at least very comely in Europe. The younger women have for long been noted for their beautiful, erect carriage, soft skin, full, firm breasts, rounded buttocks and well-formed feet.

Wallace declared that hard toil, privations and very early married life gave the women of the Aru Islands an unfeminine appearance. Ribbe's account is different. He says : " In Watulei, I saw young wives of wealthy men who wore bead chains round breast and hips as well as encircling their throats. They often hung tiny bells between their breasts and, thus decked out, these village girls looked quite graceful and pretty, though they went about half-naked. They differed from the women of allied race on neighbouring shores by reason of their fine womanly figures and grace of movement."

Przevalsky says that the Tibetan women are squat, dirty and plain, though now and again one sees tolerably good-looking faces; they have lighter skins and more evenly set teeth than their men.

The appearance of the women of Japan strikes us much more favourably than that of their Chinese neighbours. The Japanese girl of the higher social classes is very attractive; grace of movement and manner are her heritage from the cradle; her round childish face is full of expression; and her slightly oblique, black eyes have an extremely mischievous expression. Her teeth are very white, set somewhat apart and slightly prominent; her hair long and thick. Many married women in Japan stain their teeth black and pluck out their eyebrows; replacing the natural hair with a thin line of black paint, but their extremely amiable and expressive eyes are praised by all. A Japanese term for a young unmarried woman is Shiraha, or " White Teeth " (Ehmann).

[Bacon, in discussing the ideals of Japanese beauty, states the following characteristics as much admired. Face, long and narrow with forehead high and narrow in the middle. Hair, glossy, straight and smooth. Eyes, long and narrow, starting upward at the outer corners. Nose, low at the bridge, giving the face a flat appearance. Mouth, small; lips, red and full; and complexion clear ivory-white. Figure, slim and delicate, with narrow hips. The carriage should be graceful and the body slightly bent forward. The step should be short and quick with the toes turned in (p. 50).]

The Chinese women appeal far less to European æsthetic sense. They are small in stature and insignificant, and their sedentary lives induce a pallor with a sallow tinge. Their faces are so round as to be almost circular. Their racial characteristic, the shape and setting of their eyes, often gives a certain piquancy—but the salient cheek bones, short flat nose, heavy lips and smooth coarse hair are not attractive.

BEAUTY IN OCEANIA

Many travellers have praised the native women of Hawaii as pretty or comely. Their figures are very shapely below the age of 30; but they age very soon, as all observers agree. The women of the aristocratic class are, like their men, very powerfully built and often corpulent, a characteristic which Hawaiians think charming, according to Bechtinger.

On Tahiti there is a native aristocracy whose men are, as a rule, 6 ft. (or above it) in height and the women almost as tall. The Tahitian women generally wear

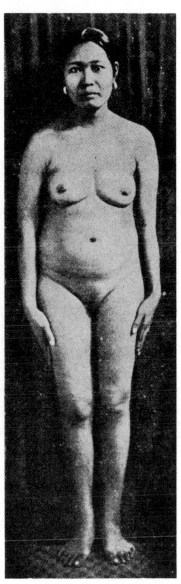

264.—Chinese woman of 22.
(Photo, B. Hagen.)

ample clothing and lead rather sedentary lives; their clothing and customs tend to make their skins pale, and they often have warm pink cheeks which show blushes. Forster describes their great laughing, lustrous eyes and sweet smiles with enthusiasm, but admits that they are not regularly handsome and that their chief charm is their affability and geniality.

Porter describes the women of the Marquesas Islands as less comely than their menfolk. They have shapely figures but ugly feet and an ugly, swaying walk. Krusenstern found them

265.—Woman from North China.   (Anthrop. Ges., Berlin.)

short in stature and with thick waists but softly rounded faces, large sparkling eyes, lovely teeth and skins glowing with health.

The Samoan girls and women are thus described by Zöller: " It would be difficult to pick out real beauties among them, but prettiness and good looks abound, at least so long as they are young." Krämer praises " the fine structure and outline of the thorax, whose ribs have never been distorted and compressed by stays. The long, classic, slightly convergent lines sweep from arm-pits to waist and then arch boldly outwards to the hips." But there is no doubt that Samoan faces can also be very regular and attractive.

The Maori women of New Zealand are not considered pretty. They have very wide mouths and broad nostrils, emphasised by the ritual tattoo marks on lower lips and chin. Rutherford compares these tattoo patterns to a crown reversed. The Maori women are not graceful, though very muscular and agile : there is something violent in their active, primitive force. But Büchner has recorded having seen some handsome and stately figures among Maori women.

The New Hebrides are inhabited by Melanesians. Forster found the Melanesian women of Tanna Island small and, in general, plain, even ugly. On Vate, another island of the New Hebridian Group, the women are tall and thin according to Erskine. But on Malekula they are ugly and badly formed ; which is not to be wondered at considering the heavy work they have to do. Their breasts are long, almost tubular, and very disfiguring. The same is said of the

266 .—Woman from Honolulu. (Photo, G. Häckel, Berlin.)

women of Aoba, and the palm for unattractiveness in the New Hebrides goes to the women of Vanikoro, as soon as they have passed their youth, which has a certain comeliness.

The natives of New Guinea or Papua are also Melanesians. They do not appear attractive to Europeans, though very pretty faces are said to occur among them ; but among the boys rather than the girls. As a rule, however, they seem to us decidedly ugly.

In the Admiralty Islands the men are tall and finely made, but the women far inferior in stature and comeliness and, as the " Challenger " reports testify, the use of betel nut makes their appearance positively repellent. Miklucho-Maclay adds further particulars : he describes the older women as very thin and bony, and their shaven heads, deep wrinkles, flat chests and skinny muscular limbs are like those of elderly men.

Amongst the Gilbert Islanders there is marked difference in height between the sexes. The Gilbert Island women have slender limbs and soft pleasant faces. Meinicke praises their "long black curls, regular features full of animation and intelligence, well-developed foreheads and bright, dark eyes. Their cheek bones project somewhat and their noses are broad. Their white teeth often suffer from chewing pandanus."

The native women of Easter Island are recorded as having curiously lax and tired-looking features even among quite young girls. Their faces were very round in youth, but lost this fullness in later years. The Easter Island women, it is said, were the smallest in stature of all the South Seas, and somewhat lighter in complexion than the men.

Among the Australian aborigines, the women are of medium height ; if they are tall they

267.—Woman from Marquesas Islands.   (Mus. f. Volkerk., Dresden.)

are greatly admired and sought after as beauties. They are in their prime from 10 to 14 years old. Mücke, who lived among the black folk of Southern Australia for years, spoke in terms of admiration of one native girl of 15 ; her figure was of the "finest symmetry," with firm, round limbs, her skin like dusky velvet and "her full lips visibly red and parting to show the best set of ivory-white teeth, gleaming like pearls."

Other writers describe the pathetic ugliness of these women, in the neighbourhood of Adelaide. And in Northern Australia they are reported by Browne as stunted, shrivelled and of wretched appearance.

In 1884 a troupe of Australian aborigines were brought to Berlin, where they were visited and studied by Rudolph Virchow. This great anthropologist emphasised his astonishment at the ease, directness and even beauty of movement in these members of a primitive race. He said : " These women have such a graceful carriage of the head, such elegance of movement—whether of body or limbs—that they might have been brought up in the highest circles of our European Society."

BEAUTY IN AMERICA

The people of the United States of America have amalgamated from many racial stocks into a nation with a distinct national type of their own. This type is manifest in their women as well ; its defects are thus pilloried by one of their own countrymen : " They have neither

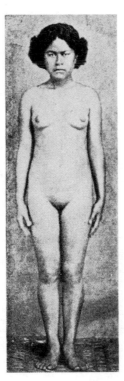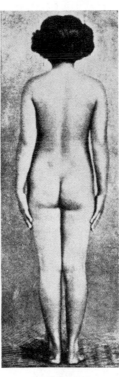

268 .—Samoan girl of 14. (Godeffroy Coll.)

bones nor muscles, nor sap of life in their veins—they have only nerves. And how, indeed could it be otherwise ? Instead of bread they eat chalk ; instead of wine, they drink iced water ; their shoes are too thin, their clothing too tight."

Schweiger-Lerchenfeld quotes the opinion of many Europeans who concur respecting the American women of the Eastern and Northern States especially ; they admit many personal charms, delicate pallor, beautiful features, and grace, but note the lack of something fundamentally vital. He maintains that the racial differences of the old Colonial days are still traceable. He claims to be able to distinguish Dutch and Flemish traits in the eyes and colouring of dwellers in the North. The New Yorker has more colour ; the Boston girl is at the same time livelier and more delicate. Be that as it may, the racial type of British beauty is still found undiminished and undimmed among the upper classes of New England and the Southern States. [The women of the United States belong to so many diverse types owing to the different nationalities resident there that any detailed considerations are impossible. Standards of beauty conform largely to

269.—Samoan Woman.   (After v. Reitzenstein.)

prevailing fashions, and correspond to the ideas of beauty current in Europe at the time.   The wide use of cosmetics and " beauty " preparations indicates the attention the American girl pays to her body.   Moreover, the cult of athleticism in the younger women tends to produce a

270.—Maori Women wearing breast ornaments (*Hei-tiki*) made of green-stone.

well-built figure with good bodily proportions. Journals such as *Beauty* and numerous text-books on beauty culture provide material for studying prevailing fashions.]

Mexican women are not pleasing to all tastes, although urban women of purely or mainly Spanish descent are worthy representatives of their racial type ; they have lustrous black eyes and raven hair and dazzling teeth. They are not tall, but move with extreme grace. The Mexican women of the country and provinces are less attractive ; their eyes, hair and teeth match those of the town dwellers, but they have prominent cheek bones, large mouths and badly formed noses.

The women of Arctic America—like their menfolk—are even less attractive in European eyes. There are great differences, however, between the inhabitants of the eastern and western

271.—Samoan girl.   (After A. Berger.)

coasts of Greenland. Finn says : " The West Greenlanders are full-blooded Eskimo and, as a rule, squat in build with a waddling gait and protruding stomach. The eastern coast has taller, slenderer women of much pleasanter physique and appearance. All Greenland Eskimo women have relatively small hands and feet."

N. A. E. Nordenskiöld writes : " A Greenland *belle* in holiday attire looks far from ill ; her brown skin is clear and wholesome, her cheeks round and smooth. Her close-fitting costume is made of selected seals' hide ; her graceful little boots have high tops and brightly-coloured beads are twisted round her neck and hair. Her physical features are enhanced by her cheerful spontaneous gaiety and by a considerable amount of coquetry. . . . She is wooed and won with some display of force, but she prefers that method. When she is a wife and brings her children into the world, she neglects her appearance ; her proud straight carriage is bowed beneath the burden of the children carried on her back, her roundness of limb and form vanishes, her walk becomes a stiff stagger, her hair falls out at the temples and her teeth are worn down to the roots, for the hides are chewed by the women in the process of ' dressing.' The girls are pleasant to behold, but, as matrons, they grow repulsively ugly and dirty."

Holmberg reports that the Tlingit women of the North-West coast walk bent and with a

272.—Woman from Fiji.   (After Friedenthal.)

waddling gait, whereas their menfolk stride proudly ; small hands and, as a rule, small feet, are characteristic of this tribe.

Among various Indian tribes of North America the women are of noticeably short stature. [G. W. James and R. W. Shufeldt have both dealt with the Indians' ideals of beauty.] Bartram states that the Creek women are rarely over 5 ft. in height. They are, as a rule, squat and broad in proportion to their height, with round massive heads and wide, round, rather flat faces (Prince M. zu Wied).   Parker describes the North American Indian squaw as generally

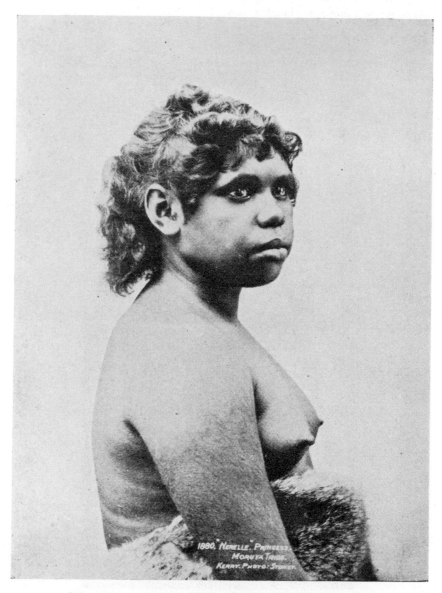

273 .—Woman from New South Wales.   (Anthrop. Soc., Berlin.)

short, strongly built, capable of incessant toil and of enduring great hardships ; with wide shoulders, long arms and massive hips in harmony with a capacious pelvis.

Among the Indian tribes of the Southern Continent, F. von Hellwald has mentioned the Conibo women on the Juruha River as small, but with less thin lower limbs and less protuberant abdomens than most others.

The young Arawak girls of Guiana have a certain fame for fine bodily proportions, round

muscular limbs and an almost classical cast of features.   Their eyes are large and black, and
according to Appun their figures are extremely graceful and feminine and their profiles " purely

274 .—Woman from the Tonga Islands.   (After Reitzenstein.)

Greek " ; and the Arecuna women are the prettiest of all their race.   On the other hand, the
Taruma are said to be the least attractive.   But tastes differ in these matters.   Appun can

hardly find words fit to praise the charms of these aboriginal women of tropical South America, whereas Sachs gives a very different description of them.

The Patagonians, at the southern extremity of the continent between the Chilean Andes and the Atlantic, are very tall muscular people. Their women are on an average much shorter and with less dense hair, but very shapely and muscular.

The women of the Magellan Strait Fuegians are also much smaller than the men. Their faces have been described as " squashed out " or flattened in appearance, as though between two boards. Their noses are very flat, their cheek bones protrude. Some writers have described them as very fat.

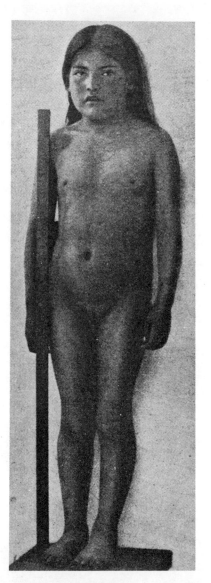

275 .—Mohegan girl. (North American.)

276 .—Aymara (Peru) girl of 10 years. The measuring rod is 1 m. high. (After Posnansky.)

The Bush negresses of Surinam have affinities with Africa. There is a strong strain of this negro blood throughout Central and South America, blended both with the coloured and white races. Prince Roland Bonaparte praises their admirable proportions and soft velvety skins, but adds : " Their evanescent beauty only lasts for a very brief time."

BEAUTY IN AFRICA

Schweiger Lerchenfeld attributes finely-shaped, delicate hands and feet to almost every Egyptian woman. They walk with a natural grace, although that rhythmic swing of the hips known to the Arabs as " Ghung " does not suit all of them. They have deep, dark, melting and very expressive eyes, which the yashmak does not entirely conceal.

R. Hartmann has remarked upon the permanence of the ancient physical type in Egypt. The modern women are very like those of ancient Egypt. The young girls are uncommonly graceful ; they are as slim and young as the royal princesses shown naked on a wall at Thebes

277.—Eskimo girl from Columbia, who received a beauty prize at a Seattle exhibition.
(Photo, Haeckel, Berlin.)

playing a sort of chess or draughts with their father Rameses III. Hartmann observed that the shoulders and arms of the women were very shapely, but their lower limbs, from thigh to foot, less so, for, when the peasants wade through the arms of the Nile and the marshes at low water, they lift their garments almost to the waist. Their shoulders and sometimes the upper portion of their arms are very well shaped. The thighs, legs and arms below the elbows are often too thin, although there are some pleasing exceptions to this rule.

As Frhr. von Maltzan has said of the maidens in the nomad tents of Tripoli, Arabs are only beautiful for a very brief season, but, in this flowering time, they are indeed fit brides for the sons of a god. They embody the poetry and mystery of the desert. Their skins are warmly golden ; their hair has a dense blackness with a tinge of metallic blue ; their eyes are the deepest wells of darkness with silken lashes, and their figures slender, with delicate bones and rounded curves. In order to appreciate Arabian grace and beauty, no Western civilisation is necessary ;

the Arab nomads of North Africa, intensely excitable and susceptible to every impression of the senses, have celebrated the charms of their women in terms of the most superlative and extravagant imagery.

But these charms begin to fade at about 16 years of age. It is the most evanescent of all feminine types, combining the most ardent passion with the most fragile elegance of form. Chavanne praises the dusky skins and the wonderful glow, half rose, half gold, in their cheeks,

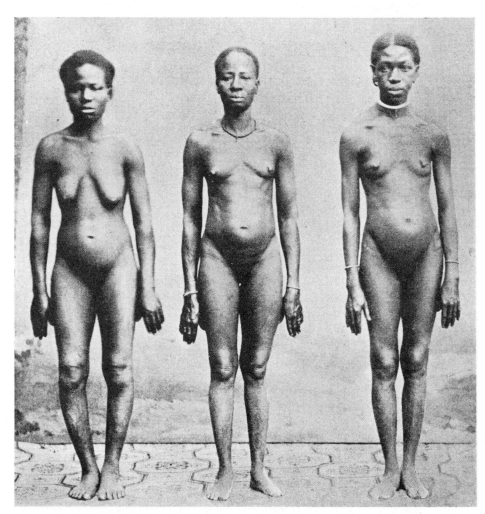

278 .—Women from Bornu and Darfur.   (Anthrop. Soc., Berlin.)

the delicate roundness of their limbs, the almost excessive brilliance of their eyes and the sable fleece of their hair ; they are phantoms of dusk and flame—but, at 30, they have become appallingly ugly, wrinkled, faded, reduced to skin and bone—excepting in such districts as Tuat, where they keep their plumpness for several years, as do the Berber women in the coast towns.

Among the Nubians (Barabra), the women are slender with spindly tapering limbs. The girls reach puberty later than the Egyptians, and even at 14 years of age their breasts have scarcely begun to develop. Like all Africans, they wither early and, in old age, according to Hartmann, the Nubian women are conspicuously ugly.

Paulitschke says : " The Somali have sometimes pleasant faces and full, well-formed breasts. I noticed also their snub noses, projecting brows and small delicately moulded ears. Their necks are finely shaped, the hips narrow, but pelvis wide with marked gluteal development ; they move with ease and agility. In their middle twenties their faces become seamed with wrinkles and their breasts wrinkled and flaccid : by the time they are 40, they are painfully ugly."

Juan Maria Schuver gives this account of the Galla (Oromo) of Abyssinia : " The women of all classes, with the exception of the very poorest, are such a contrast to their lean, bony and generally sullen and sombre looking menfolk, that I never ceased to marvel at this disparity. The younger women are so vivacious that they are hardly ever still and they retain their looks longer than the negresses, because perhaps, they have slaves to help them in their heavier daily

279 .—Hottentot woman of mixed parentage.   (Photo, E. Speer.)

tasks. They are much shorter in stature than the men (10–15 cm.), although there are a few tall figures among them." He also mentions their breadth of shoulder and full rounded arms ; and the same author found " the perfect proportions of antique statues " among the young Berta girls on the Upper Nile.

A similar account has been given of the Habab women : handsome in youth but ageing very soon.

The Beja women are not unattractive in youth. But, as they are generally given in marriage between 12 and 15, their dainty slender bodies and noticeably firm, well-developed breasts soon change and wither.

The same premature and painful decline is the rule among the tall, noble-looking and finely-made women of the Danakil and Saho in Abyssinia.

The women of Abyssinia proper are of middle height and often decidedly plump. They are often charming and most engaging in their manners. Their faces are round rather than oval, their foreheads prominent but not high, their mouths large and their chins often double. Their

280.—Berber girl of dark type from Tunis.   (After Lehnert and Landrock.)

affability and considerable diligence have made them much in demand for the harems of Arabia.

The Saurta and Terroa are two tribes living on the slopes of Mt. Gedem between Massaua and Abyssinia. Their women are much smaller than the men and have pleasant faces, but are too thin for beauty of form. The hands of both men and women are exceptionally small.

281 .—Wagaja women (East Africa).   (Photo, G. Haeckel, Berlin.)

Rohlfs remarks : " This peculiarity is common to all Abyssinians, whose hands are much too small to be pretty." One reason is weakness from idleness and lack of exercise.

Even among full-blooded negro tribes there are young women and girls of attractive appearance. But their comeliness is very evanescent and when brief youth is over, they are often positively ugly.

Again, the Bahima women (Tanganyika) are decidedly well built, as is shown by Weiss, though the lower limbs are too slender, especially between knee and ankle.

Some of the natives of the Gaboon may almost be termed pretty. Their hands and feet are shapely, their eyes full of expression and their noses comparatively high bridged. Their mouths

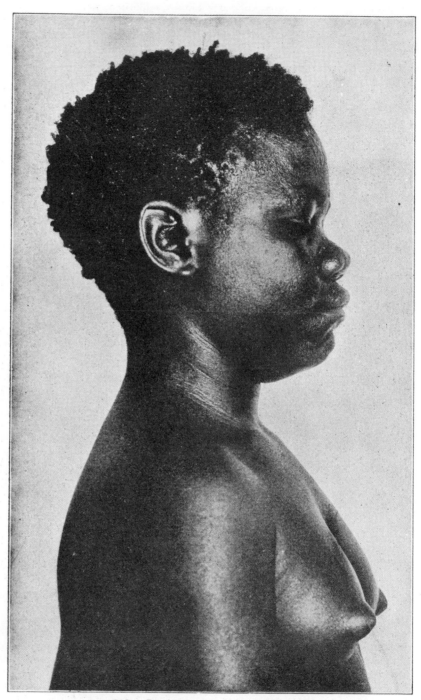

282.—Ituri pygmy.   (After v. Reitzenstein.)

283.—Zulu woman.   (After v. Reitzenstein.)

are not too large and their teeth are flawless.   The lower lip, however, is somewhat pouting and swollen.

The Wolof (Jolof) negresses might also be termed comely were it not for their undeveloped and spindly lower legs ; a Negro characteristic in exaggerated form.   Their feet are very flat and the heel projects almost like a spur.

Audebert mentions the figure and carriage of some of the natives in the interior of Madagascar.   They hold themselves erect, some protrude the abdomen excessively, but all have slender, muscular, well-proportioned shapes, unconfined by corsets.

Wangemann says that : " Some of the Basuto women and men in the Transvaal have superb figures.   But the breasts tend to sag in an almost pouch-like fashion, which is repulsive, although some of the younger girls have beautiful figures."

Among the Zulu women there are some exquisite figures with faces full of character and intelligence.   Wiese says of the women of the Angoni (a Zulu tribe north of the Zambesi River), that they are " often quite beautiful and apt to inspire enthusiastic passion in their partners."

Some African types are shown in Figs. 278 – 284

284 .—Togo woman in bridal attire.
(After Spiess.)